Acknowledgements

I have dedicated this book to Miriam Adahan. Despite living at different ends of the earth, and only meeting a handful of times, Miriam has been the biggest influence on my work in the past 25 years.

Miriam is a psychologist and author of many books. Her first book was called *EMETT*. EMETT stands for emotional maturity established through Torah and comprises psychology, Torah wisdom and a practical method to regulate emotion.

I began teaching EMETT in Johannesburg in 1989 and, despite relocating to Sydney in 1997, have continued to run at least two classes a week ever since. The four step process that I teach relies heavily on Miriam Adahan's method and I thank her for graciously giving me permission to adapt her work. When I asked her if I could adapt her material, she was delighted to hear that more people would benefit from her knowledge. From her selfless gesture it is clear Miriam has internalised the values of humility, kindness, prioritising and focusing on higher goals.

Most of the tools I teach derive directly from EMETT as does much of the language. I take no credit for being original. My contribution, I believe, has been in the evolution of Miriam's work into a form that is accessible to every willing individual no matter their identity. I am grateful to my publisher Jane Curry for giving me the opportunity to make this contribution.

Another major influence on my work has been Steven Covey (17). His work has heavily informed my thinking making it hard to isolate and index his contribution. Many of my beliefs and teachings have been inspired or validated by Steven's work. In particular, my chapter on prioritising yourself is an adaptation of his habit of "first things first".

It is difficult for me to identify all the authors, academics and clinicians who have influenced and inspired me. This book represents my life's work, and has grown from 32 years of practise as a clinical psychologist and eight years of working as an occupational therapist. Constant reading and updating my skills, attendance at countless workshops and counselling thousands of clients since 1974 have all resulted in my accumulated knowledge. I thank you all.

I also owe a huge debt of gratitude to my clients past and present. I have worked with each of you with love and a real drive to assist. Over the years I have refined my manual, its tools and processes by utilising them clinically and observing *in vivo* the effectiveness of the course. Thanks to all of you I can now say, categorically, that this method definitely works and fairly rapidly too.

It is easy to identify the wonderful people in my life who support me in my life's mission. Lisa, my personal assistant and practice manager, helps make order out of my many creative ideas and work commitments. My good friends give my life balance and perspective.

My loving husband is an ongoing cheerleader who often has had to pick up the slack at home, something which he always does cheerfully. My beloved children and their families give me joy and the ability to persevere daily. My mother continues to make sure that I look after myself as only a loving mother can. My sister, who is also my best friend, is always there to listen and provide support.

Most of all I thank my Creator who has given me such a rich life, talents, strength and passion to complete this work. If this book improves the life of only one person, my life will have been truly blessed.

Contents

Introduction

Is this book for me?

Most people in the 21st century suffer from stress and anxiety of some kind. The official statistic is that one in four people suffer from diagnosable anxiety at any given time. (1) However, millions of people struggle to get through their day-to-day lives calmly.

This book has been written to assist any individual who is suffering from anxiety or stress. Whether your anxiety is mild, moderate or severe, the tools presented here will be useful. Even if you have never received a formal diagnosis, but you feel stressed at times, the information in this book will be of use.

What makes this book different?

This book is a practical, self-help manual that gives you the tools to lower and manage anxiety. The key word here is practical. You can jump right in and begin to utilise what you have learnt immediately. The tools are provided in a weekly format so that all you have to do is read and process them exactly as prescribed.

I have chosen those tools that have proved most helpful to my clients and synthesised them in a unique way. I have taught these tools to hundreds of people over the past 30 years, so I know that they work. All you have to do is apply yourself, and work through the manual as prescribed, to manage your fears and panic.

You may already be familiar with many of the tools. However, just reading about them, or practising them only once or twice will have no positive effect on your symptoms. It is rewiring the brain that leads to change (2) and that comes through repeated application. This book provides the wherewithal to rewire your brain. (See in particular the chapter on neuropsychotherapy.)

This book is not a textbook on anxiety. Information on differing diagnoses, causes of anxiety and other treatments are available in abundance elsewhere. (3) I consciously have chosen to focus on practical strategies because, in my experience, anxiety sufferers want relief first and foremost.

There is some theory scattered throughout the chapters, but my emphasis is on practical strategies that will make a difference to your life in a short space of time. This pattern replicates, to a large extent, the clinical process that I have successfully utilised with face-to-face clients over the past three decades.

It is not an easy task to capture a therapeutic process on paper. Likewise, it is not always easy to translate what you read into practice. For such a process to work, you need to participate fully. Specifically, you will need to answer the questions, do the exercises, keep a daily monitoring diary and, MOST IMPORTANTLY, fill out a worksheet every day.

Research shows that real and lasting change takes 90 days. (4) So it is important not to try to speed through the book. If you concentrate on learning only a few tools per week as prescribed you will be able to digest the information and assimilate it into your daily routine.

What about face-to-face therapy?

Face-to-face therapy is essential in many cases. Human beings are complex with complicated mental health issues which can be separated into three main categories:

1. emotion regulation: which includes managing the symptoms of anxiety, depression and anger
2. interpersonal skills: which encapsulate the ability to sustain long-term relationships, parenting, communication, assertiveness and leadership
3. intra-personal competencies: comprising self-esteem, identity and authenticity

The majority of my work to date has been face-to-face therapy and I have witnessed many times the power of creating a safe space for clients to reflect and make changes. Since my original training was in psychodynamic therapy, I have always highly valued reflection and insight. Moreover, having worked with hundreds of parents and couples, I understand the worth in meeting face-to-face with people and working through issues or empowering them with skills training.

However, face-to-face therapy is not always possible for many people and that is where the tools in this book become important. They offer a means for people to learn and apply symptom management and self-regulation.

In the domain of emotion regulation, research has revealed that symptom management and self-regulation of emotions, can successfully be managed in different ways. My clinical experience has confirmed these findings.

Today there are hundreds of universities offering evidence-based online e-therapy courses.(5) In addition, there are apps for smart phones that have been found to be effective in keeping individuals focused and consistent, helping them to practise tools such as mindfulness.(6)

If you are self-motivated and move through the process prescribed in this book diligently, you will be successful in lowering your anxiety and managing your symptoms. However, if your motivation is lacking, or you find it hard to stay the course, a real life counsellor may be necessary.

In my experience, learning to lower anxiety and manage symptoms is the first step towards actualising yourself. Often anxiety signals deeper difficulties but you cannot move forward and deal with these difficulties because your current symptoms are so crippling.

This manual does not aim to be a substitute for face-to-face therapy. Instead, it lies in the genre of e-therapy and can certainly improve the quality of your life by teaching you effective skills while providing a format to develop new neural pathways and to stay on track.

> Thomas was referred to me by his doctor because he was unable to sleep, eat or concentrate. He gave me some background information but was unable to think about anything else except his symptoms. Therefore, we immediately launched into the 12-week process enumerated in this book.
>
> *By session eight, Thomas was feeling calmer. He could finally begin to analyse his primary relationship and admit that it was a major source of discontent. He could also begin to think*

about what he wanted from the relationship in the long-term. We completed the 12 sessions and continued working together in therapy, aiming to get clarity about his relationship.

> Allison hated her job but felt unable to make a change. Every time an acquaintance told her to stop whinging and start doing something constructive, Allison would shut down and be unable to think straight.

We plunged into the 12-week treatment process without giving much time or energy to the external issues. By session six, Allison had started to talk about work and her aspirations. By session 12, Allison was free of anxiety symptoms and she felt able to move forward in her career.

> Sally was a client who presented with parenting issues. We spent several months evaluating her parenting style, the personality profiles of herself and her children as well as trying different ways of gaining her children's cooperation. Sally's progress was slow. One day she broke down saying that she was so worried that something terrible would happen to her children that she tended to be overprotective.

Sally's admission alerted me to her anxiety and how it was interfering with her functioning as a parent. I changed direction and I began to teach Sally anxiety management tools. After seven sessions of cognitive behavioural therapy (CBT), Sally was able to implement the parenting strategies we discussed effectively.

If you are not certain whether or not you need face-to-face therapy, why not make a start here? Dedicate yourself to going through this process systematically and thoroughly. Once you are anxiety free, you may be able to work through your other issues without help. If not, then face-to-face therapy could be warranted.

I believe in empowering clients to be proactive in helping themselves. I strongly support the self-determination model (7) which has shown that being self-determined builds self-esteem and facilitates success. There is so much you can do to help yourself be well, grow and thrive. Begin wellness by taking responsibility for your health. Seek help where necessary but only after you have done all you can yourself.

At the risk of belabouring this point, take the example of the treatment of diabetes. Patients often rush to doctors to be treated. In many cases the advice a doctor gives relates to lifestyle changes, being responsible for what you eat and when, and being proactive about exercise. Those patients who do not take responsibility for their lifestyle and health, and instead insist on a medical solution can become totally dependent on doctors and medications. In giving up their responsibility to themselves they then contribute to their own inability to self-help which can in turn lead to feelings of helplessness and depression and so the cycle continues. In my expert opinion, anxiety is a lot like diabetes. There is so much that you can do to fix the problem before you have to resort to medication. Change your lifestyle as I suggest, exercise, practise the tools presented here and you may be pleasantly surprised to find that you get well without medical intervention.

Your pathway to success

This book is divided into 12 segments corresponding to 12 weeks. I recommend that you set aside an hour a week to work through the appropriate tools. You will find it easier to maintain if you designate a specific weekly time, for example: every Sunday evening at 7:00pm.

Read the material and fill in the exercises. You will get more out of the process if you write down your answers as opposed to just saying them to yourself. Commitments especially need to be put in writing.

You will also need to set aside pockets of time every day to:

> fill out an anxiety management worksheet
> fill out the daily monitoring diary
> practise relaxation, breathing and/or mindfulness
> exercise

Psychology today (8) recognises that it is not enough to simply talk about issues and gain insights. Improved mental health often requires lifestyle changes. At first, it may feel difficult to make the changes and find the time to enact them. However, once you do these activities regularly, they will become a seamless part of your day-to-day living.

Slow and steady wins the race. Good luck!

Week 1

This part covers the theory on which this course is based. It includes sections on:

> the nature of anxiety, and

> the psychological theories underpinning my treatment of anxiety.

These chapters are written for the layperson and have just enough information to give you an understanding of what anxiety is and how it can affect you. There is also information on how cognitive behavioural therapy (CBT) works.

Armed with this material, you will be an informed "client" who will increasingly become empowered to help yourself. I believe that the more you are educated about anxiety, and how to manage it, the more positive you will be. Moreover, the more likely you will be to take ownership of the process and, ultimately, for helping yourself to get better.

Clinical experience has shown me that the more hope a client has and believes in their own ability to be part of the treatment process the better the prognosis. Additionally, the more the client is active in selecting and practising the tools found in this book, the better the long-term outcome.

In contrast, the traditional medical model is very different and is based on the assertion that the doctor is the expert and you, as a patient, rely on him/her to make you well. All you have to do is take the prescription, get it filled at the pharmacy and take your medication as directed. Usually people have no idea what the medication they are taking consists of and how it really works. Frequently they can feel helpless and hopeless, particularly if they do not believe there is much they can do to get well aside from taking medication.

Let me add here that I am not against medications per se. Research has shown that for depression, a combination of anti-depressant medication and CBT is most effective. (9) Therefore, where it is indicated, I encourage my clients to take prescribed medication. However, with anxiety, long-term medication has been shown in the past to be problematic. (10)

Moreover, I have seen over years of clinical practice that many of my clients who suffer from anxiety do not need and have never needed medication. Learning my tools and the four step process is all they need to get well and stay well.

Week one is an ideal week for you to do some further reading about anxiety if you like. Information on this topic is not difficult to source. The web is literally bursting with information. However, I do advise caution. Be discerning and only read information from credible sources.

A credible source is written by someone with an academic qualification in the mental health field. Many individuals write their life stories and extrapolate from that. While it can be enlightening and interesting to hear about personal experiences of anxiety, that is all they are — personal experiences. However, since these personal stories are not backed by research, what works for one individual will not necessarily apply to you.

Psychology is a science, not an art. Psychologists base their diagnoses and treatments on research and data collected from thousands of subjects worldwide. A credible source will provide their academic qualifications plus cite their sources on which their information is based.

The nature of anxiety

What is anxiety?

It is important to understand that anxiety is a vital, in-built human function. It helps you survive when there is a real threat to your wellbeing. This can be illustrated by the following example:

A man is having his morning swim at the beach. Suddenly, some distance away he spots a fin moving through the water. The man identifies it as a shark, realises the danger and responds with fear. This is an appropriate and functional response.

This fear response is called the "fight or flight response". It occurs when a person is in danger or believes they are in danger. It is adaptive in circumstances such as the one above because it helps the man to swim away quickly, or to fight the shark, thereby saving his life.

However, the "fight or flight response" is frequently activated when there is no real danger. In the absence of a real threat, there is no outlet for the "extra steam" which your body has produced. Instead, you experience the uncomfortable feelings of anxiety, fear and panic.

The aim of this book is to teach you how to stop yourself from setting off a "fight or flight" response unnecessarily.

What happens when your "fight or flight" response is activated?

When your fight/flight response is set off, three major types of responses occur:

1. thoughts (also called cognitions)
2. actions (also called behaviours)
3. bodily reactions (also called physiological responses)

Thoughts

Specific types of negative thinking have been identified as triggering, maintaining or heightening the "fight or flight" reaction.

One type of negative thinking is to *over-estimate the chance that negative things will happen.*

For example:

> If you believe that there is a 90% chance that you will encounter a shark when entering the sea; your fear response system will be activated. In reality, the chance of encountering a shark is much less than 90% (on average there has been one shark attack per year in Australia over the past 200 years). (11)

> Such thinking may include: "I will make a mistake when I give my speech." How do you know that you will definitely make a mistake?

> Such thinking may include: "I just know that I will not meet anybody I know at the party and will stand like a wall flower all evening." How can you predict this with certainty? What evidence do you have?

Another type of negative thinking is to *over-estimate the cost of negative events.*

For example:

> > If you believe that when you went swimming you would encounter a shark, get attacked and die you would be much more fearful than if you believe that the likelihood of a shark attack being fatal is less than 30% of attacks. (11)

> > In a work context such thinking may include: "If I do this speech badly, all my colleagues will think that I am stupid, I will lose my job and never be respected again."

> > In a social context such thinking may include, "If I stand alone all evening, then people will notice and gossip about me and destroy all future dating prospects."

EXERCISE 1

Do you utilise either of the above two types of negative thinking?

If so, please tick them.

Write down an example of when you do this and what you tell yourself.

Actions/behaviours

Certain behaviours will keep your anxiety at a high level once it has been activated. Please tick those that are relevant to you:

> You avoid anxiety-provoking situations. For example, you isolate yourself because you fear meeting new people. Avoidance maintains fear and may even increase it.

> You do not stay in your feared situation long enough. For example, you fear crowds so you flee as soon as a crowd starts to build around you. Fleeing maintains the fear and may also intensify it.

> You do not do things you would really like to do nor do you achieve certain goals. For example, you do not present your work at a meeting because you are afraid of public speaking. Or you do not apply for a job you would love because you fear getting rejected.

> You over-plan to prevent your highly feared predicted event from occurring. For example, you research to the minutest detail the background of a speech you have to make for fear you will otherwise look incompetent.

> You over-prepare as a safety behaviour because you believe it will stop the feared event from happening. Over-preparing may mean practising your speech hundreds of times before you deliver it.

> You ruminate. This is a form of unproductive worry where you constantly chew on your thoughts without a result or purpose.

> You are hyper vigilant. You keep your eyes peeled for a potential threat and/or you pay greater attention to your body sensations.

> You do not practise skills you have been taught like relaxation, meditation and mindfulness.

> You do not challenge your thoughts.

> You maintain behaviours that promote anxiety. This includes continuing to consume stimulants or staying in a stressful job.

Did you know that certain substances may be contributing to your anxiety? Please tick if you consume any of the following and assign a weekly amount.

- alcohol   ____________ pw
- marijuana ____________ pw
- nicotine ____________ pw
- coffee ____________ pw
- medications that are stimulants ____________ pw
- cortisone/steroids ____________ pw
- speed ____________ pw
- appetite suppressants ____________ pw

Certain lifestyle behaviours may be contributing to your anxiety. Please tick those that apply to you and elaborate below.

> insufficient sleep
> broken sleep
> eating irregularly
> poor nutrition

EXERCISE 2

Have you identified any substances or lifestyle behaviours that may be contributing to your anxiety?   YES/NO

If yes, commit to make changes below. Make small changes that you will be able to sustain.

> *Example: My medications increase my heart rate. I will speak to my doctor about other options.*

> *Example: From today I will reduce my coffee intake by one cup per day.*

Bodily reactions

Your body reacts when you are fearful or anxious. Please tick the symptoms that you experience when you are anxious.

> Breathing rate and depth increases to make more oxygen available to the muscles for fight or flight. You can experience yawning, breathlessness, smothering feelings, tightness in the chest. This may reduce blood supply to the head (not dangerous) which can lead to dizziness, light-headedness, blurred vision, confusion, hot flushes and feelings of unreality.

> Heart rate and blood pressure increase enabling blood and oxygen to be pumped around the body more quickly. You may experience this as a "pounding heart".

> Sweating increases. This cools the body preventing it from overheating when strenuous physical activity begins.

> Muscle tension increases preparing your body to respond quickly. You may experience this as aches, pains, trembling, shaking and feelings of exhaustion.

> Digestive system activity slows allowing more energy to be diverted to the fight or flight systems. You may experience a dry mouth, nausea, heavy stomach.

> Blood redistribution to muscles occurs often resulting in tingling of fingers or toes and/or numbness.

> Immune system slows down. This allows your body to put all its efforts into escaping. You may have noticed that you frequently suffer from coughs, colds and sore throats.

Remember, these responses are vital to your survival when you are facing real danger. However, when you are not in danger, ongoing bodily reactions to stress may be harmful.

EXERCISE 3

Do you have any other symptoms that are not mentioned here? Please list them.

In reading the list above did you learn something about symptoms that you have experienced but were not aware that they were a consequence of anxiety?

If yes, please elaborate.

What causes anxiety?

Research has shown that it is your *thoughts*, and principally your thoughts, that cause your anxiety. Simply put, it is what you tell yourself in a particular situation that sets off your emotions, behaviours and bodily reactions.

Like most of us, you are not aware of what you are thinking when you get stressed. The majority of your thoughts occur automatically and at a subliminal level. This prevents you from being able to link your thoughts to your stress.

As you proceed through this manual, however, you will learn to identify your personal thinking style, and particular thoughts, that precipitate your anxiety.

Which thoughts precipitate anxiety?

Thoughts can be neutral, positive or negative.

Let us say that you notice your bicycle leaning on the fence.

> You could have a neutral thought such as "I will ride my bike later today."
> You could have a positive thought such as "I can ride a bicycle very well."
> An example of a negative thought would be "I have not ridden my bike for a few days so I will probably fall if I ride today."

It is your *negative automatic thoughts that cause distress* and can make it difficult for you to function effectively in your daily life.

Can thoughts be changed?

The simple answer is "Yes." The first step is self-awareness. As you proceed with this process, and participate in the exercises below, you will soon learn what your specific negative, unconscious thoughts are. You will also learn more helpful ways of thinking and how to replace your negative thoughts with positive ones.

Changing thoughts is an easy process which you will learn in a step-by-step manner. Practice and repetition over 90 days will ensure that your new way of thinking endures.

Psychological theories underpinning my treatment of anxiety

The treatment that I have developed and laid out in this handbook rests on two evidence-based psychological theories: neuro-psychotherapy and cognitive behavioural therapy (CBT).

Neuro-psychotherapy made simple

Many people have a pessimistic world view that they believe they cannot change. Alternatively, if change were possible, they believe it would be difficult and laborious. Some common assumptions include:

> I was born anxious
> This is just the way I am
> I have been stressed for so long I do not know how to be different
> This is my personality
> I am like this because I am a Virgo (or whatever your star sign is)
> It is genetic, everybody in my family gets stressed
> I am hardwired to be stressed
> Only medication will help

All the above assumptions are incorrect. The abundance of neuro-psychotherapy (10) research in the past 20 years has proven that:

> Even if you have a genetic tendency towards anxiety, or you have been anxious for a long time, it is still possible to make

changes. We now know that a brain is neuroplastic which means it can develop new pathways, at any age, with practice and repetition.

> Anxiety has nothing to do with your personality or your star sign. It is the result of your primitive brain firing. When you learn to stop your primitive brain from firing, and train your smart brain to fire helpful circuits, your anxiety will reduce.

> Since medication targets neurotransmitters, which is the connecting substance between neurons, it does not promote the development of new neural circuits. This means that medication may be useful in calming you down in the present moment but it does not make structural changes.

> The optimum method for treatment should aim at neurons and the development of new, adaptive neural circuits.

The Brain

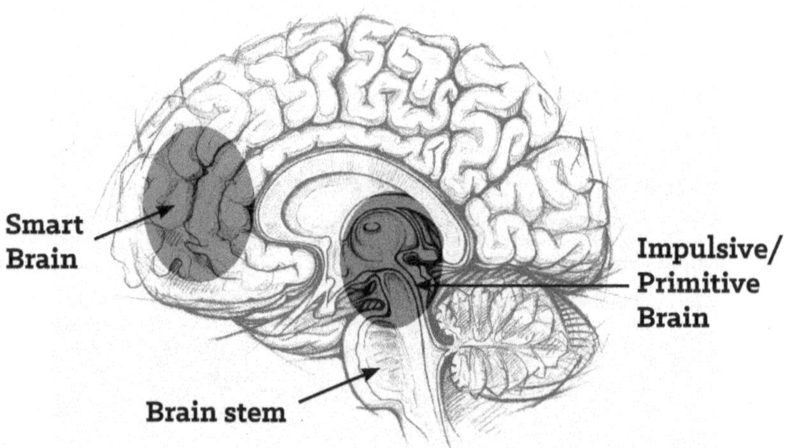

Sketch representing the brain and two key areas

Diagram 1 (10)

On this diagram of the brain, two areas are highlighted. They are called the smart brain and the primitive/impulsive brain. The part of you that is reading this book, and understanding it, is your smart brain. The primitive/impulsive brain controls your breathing and other essential lifesaving functions. It is constantly on the alert to keep you safe in dangerous situations.

Have you ever been walking along a street when suddenly, without thought, you move closer to the buildings and away from the road. At that instant, a large truck which has lost control climbs the path but misses you. Your quick movement has saved your life. You are incredulous and wonder "How did I do that? I did not even see the truck coming."

It was your primitive/impulsive brain, which is constantly on the lookout for danger that picked up cues and literally moved you to safety. This is helpful and adaptive.

However, when your primitive/impulsive brain fires often, and without cause, it leads to symptoms of anxiety. Moreover, on a neurological level, continual neural firing leads to the development of thick neural circuits.

The thick neural circuits look like this.

The Brain

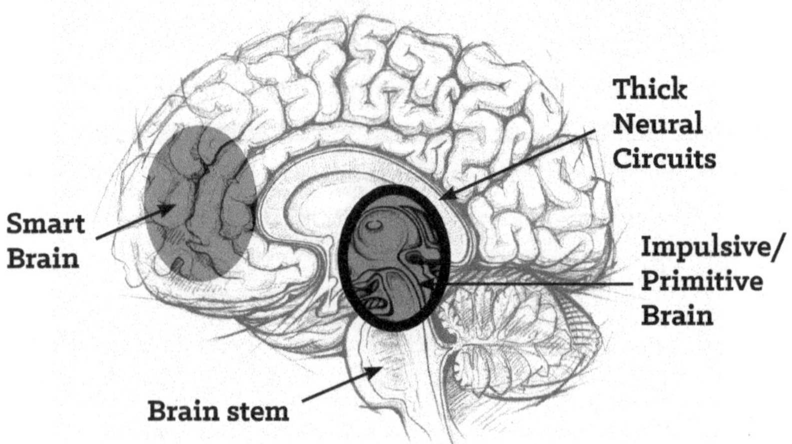

*Sketch representing thick neural circuits
when the primitive brain fires repeatedly.*

Diagram 2 (adapted) (10)

Aim of this treatment process

My aim is to assist you to develop new neural pathways in your smart brain. As the healthier neural pathways develop in your smart brain, the less the pathways in your primitive brain will fire. In fact, the old unhealthy pathways will disappear over time.

The way that you will develop new, thick neural pathways in your smart brain is by practising the new thoughts that you will learn in this workbook, over and over. Specifically, when you practise the four step process on the Anxiety Management Worksheet, you will actually be learning a new way of thinking. Moreover, when you fill out a worksheet every day for 90 days, you will ensure that you establish new neural pathways which will endure. Practically, this means that you will ensure that you are thinking "smart thoughts" most of the time.

After 90 days of practising the four step process, your smart brain will look like this.

The Brain

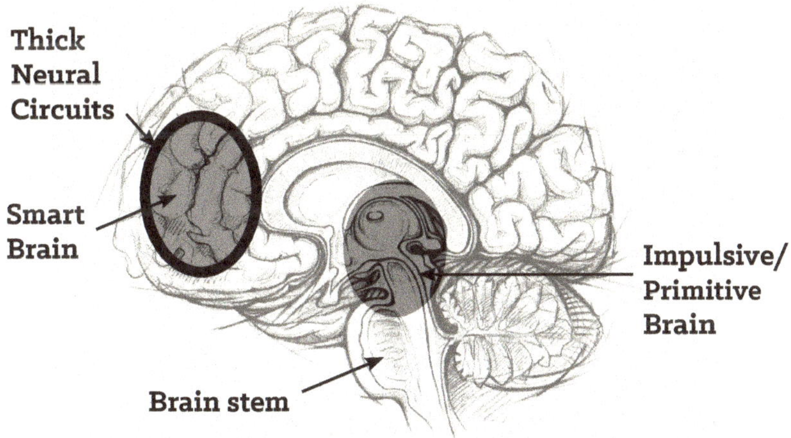

Sketch representing thick neural circuits when the smart brain fires repeatedly.

Diagram 3 (10)

Cognitive behavioural therapy (CBT)

The method that I utilise to train the brain to think differently is derived mainly from a psychological treatment called cognitive behavioural therapy (CBT). CBT has been thoroughly researched for over many years, all over the world, and on thousands of people. It has been proven to be highly effective in treating anxiety.

CBT is an approach that focuses on the relationship that exists between thoughts (cognitions), behaviours and bodily reactions. (12)

I explain CBT using my *EBB FLOW model* to indicate optimism and fluidity. Just as the sea ebbs and flows with ease, so too you will learn how to move easily from a state of stress and anxiety to a state of calm.

EBB FLOW model

EBB FLOW model
E = Event
B = Belief about the event
B = Behaviour
F = Feelings
L = Limbic system
O = Outcome
W = Win/win

It works like this:

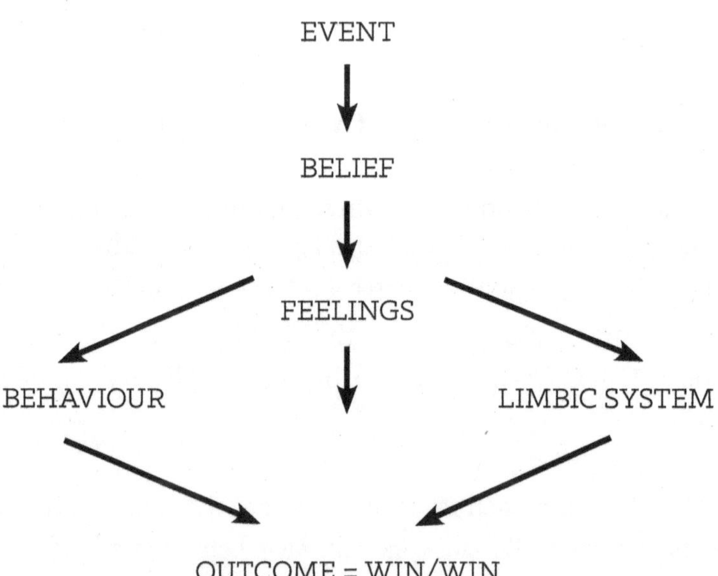

E=Event: Any occurrence, no matter how small, that takes place in your day-to-day activities.

B=Belief: When an event occurs, you will automatically have a thought about it. You may not be aware of the thought since it races through your mind automatically, unconsciously and very, very quickly. Your thought can be positive or negative. For instance, if you are thinking that it is great that you are able to have the experience of swimming with a shark, the thought is positive. Alternatively, if you are thinking that you might be killed, the thought is negative.

> neutral — "There is a shark swimming over there."
> positive — "Wow, what an interesting creature!"
> negative — "The shark is going to kill me."

I use the image of sharks to explain the "fight or flight" phenomenon in order to make a strong case for the assertion that most of life's events are neutral. Many people have argued with me saying "Come on. Sharks cannot be neutral. Everybody finds them scary." However, they are not correct. In Australia, people often pay to go swimming with sharks and are thrilled when they see them up close. Videographers working for *National Geographic* are elated if a shark comes close and they can film it. This confirms that it is not the shark itself that causes fear but the thought that goes with it.

B=Behaviour: Your behaviour during an event will be determined by your thoughts. Therefore, if you have the positive thought (eg it is a privilege that the shark is swimming nearby) you will act in a curious and accepting manner towards it. However, if you have a negative thought, namely, that sharks are dangerous and you'll be eaten, you will act in a threatened and fearful manner.

F=Feelings: Your automatic thought will influence the way you feel as well. The positive thought will result in you feeling excited, or interested, while the negative thought will result in you feeling anxious and terrified.

L=Limbic system: When you think a negative thought, it activates the limbic system which is responsible for setting off the "fight or flight" reaction in your body. The limbic system is part of your primitive brain and prepares your breathing, heart rate, muscles and digestion for danger (or perceived danger). These bodily reactions can be very distressing for an anxious person. Some individuals have been known to rush to the emergency department of the nearest hospital fearing that they are suffering from a heart attack when in fact what they are experiencing is a panic attack.

O=Outcome: The outcome of an event is totally connected to your initial thoughts about it. A positive thought may help to create a positive outcome as you may act calmly near the shark and not attract its attention. A negative thought will often result in a negative outcome, eg splashing and screaming could attract the attention of the shark.

W=Win/win: The purpose of this course is to teach you to achieve a winning solution. Your ability to reduce and manage your "fight or flight" response system will enhance your ability to find helpful solutions.

The basic philosophy of the EBB FLOW model is that everyday life events are neutral in and of themselves. What makes us react in a positive or negative manner to an event is the belief that we ascribe to an event.

Catastrophic life events, such as an airplane crash, cannot be said to be neutral. I do not attempt to address coping with cataclysmic events in this book. This book is written for people living everyday lives, with everyday problems, who suffer from anxiety and stress.

Ebb and flow

The following illustration reveals just how fluid thoughts are and how quickly we can move from one emotional state to another.

Mr Jones catches a ferry every Sunday morning. He regards it as his special time to relax and enjoy Sydney Harbour at its best. One Sunday, as the ferry leaves the city, three children begin to behave badly. They yell and jump up and down. Mr Jones is infuriated and is about to yell at them to shut up when a man comes up to him. "I am so sorry my children are being disruptive," he says, "but we have just come from the hospital. Their mum has just died."

In a flash, Mr Jones transforms from fury to compassion. Suddenly he wants to help the children and their unruly behaviour does not bother him.

When the ferry arrives in Manly, the captain of the ferry sees Mr Jones. "I hope Mr X did not tell you his fabricated story about his wife dying? He tells it to everybody so that he does not have to discipline his kids."

In an instant, Mr Jones is furious again.

See how quickly that happened? Mr Jones moved from fury to compassion and back to fury easily and quickly.

Once you learn to identify your thoughts and challenge them, you too can move from anxiety to calm quickly and easily.

You are waiting for exam results. You are convinced that you are going to fail. You are predicting gloomily that you will not get the job you had hoped for and your life will be dismal.

When the results come out, you discover that you achieved a high score. In a second you move from negativity to positivity, believing that the job you want, and its associated success, are all possible.

Again, you can see how quickly and easily you moved from fear to optimism.

How CBT works

A basic premise of CBT is that you can only think one thought at a time. When you have a negative thought and replace it with a helpful thought your anxiety will dissipate. This is analogous to watching television and changing channels. You can only watch one channel at a time.

You are watching a documentary about hospitals on Channel 7 and you start feeling sad. You change channels. Channel 9 is showing a comedy. You choose to stay with Channel 9. Your mood immediately lightens and, overall, you feel better.

When you master the four step process below, you will be able to "switch channels" too. You will be able to move from a negative thought to a neutral or positive thought with ease thereby lifting your mood and feeling calmer.

Homework

This week is "theory week". It is the time allocated for you to educate yourself about anxiety in general and the optimum way to treat it (CBT).

Spend at least one hour this week:

> going over these notes
> reading further afield (optional)

Week 2

This week, the focus is on learning how to fill in the anxiety management worksheet and the daily monitoring diary.

It is essential that you familiarise yourself with these two processes as you will be utilising them every day.

Anxiety management worksheet

The anxiety management worksheet is the major tool in my CBT program. More than anything else, filling out one worksheet every day is what will effect change in your life.

Do this for 90 days consecutively. After 90 days, you may reduce to one worksheet every second day for the next three months. After that, filling out one anxiety management worksheet per week will be sufficient to keep your new helpful thoughts wired.

Warning: If you stop filling out worksheets altogether, you could relapse and become anxious again over time.

How it works

The worksheet is the practical application of the EBB FLOW paradigm. It is a four step process (13) that is easy to do. In fact, the worksheet is self-explanatory. I recommend that you fill one in now to get the gist of it.

Date: ___________

Anxiety Management Worksheet

The purpose of this worksheet is to help you to see every stressful event as an opportunity for
1. greater understanding of yourself, your anxiety and the people around you, and
2. practicing tools to manage your anxiety.

Step One: An Event

Briefly describe an event when you became anxious. Give such details as time, place and people involved, and end with "That's when I began to work myself up..."

____

____

____

_______________________________ Rate your anxiety on a scale of 0 to 100%: [   ] %

E

Step Two: The Working-Up Process

Learn about your working up process by identifying your thoughts, feelings, behaviours and bodily reactions during the event. Tick the ones that most resonate with you.

Undermining Beliefs

B

I fear that I have lost...
- approval
- control
- co-operation
- face
- respect
- success
- trust
- validation
- love

This event proves that I am...
- stupid
- abnormal
- incompetent
- lazy
- irresponsible
- a total failure
- undisciplined
- untogether
- useless

I worry that I will suffer...
- mental collapse
- illness
- financial hardship

What I want is...
- total control
- respect
- success
- perfection
- comfort
- fairness
- tranquility
- all the answers
- for life to go smoothly
- to be all things to all people

Self-destructive Behaviour

Active
- get violent
- swear
- slam doors
- run away
- overeat
- harm myself
- criticise

Passive
- take it too seriously
- give up
- wallow in self pity
- sulk
- space out
- procrastinate
- give in
- be controlled

Intense Feelings

Angry feelings
- hateful
- aggravated
- annoyed
- hostile
- outraged
- punitive
- resentful
- vengeful

- attacked
- worn out
- rejected
- jealous
- afraid
- exploited
- lonely
- abandoned
- guilty
- insulted

Fearful feelings
- helpless
- hopeless
- disappointed
- sad

- confused
- disillusioned
- misunderstood
- trapped

Bodily Reactions (limbic system)

I am uncomfortable because I am experiencing...
- tremors
- nausea
- sweaty palms
- stomach-ache
- pounding heart
- general tension
- fatigue
- imagination on fire
- headache
- dry mouth
- jaw clenching
- shortness of breath

Continued over

B   **F**   **L**

Step Three: The Working-Down Process

Begin with, "Suddenly I realised that I was anxious and that I had choices..." This is the step of self-leadership and trust in one's ability to handle the situation.

Choose helpful thoughts:

I choose to depersonalise
There is no intention to hurt me. He is doing the best he can with the tools he has at the moment.

I choose realism over romanticism
Life presents many obstacles. I lower or raise standards as needed.

There is no right or wrong
Unless it is a moral issue, I will see it simply as a difference of opinion and/or taste.

I choose the total view of positivity
Even though this event is negative, the total view of his behaviour is positive.

I surrender control
Since I cannot change this situation, I choose to let go of it.

I choose to put this event in perspective This event is not a catastrophe because it is not life threatening. It can be viewed as a trivial life event, a normal life problem that needs to be solved not dramatised.

I choose to view this event as average, falling within the normal range
This event is not exceptional; many people have gone through this.

It's temporary - "this too shall pass"
Life is constantly changing and moving through phases and this situation will also change.

Fears or facts?
Why fear? It may not happen!

I choose to focus on this as a learning experience
Every problem that comes my way is an opportunity for me to learn about my strengths and weaknesses, others and life.

Feel soothing emotions:

I choose to feel warm, loving emotions. I do this by focusing on my heart and letting love, trust forgiveness, compassion, hope or gratitude fill my heart space.

Behave constructively:

I choose to work in part acts:
I will break the overwhelming job into manageable parts.

Do the difficult:
I will face what I fear and act with self-discipline.

I choose to solutionise:
I will find a solution by taking advice or doing research.

Prioritise myself:
I will keep my life balanced by meeting friends, doing exercise or laughing.

Compartmentalise:
I will not let this event cloud my whole day; I will focus on something else now.

Utilise calming strategies:

When I:
- relax,
- breathe deeply,
- go for a run,
- shower,
- lie down,
- read,
- watch TV,
- climb into a mental helicopter,
- practice mindfulness/meditation,

my mind and body calm down.

Step Four: The Self Motivation Process

Endorse yourself for any growth no matter how small.

In the past I would have...

____

____

But this time I...

____

____

Tick off the traits that you strengthened when you worked down your anxiety:

☐ generosity   ☐ peacefulness
☐ kindness   ☐ self-discipline
☐ compassion   ☐ forgiveness
☐ consideration   ☐ courage
☐ helpfulness   ☐ responsibility
☐ respectfulness   ☐ reliability
☐ honesty   ☐ loyalty
☐ fairness   ☐ love
☐ patience   ☐ humility

Rate your anxiety on a scale of 0 to 100%:

_______%

O

W

Now that you have completed an anxiety management worksheet, read through the steps below which provide details and an explanation of the four step process.

Step one

Step one of the worksheet is the place where you:

a) jot down an event where you worked yourself up
b) rate your anxiety as a percentage.

Step One: An Event

Briefly describe an event when you became anxious. Give such details as time, place and people involved, and end with "That's when I began to work myself up..."

____

____ E

____

_________________________________ Rate your anxiety on a scale of 0 to 100%: [   ] %

The event only requires a few lines because the details surrounding an event are less important than you taking responsibility for your emotional response by saying "That's when I began to work myself up."

Remember, events are neutral. It is what you are thinking and saying about the event that leads to anxiety. From today, start saying:

> "I work myself up when I tell myself..."
> "I stress myself when I tell myself..."
> "I anger myself when I tell myself.... "

For example:

> "Last week, I was waiting for a bus when a person pushed in the line ahead of me. That's when I began to work myself up."
> "My boss corrected my spelling. That's when I began to work myself up."
> "A letter I sent came back address unknown. That's when I began to work myself up."

It is not necessary to provide more details than that. The focus is on your working up process and not specific factors. In my experience, too many details tend to be a distraction from taking responsibility for your mental state.

Rate your anxiety on a scale of 0 to 100%. This rating is totally subjective and only you can rate yourself. Rate it as highly as you felt was appropriate at the time of the event even if now it seems ridiculously high.

Step two

Step two leads to self-awareness. It will help you to identify the underlying beliefs that led to self-destructive behaviours, intense feelings and uncomfortable bodily reactions.

Beliefs

Discover what your insecure thoughts/beliefs were that led to your anxiety by reading through the lists provided and ticking those that resonate. Act quickly and spontaneously. Do not over-think your answers. Even if now they seem irrational, tick those beliefs that you had at the time of the event.

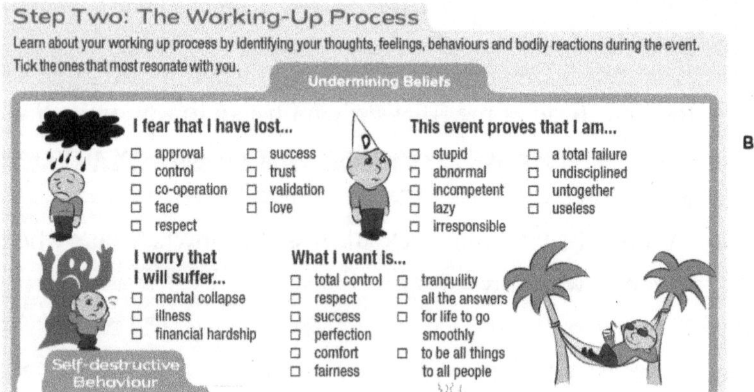

There are four main types of insecure thoughts:

1. Thoughts about loss or insecurity:
    "I fear that I have lost approval, control, cooperation, face, respect, success, trust, validation or love."

2. Thoughts concerning shame or inferiority:
    "This event proves that I am stupid, abnormal, incompetent, lazy, irresponsible, a total failure, undisciplined, untogether or useless."

3. Catastrophic thoughts:
    "I worry that I will suffer illness or a mental or physical collapse."

4. Unrealistic wishes which stir up feelings of anxiety:
    "What I want is total control, respect, success, perfection, comfort, fairness, tranquillity, all the answers, for life to go smoothly or to be all things to all people."

Self-destructive behaviours

Undermining beliefs can cause active and/or passive self-destructive behaviours. These are behaviours you indulge in when you have worked yourself up.

Active self-destructive behaviours include:

- get violent
- swear
- slam doors
- run away
- overeat
- harm myself
- criticise

Passive self-destructive behaviours include:

- take it too seriously
- give up
- wallow in self-pity
- sulk
- space out
- procrastinate
- give in
- be controlled

Intense feelings

Undermining beliefs can lead to intense feelings which may be angry or fearful. Angry feelings are feelings that are directed

outwards, towards others, while fearful feelings are directed inwards, towards yourself.

You are driving in traffic and accidently bump into the car in front of you causing a dent.

Angry response: "You stupid idiot. Why did you slow down like that? You are responsible for this!"

Fearful response: "I am such an idiot. I always mess things up. Trust me to drive too close to the car in front."

Angry feelings include:

- hateful
- aggravated
- annoyed
- hostile
- outraged
- punitive
- resentful
- vengeful

Fearful feelings include:

- helpless
- hopeless
- disappointed
- sad
- attacked

- worn out
- rejected
- afraid
- exploited
- lonely
- abandoned
- guilty
- insulted
- confused
- disillusioned
- misunderstood
- trapped

Uncomfortable bodily reactions

Unhelpful beliefs may set off the limbic system in the brain which, in turn, cause uncomfortable bodily reactions including:

- tremors
- nausea
- sweaty palms
- stomach ache
- pounding heart
- general tension
- fatigue
- imagination on fire
- headache
- dry mouth
- jaw clenching
- shortness of breath

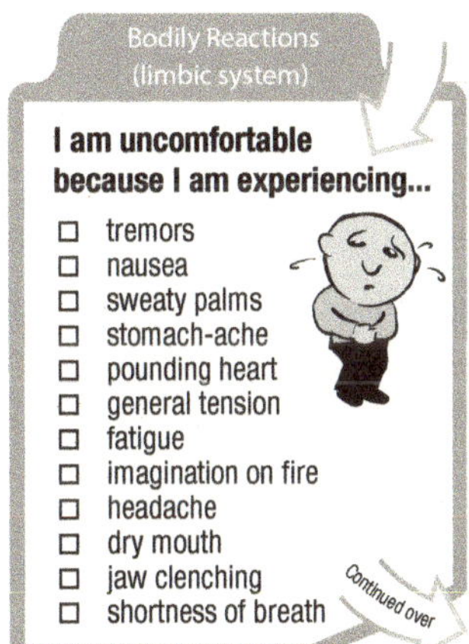

Step three

Step three is the section of the worksheet where you make a choice to move from negative thinking to helpful thinking. I specifically use the term "helpful thinking" as opposed to positive thinking. There is a whole industry devoted to teaching people how to turn a negative into a positive. My experience has taught me that you cannot always make things look positive. What you can do, however, is to think in a way that helps you to stay calm.

Jimmy is struggling to find a job. He starts to lose hope and cannot find anything positive in his situation. However, a helpful thought would assist him to persevere.

*If Jim utilised the tool "**perspective**," he would remind himself that while he is going through a challenging time, he is not in any danger. This would keep him calm. Or if he utilised the tool "**average**," he could view his problem as a common problem that many people have gone through. This would help him feel normal and hopeful.*

At no time is Jimmy trying to convince himself that there is no problem or that it does not hurt. Nor is he looking for a hidden silver lining. He is feeling calm by being realistic.

Before choosing a tool, you must ALWAYS read the top lines of the worksheet which state: *"Suddenly I realised that I was anxious and that I had choices."* This is the step of self-leadership and trust in your own ability to handle the situation.

Read these words even if you do not believe them at first. Over time you will grow to believe them. Repetition will ensure that they will become ongoing, empowering words that will automatically pop into your mind when you start to feel anxious.

There are four categories of tools that can be utilised by you to offset your negative beliefs, self-destructive behaviours, intense feelings and uncomfortable bodily reactions.

1. thinking tools
2. behaviour tools
3. feeling tools
4. calming tools

Thinking tools

When you move from negative, insecure, irrational thinking to measured, rational and secure thinking your "fight or flight" reaction will disappear. This is an *inside-out* method of changing an anxious reaction to a balanced one.

On the worksheet, there are ten helpful thoughts which you can use to challenge your insecure thoughts. I have found them to be universally helpful.

Choose helpful thoughts:

I choose to depersonalise
There is no intention to hurt me. He is doing the best he can with the tools he has at the moment.

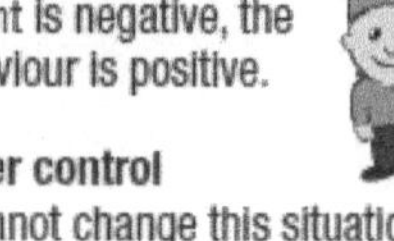

I choose realism over romanticism
Life presents many obstacles. I lower or raise standards as needed.

There is no right or wrong
Unless it is a moral issue, I will see it simply as a difference of opinion and/or taste.

I choose the total view of positivity
Even though this event is negative, the total view of his behaviour is positive.

I surrender control
Since I cannot change this situation, I choose to let go of it.

I choose to put this event in perspective This event is not a catastrophe because it is not life threatening. It can be viewed as a trivial life event, a normal life problem that needs to be solved not dramatised.

I choose to view this event as average, falling within the normal range
This event is not exceptional; many people have gone through this.

It's temporary - "this too shall pass"
Life is constantly changing and moving through phases and this situation will also change.

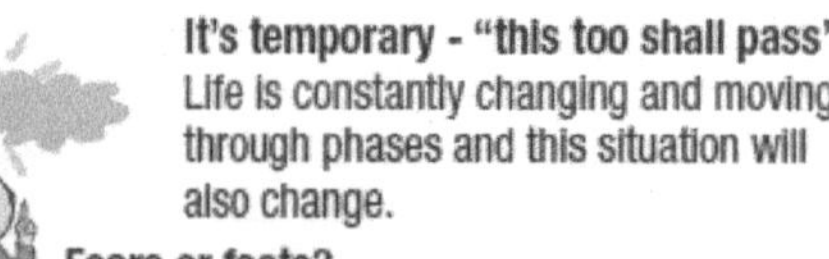

Fears or facts?
Why fear? It may not happen!

I choose to focus on this as a learning experience
Every problem that comes my way is an opportunity for me to learn about my strengths and weaknesses, others and life.

You can choose one or more of these secure thoughts to assist you to work down your anxiety. Your choice will differ from event to event.

> depersonalise
> realism

> no right or wrong
> total view of positivity
> surrender control
> perspective
> average
> temporary
> fears or facts?
> learning experience

If you ticked off a catastrophic thought like "I worry that I will suffer mental collapse," then utilising the tool "**perspective**" will help you to calm down. While, if you ticked off "What I want is total control," you could use the tool "**surrender control**" to work down your distress. If you thought that a party was a failure because it started late, choosing the tool "**total view of positivity**" will help you to feel better by looking at the overall success it truly was.

Behavioural tools

There are five behavioural tools on the worksheet. They encompass an *outside-in* approach where you become calmer through action. What this means is that you literally take action and "just do it" regardless of your thoughts or feelings at the time.

> part acts
> do the difficult
> solutionise
> prioritise myself
> compartmentalise

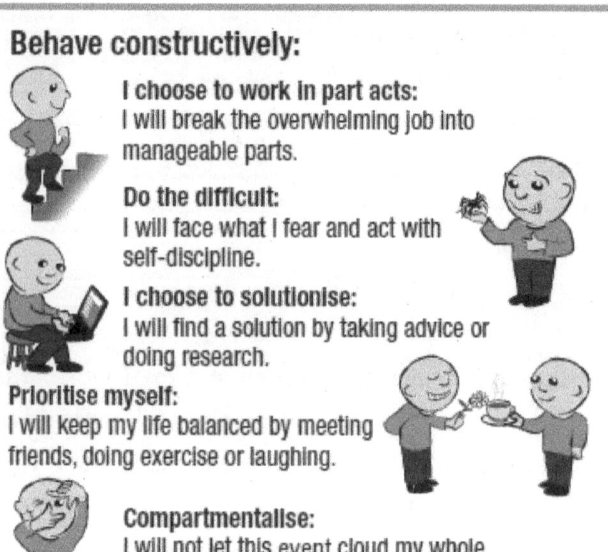

For example:

> You are moving house and are feeling overwhelmed. The tool "part acts" will assist you. Without any thought or diagnosis, begin breaking the job up into smaller pieces and you will quickly feel less anxious and more on top of things.

> If you are afraid of lifts, for example, the tool "do the difficult" is the tool of choice. Develop an exposure ladder (see page 201) and start approaching a lift ASAP.

> When you find yourself dwelling on an outburst that happened yesterday, the tool "compartmentalise" will enable you to focus on the here and now.

Feeling tools

Just as you can only think one thought at a time, you can only feel one feeling at a time. When you are experiencing a strong negative feeling and you wish to change it to a positive feeling, utilise visualisation. This is an *inside-out* approach to change.

I choose to feel warm, loving emotions. I do this by focusing on my heart and letting love, trust, forgiveness, compassion, or gratitude fill my heart space.

> You are jealous of your rich friend. You do not like having these horrible feelings and you would rather feel gratitude. Close your eyes and visualise your heart space, the space around your heart. Now begin to remember all the times that your friend invited you over and how kind she has been to you. As you visualise her kindness, gratitude will fill your heart space and replace the jealousy.

> You are furious at the mess your child has made. You would prefer to be loving and to discipline with love. Close your eyes and visualise your heart space. Now remember the day your child was born and how excited you felt. Remember the first time she smiled at you. As you remember, watch love fill your heart space.

> You are terrified you will fail an exam. Close your eyes and visualise your heart space. Relive all the times you succeeded. Observe your heart space fill with hope.

Calming tools

There are various practices that will assist you to calm your bodily reactions down. By utilising them, you are harnessing *outside-in* agents of change.

The more you practise calming tools, the more your body will become acclimatised to operating at a relaxed pace and ultimately the relaxed state will become your default mode of operation.

Calming tools include deep breathing, relaxation, mindfulness, and meditation.

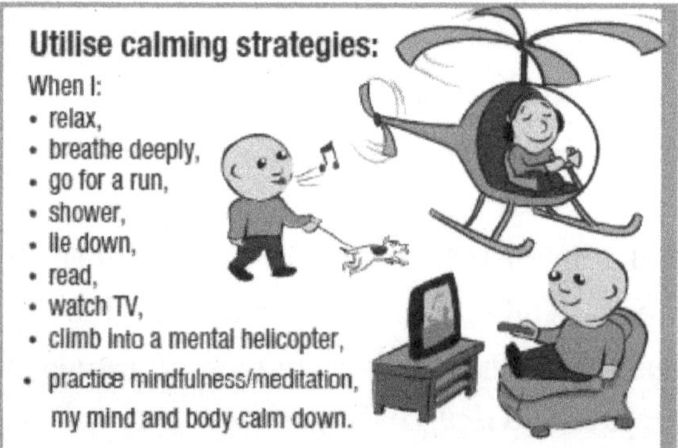

Step four

Step four incorporates:

> learning how to stay positive and motivated
> developing character
> rating your anxiety again, as a percentage

Staying positive

In step four, you are required to comment on the progress that you have made relating to the specific event that you chose. Every small achievement deserves recognition. You do not have to wait for some mammoth achievement to feel that you can congratulate yourself.

Step Four: The Self Motivation Process

Endorse yourself for any growth no matter how small.

In the past I would have...

But this time I...

Tick off the traits that you strengthened when you worked down your anxiety:

- generosity
- kindness
- compassion
- consideration
- helpfulness
- respectfulness
- honesty
- fairness
- patience
- peacefulness
- self-discipline
- forgiveness
- courage
- responsibility
- reliability
- loyalty
- love
- humility

Rate your anxiety on a scale of 0 to 100%:

_____ %

Be sure not to mention anything that you omitted to do. Focus only on the positive and validate each small victory. This is the secret of staying motivated. As you monitor and acknowledge each positive growth, you will have the grit to keep moving forward no matter what challenges lie ahead.

> "In the past I would have been awake all night, but last night I slept for 30 minutes."
> "In the past I would have run away, but this time I confronted the problem."
> "In the past I would have sulked for hours but this time I stopped sulking after one hour."

Develop character

Step four also functions to strengthen important character traits. A good character is attainable by every person no matter their intelligence or talents. As you build your sense of character by filling in this section of the worksheet, you will feel less anxious. This is because your increasingly ethical behaviour builds your self-esteem and trust in yourself.

There is a list of traits for you to tick off which you believe you strengthened when you worked down your anxiety. The list I provide below is by no means exhaustive so please feel free to add your own:

> generosity
> kindness
> compassion
> consideration
> helpfulness
> respectfulness
> honesty
> fairness
> patience

> peacefulness
> self-discipline
> forgiveness
> courage
> responsibility
> reliability
> loyalty
> love
> humility

Rate your anxiety

How do you feel now after filling in the worksheet? Rate you anxiety on a scale of 0 to 100%. Again this is a subjective score which you give to yourself. Compare it to the score you gave yourself in step one. Even a reduction of 1% can be regarded as a victory.

Daily monitoring diary

As part of this course you are requested to fill out a daily diary.(14) When you write something down, and measure it, it leads to change.

Each day you will need to fill out the following information:

> If you exercised and for how long — what was your anxiety level before and after?

> If, and for how long, you engaged in relaxation/meditation/mindfulness — what was your anxiety level before and after?

> How often you had a catastrophic/negative thought — what was your belief in that thought before and after challenging it?

> Your overall anxiety rating for the day on a scale from 0–10 (0 being not at all anxious; 10 being extremely anxious).

The benefits of completing this diary every day include:

> You will be writing down facts on the given day. It can be difficult to remember on a Wednesday for example, what you felt on the previous Monday. Facts are important in CBT because we challenge thoughts and fears with facts.

> You will be keeping track of your anxiety levels. This is often informative because you may pick up a trend such as: "I am worse on the days I go to work."

> You will learn to identify your negative thoughts when they arise.

> You will be rating the benefits of relaxation/meditation/mindfulness and exercise. Once you document the improvements, you will feel reassured that you have tools at your disposal for difficult moments.

> By taking notice of the changes you experience, you will feel motivated to keep using the tools.

The diary looks like this.

DAILY MONITORING DIARY WEEK ENDING

Day	M	T	W	T	F	S	S
Overall Anxiety Rating for the day (0-10)							
1. EXERCISE							
How long?							
Anxiety level before (0-10)							
Anxiety level after (0-10)							
2. BREATHING							
How long?							
Anxiety level before (0-10)							
Anxiety level after (0-10)							
3. RELAXATION							
How long?							
Anxiety level before (0-10)							
Anxiety level after (0-10)							
4. PERVASIVE PESSIMISTIC THINKING							
How often this type of thought occurred							
Belief in thoughts before challenging (0-10)							
Belief in thoughts after challenging (0-10)							
5. CATASTROPHIC THINKING							
How often this type of thought occurred							
Belief in thoughts before challenging (0-10)							
Belief in thoughts after challenging (0-10)							
6. PERMANENT PESSIMISTIC THINKING							
How often this type of thought occurred							
Belief in thoughts before challenging (0-10)							
Belief in thoughts after challenging (0-10)							

Day	M	T	W	T	F	S	S
7. MINDFULNESS (FORMAL, GROUNDING, INFORMAL MINDFULNESS)							
How long?							
Anxiety level before (0-10)							
Anxiety level after (0-10)							
8. ROMANTIC THINKING							
How often this type of thought occurred							
Belief in thoughts before challenging (0-10)							
Belief in thoughts after challenging (0-10)							
9. NEGATIVE JUDGEMENTAL THINKING							
How often this type of thought occurred							
Belief in thoughts before challenging (0-10)							
Belief in thoughts after challenging (0-10)							
10. CAN'T LET GO THINKING							
How often this type of thought occurred							
Belief in thoughts before challenging (0-10)							
Belief in thoughts after challenging (0-10)							
11. MEDITATION							
How long?							
Anxiety level before (0-10)							
Anxiety level after (0-10)							
12. EXCEPTIONAL THINKING							
How often this type of thought occurred							
Belief in thoughts before challenging (0-10)							
Belief in thoughts after challenging (0-10)							

When you fill it in, it will look like this:

DAILY MONITORING DIARY WEEK ENDING

Day	M	T	W	T	F	S	S
Overall Anxiety Rating for the day (0-10)	9	8	6	8	4	0	0
1. EXERCISE							
How long?	45 min		60 min			120 min	
Anxiety level before (0-10)	8		7			4	
Anxiety level after (0-10)	4		4			0	
2. BREATHING							
How long?	2 min	2 min	2 min	2 min	2 min	2 min	2 min
Anxiety level before (0-10)	8	8	7	6	6	5	4
Anxiety level after (0-10)	4	3	3	2	1	1	1
3. RELAXATION							
How long?	10 min		10 min		10 min	10 min	10 min
Anxiety level before (0-10)	7		6		6	4	3
Anxiety level after (0-10)	4		3		3	1	0
4. PERVASIVE PESSIMISTIC THINKING							
How often this type of thought occurred	5		11	5			
Belief in thoughts before challenging (0-10)	10		10	10			
Belief in thoughts after challenging (0-10)	8		7	5			
5. CATASTROPHIC THINKING							
How often this type of thought occurred	20	20	10	5	4	2	2
Belief in thoughts before challenging (0-10)	10	10	8	7	6	6	6
Belief in thoughts after challenging (0-10)	9	5	2	2	2	1	1
6. PERMANENT PESSIMISTIC THINKING							
How often this type of thought occurred	0	0	0	0	1	0	0
Belief in thoughts before challenging (0-10)					6		
Belief in thoughts after challenging (0-10)					1		

Day	M	T	W	T	F	S	S
7. MINDFULNESS **(FORMAL, GROUNDING, INFORMAL MINDFULNESS)**							
How long?	2 min		10 min		2 min		10 min
Anxiety level before (0-10)	6		8		5		4
Anxiety level after (0-10)	2		2		2		0
8. ROMANTIC THINKING							
How often this type of thought occurred	0	0	0	0	0	0	0
Belief in thoughts before challenging (0-10)							
Belief in thoughts after challenging (0-10)							
9. NEGATIVE JUDGEMENTAL THINKING							
How often this type of thought occurred	15	14	13	10	7	5	4
Belief in thoughts before challenging (0-10)	10	10	9	8	7	3	3
Belief in thoughts after challenging (0-10)	8	8	5	3	2	1	0
10. CAN'T LET GO THINKING							
How often this type of thought occurred	1			1	1		
Belief in thoughts before challenging (0-10)	10			8	6		
Belief in thoughts after challenging (0-10)	4			4	2		
11. MEDITATION							
How long?						20 min	20 min
Anxiety level before (0-10)						6	6
Anxiety level after (0-10)						2	1
12. EXCEPTIONAL THINKING							
How often this type of thought occurred	5		7		6		
Belief in thoughts before challenging (0-10)	9		8		6		
Belief in thoughts after challenging (0-10)	5		4		2		

How to get the most out of this workbook

You now have completed the groundwork for the rest of the course.

You have learned about anxiety and what happens to you when you are anxious. You have also learned about CBT and the EBB FLOW paradigm which is the primary treatment modality that you will be utilising.

The neurological reasons for practising the worksheets and tools over 90 days have been explained to you. The daily monitoring diary and its benefits have also been explained. Armed with this information, you are now geared up and ready to begin the practical (and most important part) of improving yourself.

The reason it is the most important part is that the theory alone does not lead to change. Developing new thoughts and behaviours, and practising them over 90 days, will ensure progress. In the next 12 weeks, you will have the opportunity to learn each tool in depth and to apply them to your personal life.

This workbook has been divided into 12 weeks/segments. Every week you are encouraged to:

1. Read through the recommended tools. Every week you will be exposed to at least one thinking tool, one behavioural tool and one calming tool.
2. Fill out the relevant exercises relating to the tools.
3. Practise your calming tools daily.
4. Exercise regularly.
5. Fill out your daily monitoring diary.
6. Fill out a worksheet every day.

You will need a maximum of one hour per week to read and fill in the exercises for the prescribed three tools. You should require no more than 30 minutes a day to fill in an anxiety management worksheet and the daily monitoring diary and to practise relaxation/mindfulness/meditation.

In case you are worried that this is a big commitment, you are right, it is. It is a commitment to your mental health and well-being. In my opinion, there is nothing more valuable than that. Therefore, it is my sincere hope that by the end of 90 days, you will have incorporated these essential and wonderful practices into your life and will continue to practise them indefinitely.

Homework

There are seven worksheets (one for each day) at the end of this chapter and at the end of every chapter.

From today, you can begin to fill out a worksheet every day. Also, from today, please start to fill out the daily monitoring diary. For this week, you are only required to rate your daily anxiety level.

DAILY MONITORING DIARY WEEK ENDING ______________________

Day	M	T	W	T	F	S	S
Overall Anxiety Rating for the day (0-10)							

Date: _______________

Anxiety Management Worksheet

The purpose of this worksheet is to help you to see every stressful event as an opportunity for
1. greater understanding of yourself, your anxiety and the people around you, and
2. practicing tools to manage your anxiety.

Step One: An Event

Briefly describe an event when you became anxious. Give such details as time, place and people involved, and end with "That's when I began to work myself up..."

____

____

____

____ Rate your anxiety on a scale of 0 to 100%: [____] %

E

Step Two: The Working-Up Process

Learn about your working up process by identifying your thoughts, feelings, behaviours and bodily reactions during the event. Tick the ones that most resonate with you.

Undermining Beliefs

B

I fear that I have lost...

- ☐ approval
- ☐ success
- ☐ control
- ☐ trust
- ☐ co-operation
- ☐ validation
- ☐ face
- ☐ love
- ☐ respect

This event proves that I am...

- ☐ stupid
- ☐ a total failure
- ☐ abnormal
- ☐ undisciplined
- ☐ incompetent
- ☐ untogether
- ☐ lazy
- ☐ useless
- ☐ irresponsible

I worry that I will suffer...

- ☐ mental collapse
- ☐ illness
- ☐ financial hardship

What I want is...

- ☐ total control
- ☐ tranquility
- ☐ respect
- ☐ all the answers
- ☐ success
- ☐ for life to go smoothly
- ☐ perfection
- ☐ comfort
- ☐ to be all things to all people
- ☐ fairness

Self-destructive Behaviour

Active

- ☐ get violent
- ☐ swear
- ☐ slam doors
- ☐ run away
- ☐ overeat
- ☐ harm myself
- ☐ criticise

Passive

- ☐ take it too seriously
- ☐ give up
- ☐ wallow in self pity
- ☐ sulk
- ☐ space out
- ☐ procrastinate
- ☐ give in
- ☐ be controlled

Intense Feelings

Angry feelings

- ☐ hateful
- ☐ attacked
- ☐ aggravated
- ☐ worn out
- ☐ annoyed
- ☐ rejected
- ☐ hostile
- ☐ jealous
- ☐ outraged
- ☐ afraid
- ☐ punitive
- ☐ exploited
- ☐ resentful
- ☐ lonely
- ☐ vengeful
- ☐ abandoned
- ☐ guilty

Fearful feelings

- ☐ insulted
- ☐ helpless
- ☐ confused
- ☐ hopeless
- ☐ disillusioned
- ☐ disappointed
- ☐ misunderstood
- ☐ sad
- ☐ trapped

Bodily Reactions (limbic system)

I am uncomfortable because I am experiencing...

- ☐ tremors
- ☐ nausea
- ☐ sweaty palms
- ☐ stomach-ache
- ☐ pounding heart
- ☐ general tension
- ☐ fatigue
- ☐ imagination on fire
- ☐ headache
- ☐ dry mouth
- ☐ jaw clenching
- ☐ shortness of breath

Continued over

B   **F**   **L**

Step Three: The Working-Down Process

Begin with, "Suddenly I realised that I was anxious and that I had choices..." This is the step of self-leadership and trust in one's ability to handle the situation.

Choose helpful thoughts:

I choose to depersonalise
There is no intention to hurt me. He is doing the best he can with the tools he has at the moment.

I choose realism over romanticism
Life presents many obstacles. I lower or raise standards as needed.

There is no right or wrong
Unless it is a moral issue, I will see it simply as a difference of opinion and/or taste.

I choose the total view of positivity
Even though this event is negative, the total view of his behaviour is positive.

I surrender control
Since I cannot change this situation, I choose to let go of it.

I choose to put this event in perspective This event is not a catastrophe because it is not life threatening. It can be viewed as a trivial life event, a normal life problem that needs to be solved not dramatised.

I choose to view this event as average, falling within the normal range
This event is not exceptional; many people have gone through this.

It's temporary - "this too shall pass"
Life is constantly changing and moving through phases and this situation will also change.

Fears or facts?
Why fear? It may not happen!

I choose to focus on this as a learning experience
Every problem that comes my way is an opportunity for me to learn about my strengths and weaknesses, others and life.

Feel soothing emotions:

I choose to feel warm, loving emotions. I do this by focusing on my heart and letting love, trust forgiveness, compassion, hope or gratitude fill my heart space.

Behave constructively:

I choose to work in part acts:
I will break the overwhelming job into manageable parts.

Do the difficult:
I will face what I fear and act with self-discipline.

I choose to solutionise:
I will find a solution by taking advice or doing research.

Prioritise myself:
I will keep my life balanced by meeting friends, doing exercise or laughing.

Compartmentalise:
I will not let this event cloud my whole day; I will focus on something else now.

Utilise calming strategies:

When I:
- relax,
- breathe deeply,
- go for a run,
- shower,
- lie down,
- read,
- watch TV,
- climb into a mental helicopter,
- practice mindfulness/meditation,

my mind and body calm down.

Step Four: The Self Motivation Process

Endorse yourself for any growth no matter how small.

In the past I would have...

____

____

But this time I...

____

____

Tick off the traits that you strengthened when you worked down your anxiety:

- ☐ generosity
- ☐ kindness
- ☐ compassion
- ☐ consideration
- ☐ helpfulness
- ☐ respectfulness
- ☐ honesty
- ☐ fairness
- ☐ patience
- ☐ peacefulness
- ☐ self-discipline
- ☐ forgiveness
- ☐ courage
- ☐ responsibility
- ☐ reliability
- ☐ loyalty
- ☐ love
- ☐ humility

Rate your anxiety on a scale of 0 to 100%:

☐ %

Anxiety Management Worksheet

The purpose of this worksheet is to help you to see every stressful event as an opportunity for
1. greater understanding of yourself, your anxiety and the people around you, and
2. practicing tools to manage your anxiety.

Step One: An Event

Briefly describe an event when you became anxious. Give such details as time, place and people involved, and end with "That's when I began to work myself up..."

____

____

____

____ Rate your anxiety on a scale of 0 to 100%: [ ] %

E

Step Two: The Working-Up Process

Learn about your working up process by identifying your thoughts, feelings, behaviours and bodily reactions during the event.

Tick the ones that most resonate with you.

Undermining Beliefs

B

I fear that I have lost...

- ☐ approval
- ☐ control
- ☐ co-operation
- ☐ face
- ☐ respect
- ☐ success
- ☐ trust
- ☐ validation
- ☐ love

This event proves that I am...

- ☐ stupid
- ☐ abnormal
- ☐ incompetent
- ☐ lazy
- ☐ irresponsible
- ☐ a total failure
- ☐ undisciplined
- ☐ untogether
- ☐ useless

I worry that I will suffer...

- ☐ mental collapse
- ☐ illness
- ☐ financial hardship

What I want is...

- ☐ total control
- ☐ respect
- ☐ success
- ☐ perfection
- ☐ comfort
- ☐ fairness
- ☐ tranquility
- ☐ all the answers
- ☐ for life to go smoothly
- ☐ to be all things to all people

Self-destructive Behaviour

Active
- ☐ get violent
- ☐ swear
- ☐ slam doors
- ☐ run away
- ☐ overeat
- ☐ harm myself
- ☐ criticise

Passive
- ☐ take it too seriously
- ☐ give up
- ☐ wallow in self pity
- ☐ sulk
- ☐ space out
- ☐ procrastinate
- ☐ give in
- ☐ be controlled

Intense Feelings

Angry feelings
- ☐ hateful
- ☐ aggravated
- ☐ annoyed
- ☐ hostile
- ☐ outraged
- ☐ punitive
- ☐ resentful
- ☐ vengeful
- ☐ attacked
- ☐ worn out
- ☐ rejected
- ☐ jealous
- ☐ afraid
- ☐ exploited
- ☐ lonely
- ☐ abandoned
- ☐ guilty

Fearful feelings
- ☐ helpless
- ☐ hopeless
- ☐ disappointed
- ☐ sad
- ☐ insulted
- ☐ confused
- ☐ disillusioned
- ☐ misunderstood
- ☐ trapped

Bodily Reactions (limbic system)

I am uncomfortable because I am experiencing...
- ☐ tremors
- ☐ nausea
- ☐ sweaty palms
- ☐ stomach-ache
- ☐ pounding heart
- ☐ general tension
- ☐ fatigue
- ☐ imagination on fire
- ☐ headache
- ☐ dry mouth
- ☐ jaw clenching
- ☐ shortness of breath

Continued over

B   F   L

Step Three: The Working-Down Process

Begin with, "Suddenly I realised that I was anxious and that I had choices..." This is the step of self-leadership and trust in one's ability to handle the situation.

Choose helpful thoughts:

I choose to depersonalise
There is no intention to hurt me. He is doing the best he can with the tools he has at the moment.

I choose realism over romanticism
Life presents many obstacles. I lower or raise standards as needed.

There is no right or wrong
Unless it is a moral issue, I will see it simply as a difference of opinion and/or taste.

I choose the total view of positivity
Even though this event is negative, the total view of his behaviour is positive.

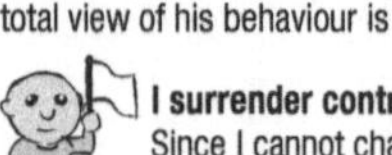

I surrender control
Since I cannot change this situation, I choose to let go of it.

I choose to put this event in perspective This event is not a catastrophe because it is not life threatening. It can be viewed as a trivial life event, a normal life problem that needs to be solved not dramatised.

I choose to view this event as average, falling within the normal range
This event is not exceptional; many people have gone through this.

It's temporary - "this too shall pass"
Life is constantly changing and moving through phases and this situation will also change.

Fears or facts?
Why fear? It may not happen!

I choose to focus on this as a learning experience
Every problem that comes my way is an opportunity for me to learn about my strengths and weaknesses, others and life.

Feel soothing emotions:

I choose to feel warm, loving emotions. I do this by focusing on my heart and letting love, trust forgiveness, compassion, hope or gratitude fill my heart space.

Behave constructively:

I choose to work in part acts:
I will break the overwhelming job into manageable parts.

Do the difficult:
I will face what I fear and act with self-discipline.

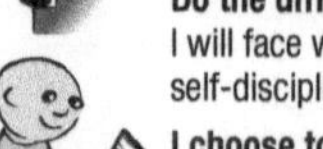

I choose to solutionise:
I will find a solution by taking advice or doing research.

Prioritise myself:
I will keep my life balanced by meeting friends, doing exercise or laughing.

Compartmentalise:
I will not let this event cloud my whole day; I will focus on something else now.

Utilise calming strategies:

When I:
- relax,
- breathe deeply,
- go for a run,
- shower,
- lie down,
- read,
- watch TV,
- climb into a mental helicopter,
- practice mindfulness/meditation,

my mind and body calm down.

Step Four: The Self Motivation Process

Endorse yourself for any growth no matter how small.

In the past I would have...

____

____

But this time I...

____

____

Tick off the traits that you strengthened when you worked down your anxiety:

☐ generosity ☐ peacefulness
☐ kindness ☐ self-discipline
☐ compassion ☐ forgiveness
☐ consideration ☐ courage
☐ helpfulness ☐ responsibility
☐ respectfulness ☐ reliability
☐ honesty ☐ loyalty
☐ fairness ☐ love
☐ patience ☐ humility

Rate your anxiety on a scale of 0 to 100%:

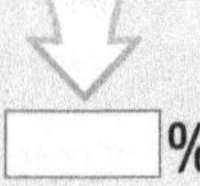

______ %

O

W

Date: _______________

Anxiety Management Worksheet

The purpose of this worksheet is to help you to see every stressful event as an opportunity for
1. greater understanding of yourself, your anxiety and the people around you, and
2. practicing tools to manage your anxiety.

Step One: An Event

Briefly describe an event when you became anxious. Give such details as time, place and people involved, and end with "That's when I began to work myself up..."

____

____

____

____ Rate your anxiety on a scale of 0 to 100%: [   ] %

E

Step Two: The Working-Up Process

Learn about your working up process by identifying your thoughts, feelings, behaviours and bodily reactions during the event. Tick the ones that most resonate with you.

Undermining Beliefs

B

I fear that I have lost...

- ☐ approval
- ☐ control
- ☐ co-operation
- ☐ face
- ☐ respect
- ☐ success
- ☐ trust
- ☐ validation
- ☐ love

This event proves that I am...

- ☐ stupid
- ☐ abnormal
- ☐ incompetent
- ☐ lazy
- ☐ irresponsible
- ☐ a total failure
- ☐ undisciplined
- ☐ untogether
- ☐ useless

I worry that I will suffer...

- ☐ mental collapse
- ☐ illness
- ☐ financial hardship

What I want is...

- ☐ total control
- ☐ respect
- ☐ success
- ☐ perfection
- ☐ comfort
- ☐ fairness
- ☐ tranquility
- ☐ all the answers
- ☐ for life to go smoothly
- ☐ to be all things to all people

Self-destructive Behaviour

Active
- ☐ get violent
- ☐ swear
- ☐ slam doors
- ☐ run away
- ☐ overeat
- ☐ harm myself
- ☐ criticise

Passive
- ☐ take it too seriously
- ☐ give up
- ☐ wallow in self pity
- ☐ sulk
- ☐ space out
- ☐ procrastinate
- ☐ give in
- ☐ be controlled

Intense Feelings

Angry feelings
- ☐ hateful
- ☐ aggravated
- ☐ annoyed
- ☐ hostile
- ☐ outraged
- ☐ punitive
- ☐ resentful
- ☐ vengeful
- ☐ attacked
- ☐ worn out
- ☐ rejected
- ☐ jealous
- ☐ afraid
- ☐ exploited
- ☐ lonely
- ☐ abandoned
- ☐ guilty
- ☐ insulted

Fearful feelings
- ☐ helpless
- ☐ hopeless
- ☐ disappointed
- ☐ sad
- ☐ confused
- ☐ disillusioned
- ☐ misunderstood
- ☐ trapped

Bodily Reactions (limbic system)

I am uncomfortable because I am experiencing...
- ☐ tremors
- ☐ nausea
- ☐ sweaty palms
- ☐ stomach-ache
- ☐ pounding heart
- ☐ general tension
- ☐ fatigue
- ☐ imagination on fire
- ☐ headache
- ☐ dry mouth
- ☐ jaw clenching
- ☐ shortness of breath

Continued over

B   **F**   **L**

Step Three: The Working-Down Process

Begin with, "Suddenly I realised that I was anxious and that I had choices..." This is the step of self-leadership and trust in one's ability to handle the situation.

Choose helpful thoughts:

I choose to depersonalise
There is no intention to hurt me. He is doing the best he can with the tools he has at the moment.

I choose realism over romanticism
Life presents many obstacles. I lower or raise standards as needed.

There is no right or wrong
Unless it is a moral issue, I will see it simply as a difference of opinion and/or taste.

I choose the total view of positivity
Even though this event is negative, the total view of his behaviour is positive.

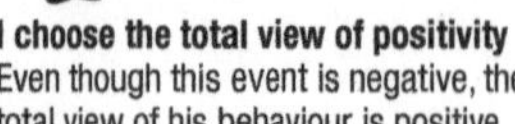

I surrender control
Since I cannot change this situation, I choose to let go of it.

I choose to put this event in perspective This event is not a catastrophe because it is not life threatening. It can be viewed as a trivial life event, a normal life problem that needs to be solved not dramatised.

I choose to view this event as average, falling within the normal range
This event is not exceptional; many people have gone through this.

It's temporary - "this too shall pass"
Life is constantly changing and moving through phases and this situation will also change.

Fears or facts?
Why fear? It may not happen!

I choose to focus on this as a learning experience
Every problem that comes my way is an opportunity for me to learn about my strengths and weaknesses, others and life.

Feel soothing emotions:

I choose to feel warm, loving emotions. I do this by focusing on my heart and letting love, trust forgiveness, compassion, hope or gratitude fill my heart space.

Behave constructively:

I choose to work in part acts:
I will break the overwhelming job into manageable parts.

Do the difficult:
I will face what I fear and act with self-discipline.

I choose to solutionise:
I will find a solution by taking advice or doing research.

Prioritise myself:
I will keep my life balanced by meeting friends, doing exercise or laughing.

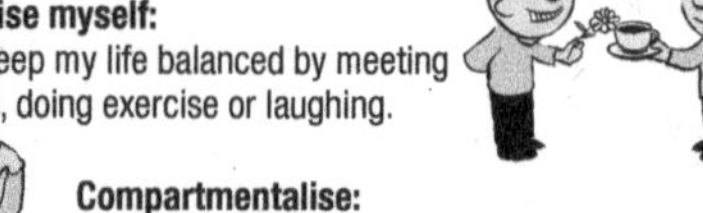

Compartmentalise:
I will not let this event cloud my whole day; I will focus on something else now.

Utilise calming strategies:

When I:
- relax,
- breathe deeply,
- go for a run,
- shower,
- lie down,
- read,
- watch TV,
- climb into a mental helicopter,
- practice mindfulness/meditation,

my mind and body calm down.

Step Four: The Self Motivation Process

Endorse yourself for any growth no matter how small.

In the past I would have...

____

____

But this time I...

____

____

Tick off the traits that you strengthened when you worked down your anxiety:

- ☐ generosity
- ☐ kindness
- ☐ compassion
- ☐ consideration
- ☐ helpfulness
- ☐ respectfulness
- ☐ honesty
- ☐ fairness
- ☐ patience
- ☐ peacefulness
- ☐ self-discipline
- ☐ forgiveness
- ☐ courage
- ☐ responsibility
- ☐ reliability
- ☐ loyalty
- ☐ love
- ☐ humility

Rate your anxiety on a scale of 0 to 100%:

____ %

O

W

Date: ______________

Anxiety Management Worksheet

The purpose of this worksheet is to help you to see every stressful event as an opportunity for
1. greater understanding of yourself, your anxiety and the people around you, and
2. practicing tools to manage your anxiety.

Step One: An Event

Briefly describe an event when you became anxious. Give such details as time, place and people involved, and end with "That's when I began to work myself up..."

____

____

____

____ Rate your anxiety on a scale of 0 to 100%: [   ] %

E

Step Two: The Working-Up Process

Learn about your working up process by identifying your thoughts, feelings, behaviours and bodily reactions during the event.
Tick the ones that most resonate with you.

B

Undermining Beliefs

I fear that I have lost...

- ☐ approval
- ☐ control
- ☐ co-operation
- ☐ face
- ☐ respect
- ☐ success
- ☐ trust
- ☐ validation
- ☐ love

This event proves that I am...

- ☐ stupid
- ☐ abnormal
- ☐ incompetent
- ☐ lazy
- ☐ irresponsible
- ☐ a total failure
- ☐ undisciplined
- ☐ untogether
- ☐ useless

I worry that I will suffer...

- ☐ mental collapse
- ☐ illness
- ☐ financial hardship

What I want is...

- ☐ total control
- ☐ respect
- ☐ success
- ☐ perfection
- ☐ comfort
- ☐ fairness
- ☐ tranquility
- ☐ all the answers
- ☐ for life to go smoothly
- ☐ to be all things to all people

Self-destructive Behaviour

Active
- ☐ get violent
- ☐ swear
- ☐ slam doors
- ☐ run away
- ☐ overeat
- ☐ harm myself
- ☐ criticise

Passive
- ☐ take it too seriously
- ☐ give up
- ☐ wallow in self pity
- ☐ sulk
- ☐ space out
- ☐ procrastinate
- ☐ give in
- ☐ be controlled

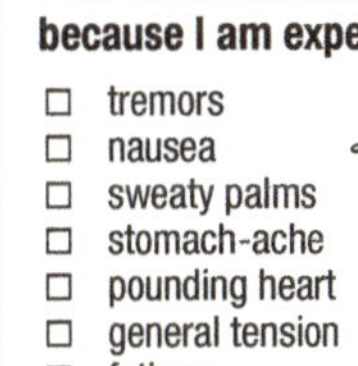

Intense Feelings

Angry feelings
- ☐ hateful
- ☐ aggravated
- ☐ annoyed
- ☐ hostile
- ☐ outraged
- ☐ punitive
- ☐ resentful
- ☐ vengeful

Fearful feelings
- ☐ helpless
- ☐ hopeless
- ☐ disappointed
- ☐ sad

- ☐ attacked
- ☐ worn out
- ☐ rejected
- ☐ jealous
- ☐ afraid
- ☐ exploited
- ☐ lonely
- ☐ abandoned
- ☐ guilty
- ☐ insulted
- ☐ confused
- ☐ disillusioned
- ☐ misunderstood
- ☐ trapped

Bodily Reactions (limbic system)

I am uncomfortable because I am experiencing...

- ☐ tremors
- ☐ nausea
- ☐ sweaty palms
- ☐ stomach-ache
- ☐ pounding heart
- ☐ general tension
- ☐ fatigue
- ☐ imagination on fire
- ☐ headache
- ☐ dry mouth
- ☐ jaw clenching
- ☐ shortness of breath

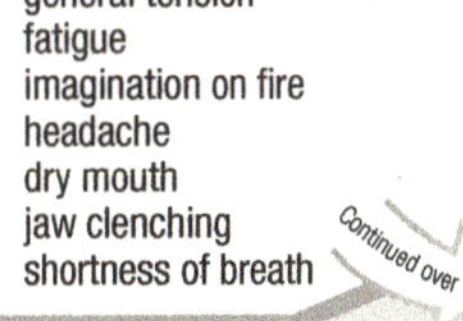

Continued over

B   **F**   **L**

Step Three: The Working-Down Process

Begin with, "Suddenly I realised that I was anxious and that I had choices..." This is the step of self-leadership and trust in one's ability to handle the situation.

Choose helpful thoughts:

I choose to depersonalise
There is no intention to hurt me. He is doing the best he can with the tools he has at the moment.

I choose realism over romanticism
Life presents many obstacles. I lower or raise standards as needed.

There is no right or wrong
Unless it is a moral issue, I will see it simply as a difference of opinion and/or taste.

I choose the total view of positivity
Even though this event is negative, the total view of his behaviour is positive.

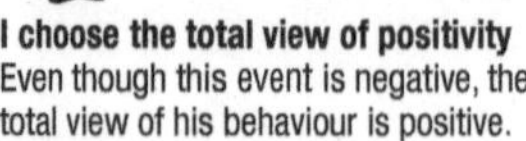

I surrender control
Since I cannot change this situation, I choose to let go of it.

I choose to put this event in perspective
This event is not a catastrophe because it is not life threatening. It can be viewed as a trivial life event, a normal life problem that needs to be solved not dramatised.

I choose to view this event as average, falling within the normal range
This event is not exceptional; many people have gone through this.

It's temporary - "this too shall pass"
Life is constantly changing and moving through phases and this situation will also change.

Fears or facts?
Why fear? It may not happen!

I choose to focus on this as a learning experience
Every problem that comes my way is an opportunity for me to learn about my strengths and weaknesses, others and life.

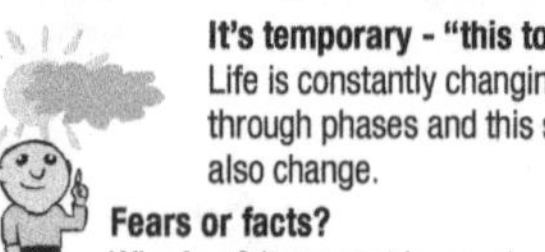

Feel soothing emotions:

I choose to feel warm, loving emotions. I do this by focusing on my heart and letting love, trust forgiveness, compassion, hope or gratitude fill my heart space.

Behave constructively:

I choose to work in part acts:
I will break the overwhelming job into manageable parts.

Do the difficult:
I will face what I fear and act with self-discipline.

I choose to solutionise:
I will find a solution by taking advice or doing research.

Prioritise myself:
I will keep my life balanced by meeting friends, doing exercise or laughing.

Compartmentalise:
I will not let this event cloud my whole day; I will focus on something else now.

Utilise calming strategies:

When I:
- relax,
- breathe deeply,
- go for a run,
- shower,
- lie down,
- read,
- watch TV,
- climb into a mental helicopter,
- practice mindfulness/meditation,

my mind and body calm down.

Step Four: The Self Motivation Process

Endorse yourself for any growth no matter how small.

In the past I would have...

____

____

But this time I...

____

____

Tick off the traits that you strengthened when you worked down your anxiety:

☐ generosity	☐ peacefulness
☐ kindness	☐ self-discipline
☐ compassion	☐ forgiveness
☐ consideration	☐ courage
☐ helpfulness	☐ responsibility
☐ respectfulness	☐ reliability
☐ honesty	☐ loyalty
☐ fairness	☐ love
☐ patience	☐ humility

Rate your anxiety on a scale of 0 to 100%:

[ ] %

O

W

Date: _____________

Anxiety Management Worksheet

The purpose of this worksheet is to help you to see every stressful event as an opportunity for
1. greater understanding of yourself, your anxiety and the people around you, and
2. practicing tools to manage your anxiety.

Step One: An Event

Briefly describe an event when you became anxious. Give such details as time, place and people involved, and end with "That's when I began to work myself up..."

____

____ **E**

____

_______________________________________ Rate your anxiety on a scale of 0 to 100%: [   ] %

Step Two: The Working-Up Process

Learn about your working up process by identifying your thoughts, feelings, behaviours and bodily reactions during the event. Tick the ones that most resonate with you.

Undermining Beliefs **B**

I fear that I have lost...
- ☐ approval
- ☐ control
- ☐ co-operation
- ☐ face
- ☐ respect
- ☐ success
- ☐ trust
- ☐ validation
- ☐ love

This event proves that I am...
- ☐ stupid
- ☐ abnormal
- ☐ incompetent
- ☐ lazy
- ☐ irresponsible
- ☐ a total failure
- ☐ undisciplined
- ☐ untogether
- ☐ useless

I worry that I will suffer...
- ☐ mental collapse
- ☐ illness
- ☐ financial hardship

What I want is...
- ☐ total control
- ☐ respect
- ☐ success
- ☐ perfection
- ☐ comfort
- ☐ fairness
- ☐ tranquility
- ☐ all the answers
- ☐ for life to go smoothly
- ☐ to be all things to all people

Self-destructive Behaviour

Active
- ☐ get violent
- ☐ swear
- ☐ slam doors
- ☐ run away
- ☐ overeat
- ☐ harm myself
- ☐ criticise

Passive
- ☐ take it too seriously
- ☐ give up
- ☐ wallow in self pity
- ☐ sulk
- ☐ space out
- ☐ procrastinate
- ☐ give in
- ☐ be controlled

Intense Feelings

Angry feelings
- ☐ hateful
- ☐ aggravated
- ☐ annoyed
- ☐ hostile
- ☐ outraged
- ☐ punitive
- ☐ resentful
- ☐ vengeful

Fearful feelings
- ☐ helpless
- ☐ hopeless
- ☐ disappointed
- ☐ sad
- ☐ attacked
- ☐ worn out
- ☐ rejected
- ☐ jealous
- ☐ afraid
- ☐ exploited
- ☐ lonely
- ☐ abandoned
- ☐ guilty
- ☐ insulted
- ☐ confused
- ☐ disillusioned
- ☐ misunderstood
- ☐ trapped

Bodily Reactions (limbic system)

I am uncomfortable because I am experiencing...
- ☐ tremors
- ☐ nausea
- ☐ sweaty palms
- ☐ stomach-ache
- ☐ pounding heart
- ☐ general tension
- ☐ fatigue
- ☐ imagination on fire
- ☐ headache
- ☐ dry mouth
- ☐ jaw clenching
- ☐ shortness of breath

Continued over

B   **F**   **L**

Step Three: The Working-Down Process

Begin with, "Suddenly I realised that I was anxious and that I had choices..." This is the step of self-leadership and trust in one's ability to handle the situation.

Choose helpful thoughts:

I choose to depersonalise
There is no intention to hurt me. He is doing the best he can with the tools he has at the moment.

I choose realism over romanticism
Life presents many obstacles. I lower or raise standards as needed.

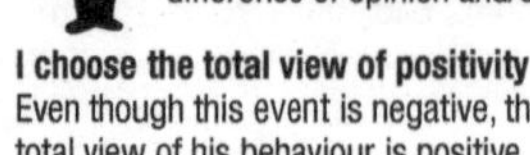

There is no right or wrong
Unless it is a moral issue, I will see it simply as a difference of opinion and/or taste.

I choose the total view of positivity
Even though this event is negative, the total view of his behaviour is positive.

I surrender control
Since I cannot change this situation, I choose to let go of it.

I choose to put this event in perspective This event is not a catastrophe because it is not life threatening. It can be viewed as a trivial life event, a normal life problem that needs to be solved not dramatised.

I choose to view this event as average, falling within the normal range
This event is not exceptional; many people have gone through this.

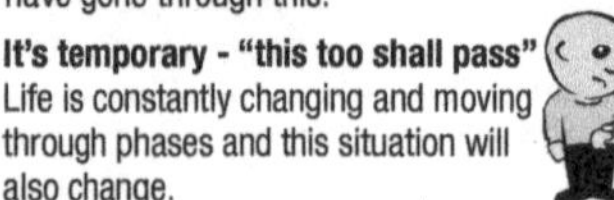

It's temporary - "this too shall pass"
Life is constantly changing and moving through phases and this situation will also change.

Fears or facts?
Why fear? It may not happen!

I choose to focus on this as a learning experience
Every problem that comes my way is an opportunity for me to learn about my strengths and weaknesses, others and life.

Feel soothing emotions:

I choose to feel warm, loving emotions. I do this by focusing on my heart and letting love, trust forgiveness, compassion, hope or gratitude fill my heart space.

Behave constructively:

I choose to work in part acts:
I will break the overwhelming job into manageable parts.

Do the difficult:
I will face what I fear and act with self-discipline.

I choose to solutionise:
I will find a solution by taking advice or doing research.

Prioritise myself:
I will keep my life balanced by meeting friends, doing exercise or laughing.

Compartmentalise:
I will not let this event cloud my whole day; I will focus on something else now.

Utilise calming strategies:

When I:
- relax,
- breathe deeply,
- go for a run,
- shower,
- lie down,
- read,
- watch TV,
- climb into a mental helicopter,
- practice mindfulness/meditation,

my mind and body calm down.

Step Four: The Self Motivation Process

Endorse yourself for any growth no matter how small.

In the past I would have...

____

____

But this time I...

____

____

Tick off the traits that you strengthened when you worked down your anxiety:

☐ generosity	☐ peacefulness	
☐ kindness	☐ self-discipline	
☐ compassion	☐ forgiveness	
☐ consideration	☐ courage	
☐ helpfulness	☐ responsibility	
☐ respectfulness	☐ reliability	
☐ honesty	☐ loyalty	
☐ fairness	☐ love	
☐ patience	☐ humility	

Rate your anxiety on a scale of 0 to 100%:

______ %

o   w

Date: _______________

Anxiety Management Worksheet

The purpose of this worksheet is to help you to see every stressful event as an opportunity for
1. greater understanding of yourself, your anxiety and the people around you, and
2. practicing tools to manage your anxiety.

Step One: An Event

Briefly describe an event when you became anxious. Give such details as time, place and people involved, and end with "That's when I began to work myself up..."

____

____

____

____ Rate your anxiety on a scale of 0 to 100%: [   ] %

E

Step Two: The Working-Up Process

Learn about your working up process by identifying your thoughts, feelings, behaviours and bodily reactions during the event.
Tick the ones that most resonate with you.

B

Undermining Beliefs

I fear that I have lost...

- ☐ approval
- ☐ control
- ☐ co-operation
- ☐ face
- ☐ respect
- ☐ success
- ☐ trust
- ☐ validation
- ☐ love

This event proves that I am...

- ☐ stupid
- ☐ abnormal
- ☐ incompetent
- ☐ lazy
- ☐ irresponsible
- ☐ a total failure
- ☐ undisciplined
- ☐ untogether
- ☐ useless

I worry that I will suffer...

- ☐ mental collapse
- ☐ illness
- ☐ financial hardship

What I want is...

- ☐ total control
- ☐ respect
- ☐ success
- ☐ perfection
- ☐ comfort
- ☐ fairness
- ☐ tranquility
- ☐ all the answers
- ☐ for life to go smoothly
- ☐ to be all things to all people

Self-destructive Behaviour

Active

- ☐ get violent
- ☐ swear
- ☐ slam doors
- ☐ run away
- ☐ overeat
- ☐ harm myself
- ☐ criticise

Passive

- ☐ take it too seriously
- ☐ give up
- ☐ wallow in self pity
- ☐ sulk
- ☐ space out
- ☐ procrastinate
- ☐ give in
- ☐ be controlled

Intense Feelings

Angry feelings

- ☐ hateful
- ☐ aggravated
- ☐ annoyed
- ☐ hostile
- ☐ outraged
- ☐ punitive
- ☐ resentful
- ☐ vengeful

Fearful feelings

- ☐ helpless
- ☐ hopeless
- ☐ disappointed
- ☐ sad
- ☐ attacked
- ☐ worn out
- ☐ rejected
- ☐ jealous
- ☐ afraid
- ☐ exploited
- ☐ lonely
- ☐ abandoned
- ☐ guilty
- ☐ insulted
- ☐ confused
- ☐ disillusioned
- ☐ misunderstood
- ☐ trapped

Bodily Reactions (limbic system)

I am uncomfortable because I am experiencing...

- ☐ tremors
- ☐ nausea
- ☐ sweaty palms
- ☐ stomach-ache
- ☐ pounding heart
- ☐ general tension
- ☐ fatigue
- ☐ imagination on fire
- ☐ headache
- ☐ dry mouth
- ☐ jaw clenching
- ☐ shortness of breath

Continued over

B   **F**   **L**

Step Three: The Working-Down Process

Begin with, "Suddenly I realised that I was anxious and that I had choices..." This is the step of self-leadership and trust in one's ability to handle the situation.

Choose helpful thoughts:

I choose to depersonalise
There is no intention to hurt me. He is doing the best he can with the tools he has at the moment.

I choose realism over romanticism
Life presents many obstacles. I lower or raise standards as needed.

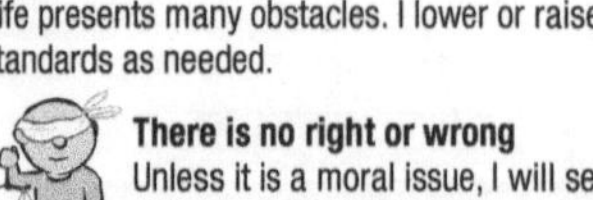

There is no right or wrong
Unless it is a moral issue, I will see it simply as a difference of opinion and/or taste.

I choose the total view of positivity
Even though this event is negative, the total view of his behaviour is positive.

I surrender control
Since I cannot change this situation, I choose to let go of it.

I choose to put this event in perspective This event is not a catastrophe because it is not life threatening. It can be viewed as a trivial life event, a normal life problem that needs to be solved not dramatised.

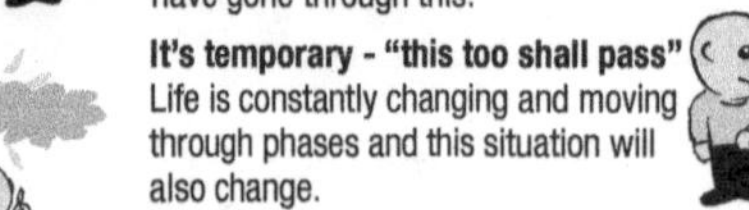

I choose to view this event as average, falling within the normal range
This event is not exceptional; many people have gone through this.

It's temporary - "this too shall pass"
Life is constantly changing and moving through phases and this situation will also change.

Fears or facts?
Why fear? It may not happen!

I choose to focus on this as a learning experience
Every problem that comes my way is an opportunity for me to learn about my strengths and weaknesses, others and life.

Feel soothing emotions:

I choose to feel warm, loving emotions. I do this by focusing on my heart and letting love, trust forgiveness, compassion, hope or gratitude fill my heart space.

Behave constructively:

I choose to work in part acts:
I will break the overwhelming job into manageable parts.

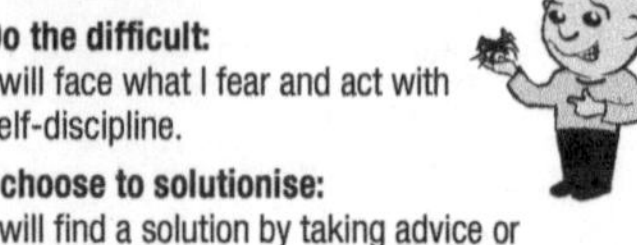

Do the difficult:
I will face what I fear and act with self-discipline.

I choose to solutionise:
I will find a solution by taking advice or doing research.

Prioritise myself:
I will keep my life balanced by meeting friends, doing exercise or laughing.

Compartmentalise:
I will not let this event cloud my whole day; I will focus on something else now.

Utilise calming strategies:

When I:
- relax,
- breathe deeply,
- go for a run,
- shower,
- lie down,
- read,
- watch TV,
- climb into a mental helicopter,
- practice mindfulness/meditation,

my mind and body calm down.

Step Four: The Self Motivation Process

Endorse yourself for any growth no matter how small.

In the past I would have...

____

____

But this time I...

____

____

Tick off the traits that you strengthened when you worked down your anxiety:

- ☐ generosity
- ☐ kindness
- ☐ compassion
- ☐ consideration
- ☐ helpfulness
- ☐ respectfulness
- ☐ honesty
- ☐ fairness
- ☐ patience
- ☐ peacefulness
- ☐ self-discipline
- ☐ forgiveness
- ☐ courage
- ☐ responsibility
- ☐ reliability
- ☐ loyalty
- ☐ love
- ☐ humility

Rate your anxiety on a scale of 0 to 100%:

☐ %

O

W

Date: _____________

Anxiety Management Worksheet

The purpose of this worksheet is to help you to see every stressful event as an opportunity for
1. greater understanding of yourself, your anxiety and the people around you, and
2. practicing tools to manage your anxiety.

Step One: An Event

Briefly describe an event when you became anxious. Give such details as time, place and people involved, and end with "That's when I began to work myself up..."

____   **E**

____

____

____ Rate your anxiety on a scale of 0 to 100%: [   ] %

Step Two: The Working-Up Process

Learn about your working up process by identifying your thoughts, feelings, behaviours and bodily reactions during the event.
Tick the ones that most resonate with you.

Undermining Beliefs   **B**

I fear that I have lost...

- ☐ approval
- ☐ control
- ☐ co-operation
- ☐ face
- ☐ respect
- ☐ success
- ☐ trust
- ☐ validation
- ☐ love

This event proves that I am...

- ☐ stupid
- ☐ abnormal
- ☐ incompetent
- ☐ lazy
- ☐ irresponsible
- ☐ a total failure
- ☐ undisciplined
- ☐ untogether
- ☐ useless

I worry that I will suffer...

- ☐ mental collapse
- ☐ illness
- ☐ financial hardship

What I want is...

- ☐ total control
- ☐ respect
- ☐ success
- ☐ perfection
- ☐ comfort
- ☐ fairness
- ☐ tranquility
- ☐ all the answers
- ☐ for life to go smoothly
- ☐ to be all things to all people

Self-destructive Behaviour

Active

- ☐ get violent
- ☐ swear
- ☐ slam doors
- ☐ run away
- ☐ overeat
- ☐ harm myself
- ☐ criticise

Passive

- ☐ take it too seriously
- ☐ give up
- ☐ wallow in self pity
- ☐ sulk
- ☐ space out
- ☐ procrastinate
- ☐ give in
- ☐ be controlled

Intense Feelings

Angry feelings

- ☐ hateful
- ☐ aggravated
- ☐ annoyed
- ☐ hostile
- ☐ outraged
- ☐ punitive
- ☐ resentful
- ☐ vengeful

Fearful feelings

- ☐ helpless
- ☐ hopeless
- ☐ disappointed
- ☐ sad
- ☐ attacked
- ☐ worn out
- ☐ rejected
- ☐ jealous
- ☐ afraid
- ☐ exploited
- ☐ lonely
- ☐ abandoned
- ☐ guilty
- ☐ insulted
- ☐ confused
- ☐ disillusioned
- ☐ misunderstood
- ☐ trapped

Bodily Reactions (limbic system)

I am uncomfortable because I am experiencing...

- ☐ tremors
- ☐ nausea
- ☐ sweaty palms
- ☐ stomach-ache
- ☐ pounding heart
- ☐ general tension
- ☐ fatigue
- ☐ imagination on fire
- ☐ headache
- ☐ dry mouth
- ☐ jaw clenching
- ☐ shortness of breath

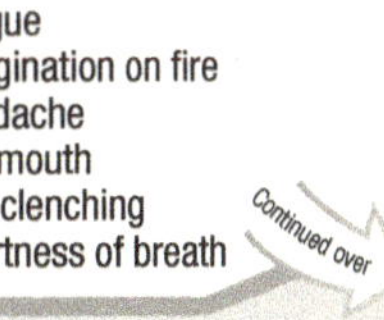

B   **F**   **L**

Step Three: The Working-Down Process

Begin with, "Suddenly I realised that I was anxious and that I had choices..." This is the step of self-leadership and trust in one's ability to handle the situation.

Choose helpful thoughts:

I choose to depersonalise
There is no intention to hurt me. He is doing the best he can with the tools he has at the moment.

I choose realism over romanticism
Life presents many obstacles. I lower or raise standards as needed.

There is no right or wrong
Unless it is a moral issue, I will see it simply as a difference of opinion and/or taste.

I choose the total view of positivity
Even though this event is negative, the total view of his behaviour is positive.

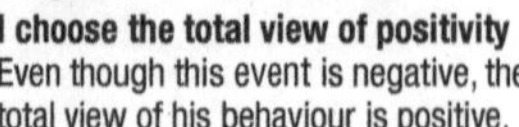

I surrender control
Since I cannot change this situation, I choose to let go of it.

I choose to put this event in perspective This event is not a catastrophe because it is not life threatening. It can be viewed as a trivial life event, a normal life problem that needs to be solved not dramatised.

I choose to view this event as average, falling within the normal range
This event is not exceptional; many people have gone through this.

It's temporary - "this too shall pass"
Life is constantly changing and moving through phases and this situation will also change.

Fears or facts?
Why fear? It may not happen!

I choose to focus on this as a learning experience
Every problem that comes my way is an opportunity for me to learn about my strengths and weaknesses, others and life.

Feel soothing emotions:

I choose to feel warm, loving emotions. I do this by focusing on my heart and letting love, trust forgiveness, compassion, hope or gratitude fill my heart space.

Behave constructively:

I choose to work in part acts:
I will break the overwhelming job into manageable parts.

Do the difficult:
I will face what I fear and act with self-discipline.

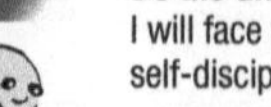

I choose to solutionise:
I will find a solution by taking advice or doing research.

Prioritise myself:
I will keep my life balanced by meeting friends, doing exercise or laughing.

Compartmentalise:
I will not let this event cloud my whole day; I will focus on something else now.

Utilise calming strategies:

When I:
- relax,
- breathe deeply,
- go for a run,
- shower,
- lie down,
- read,
- watch TV,
- climb into a mental helicopter,
- practice mindfulness/meditation,

my mind and body calm down.

Step Four: The Self Motivation Process

Endorse yourself for any growth no matter how small.

In the past I would have...

____

____

But this time I...

____

____

Tick off the traits that you strengthened when you worked down your anxiety:

☐ generosity	☐ peacefulness		
☐ kindness	☐ self-discipline		
☐ compassion	☐ forgiveness		
☐ consideration	☐ courage		
☐ helpfulness	☐ responsibility		
☐ respectfulness	☐ reliability		
☐ honesty	☐ loyalty		
☐ fairness	☐ love		
☐ patience	☐ humility		

Rate your anxiety on a scale of 0 to 100%:

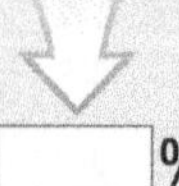

__________ %

O

W

Week 3

The week three segment comprises these tools:

1. total view: thinking tool
2. exercise: behavioural tool
3. breathing: calming tool
4. relaxation: calming tool

Total view: thinking tool

"I choose the total view of positivity. Even though this incident is negative, the total view of my situation is positive."

OR

"I choose the total view of positivity. Even though this incident is negative, the total view of his behaviour is positive."

When we go through a *specific* negative situation, it often feels to us as though the *whole* situation is negative. For instance, let us say one friend has let you down, you might feel then that you cannot trust any of your other friends.

This manner of pessimistic thinking is called "pervasive pessimistic thinking." (15) It is what happens when you take one negative detail and allow it to contaminate (pervade) the whole picture. This tool helps you to see the total view as positive with only one negative aspect.

EXERCISE 4

Take a pen and draw a small circle anywhere on the picture of the world (see image above). This action is symbolic of you making a note of an area in your life that hurts or needs attention.

When you utilise this tool, you are not being hyper positive and denying that there is pain or stress in your situation. You are acknowledging your pain while being realistic about its size in comparison to all the positives in your life.

Viewing the problem in relation to a bigger picture reduces anxiety because the problem becomes small and manageable.

When you next feel anxious about a situation, this tool will help you to step back and look at the total picture in a more realistic light. It will encourage you to see only the specific situation as negative and will prevent you from generalising negativity to the whole situation.

Here are some examples of how to utilise the tool "**total view**":

> You are studying various subjects at school. Your score in maths is below average. You tell yourself "I am stupid" which is a pervasive pessimistic way of thinking because, you are not stupid.

> *Using this tool, you would instead say "Even though I am struggling with maths, I am not stupid in every respect. My scores for other subjects are above average. Therefore, the total view of my scholastic ability is positive."*

> You have prepared a four-course dinner. The soufflé which you made for dessert flopped. Instead of berating yourself and thinking "I am not a good cook," say "Even though the soufflé failed to rise, the total view of my cooking ability is good."

> Your boss yells at you. You feel humiliated and want to leave your job in a fit of anger. Take a minute and ask yourself how many things are bad at your place of employment. If you find that you are satisfied with the income, the hours, your colleagues and the tasks, then calm yourself by saying "Even though my boss yells at me on occasion and I do not like it, the total view of my job is positive."

Of course, there will be times when a situation is negative as a whole and this tool would not then be applicable. In such a case, you must take action! For instance, if your boss yells at you and underpays you plus the team is unfriendly, then you probably should leave the job.

This tool is appropriate when it feels to you as though a whole situation is negative when, in fact, it isn't and you need assistance to gain perspective. Gaining that perspective will motivate you and lift your mood.

EXERCISE 5

Circle one response for each of the scenarios below:

1. When you miss an important meeting at work, do you think:
   a) My memory is poor
   b) I sometimes forget to check my appointment book

2. When you have prepared an outing with your family and they do not agree with any of your ideas, do you think:
   a) I don't know how to plan outings
   b) I planned it without asking if they were interested or had free time

3. When your shares drop to an all-time low, do you think:
   a) I don't know much about the business climate
   b) I made a poor choice of shares

4. Do you tend to think:
   a) All people are untrustworthy
   b) Peter Smith is untrustworthy

5. Do you ever feel:
   a) I am repulsive
   b) I am repulsive to Peter Jones

6. Do you believe:
   a) No courses will ever be able to benefit me
   b) That course on "swimming therapy" was not helpful to me

7. If you are penalised for not returning your income tax forms on time, do you think:
   a) I am disorganised and irresponsible
   b) I was lazy about getting my taxes done this year

8. Should a shop refuse to honour your credit card, do you think:
   a) I am useless at budgeting
   b) I sometimes forget to check my balance before I shop

How many a)'s did you score?
How many b)'s did you score?

In the examples laid out in the above exercise, a) responses are indicative of pervasive pessimistic thinking, while b) responses indicate a negative assessment of a specific area.

Put another way, when you think, "My memory is poor," you are basically saying that the "total view of my memory ability is poor." However, when you say, "I sometimes forget to check my appointment book," you are saying, "When I look at the total picture of my memory ability, I can see that it is adequate. However, there are times when I sometimes forget to check my appointment book."

When you think, "I am not very good at planning things," you are undermining your organisational abilities in an overall way. However, when you think, "I planned it without asking if others were interested or had free time," you acknowledge that your organisational abilities as a whole are fine, but in this instance they did not shine through due to a lack of consultation with the people involved.

Similarly, when your shares drop to an all-time low and you attribute it to your lack of knowledge of the entire business climate, it is a pervasive pessimistic belief. On the other hand, when you think that you have a generally thorough understanding of the business climate but in this particular case you erred in your choice, you are looking at the total view of your business abilities in a positive light.

A pervasive pessimistic outlook is de-motivating and de-energising. Seeing the total view as positive will give you a good feeling about yourself, and/or the situation. You will not feel anxious and you will be motivated to persevere and solve the problem.

Daily monitoring diary

From this week, start to keep a record of every time you catch yourself thinking in a pervasive, pessimistic way. This will help you to catch yourself when you start thinking negatively. It will also assist you to learn more about your unique pattern of negative thinking.

For instance, if you come to realise that you utilise pervasive pessimistic thinking a lot, you now have a tool to change this thinking style.

Exercise: behavioural tool

"Exercise lifts my mood."

There is no health discipline today that does not encourage regular exercise.

When you exercise, your body releases endorphins (neurotransmitters). Endorphins elevate your mood resulting in you feeling happier and more energetic. Furthermore, exercise leads to an agile body which is better able to cope with stress and illness, and generally results in a better immune system.

81

Since all types of exercise will enhance your feeling of wellbeing, choose one that you enjoy. You will be more likely to keep exercising if you find it pleasurable.

Exercise can be used either to lower anxiety when you feel anxious or to prevent anxiety in the future. In other words, when you feel anxious and choose exercise as a tool, your anxiety will reduce. Moreover, when you exercise regularly as part of your daily practice, you will be less anxious overall.

At least three exercise sessions per week is ideal. However, if you have not exercised recently, commit to once a week to get going and then slowly increase it. This way you are more likely to keep your commitment.

EXERCISE 6

What types of exercise do you enjoy?

What exercise do you actually do?

Make a commitment, now, on paper as follows:

I commit to (type of exercise) ....

....

.... times a week, starting ....

....

....

Daily monitoring diary

Keep a daily record of when you exercise and the effect exercise has on lowering your anxiety. This record will motivate you to keep exercising regularly because you will have proof of the benefits of exercise.

Breathing: calming tool

Deep breathing lowers anxiety.

There are many different types of breathing that are taught by health professionals. If you already practise deep breathing regularly, and are happy with the benefits, then continue with your familiar routine on a daily basis.

If you are not happy with your routine, or do not have a deep breathing method, I recommend that you utilise my preferred method and make it a daily practice.

I teach "five breaths to calm."

When you practise "five breaths to calm," keep the following in mind:

1. Focus on your breath.
2. When you inhale, fill your lungs to maximum capacity.
3. When you exhale, push out as much air as possible.
4. The word "relax" must be said aloud, as an instruction.
5. Breathe in deeply and as you exhale, say the word "relax" out loud.

Repeat five times.

For maximum benefit, breathing this way should be done at least twice a day.

This type of breathing can be used as a tool when you are feeling anxious. Over time, it will train your body to be in an ongoing relaxed state.

This easy, effective method is available on my website at http://anxietysolutionscbt.com/services/relaxation-therapy/

Daily monitoring diary

Keep a daily record of when you practise your deep breathing and the effect it has on your anxiety. This record will motivate you to keep practising diligently as you will have proof of the benefits of deep breathing on reducing your anxiety.

Relaxation: calming tool

It is beneficial to practice a relaxation method at least twice a day. First thing in the morning and last thing at night is easy to work into your schedule. You cannot overdose on relaxation, so feel free to do it as many times a day as you need. Any method of relaxation that you enjoy can be utilised.

My preferred method involves tensing up then relaxing.

Tense your whole body. Hold it. Let go rapidly. As you let go, feel all the tension drain out of your body. Wait for five seconds, and then tense up again. Hold. Release. Feel all your tension exit your body. You now feel relaxed, "heavy" in your chair. Focus on each body part and how it feels. For example, "My head feels very heavy against the chair. My neck is completely relaxed, there is no tension in my neck."

After you have focused on and relaxed each part of your body, count to three and then sit up normally, ending the relaxation.

The reason I prefer this method is because it has a focus — tensing your muscles. In my experience, doing a progressive relaxation is extremely difficult for individuals who are highly anxious. They are simply not able to still their thoughts and focus on relaxation.

Whereas in this method, you are active and do not have to still your mind.

There are hundreds of effective methods of relaxation. If you have a method that works for you, there is no need to change. Keep utilising it regularly.

Daily monitoring diary

Keep a daily record of when you practise relaxation and the effect it has on your anxiety. Seeing the benefits of relaxation recorded will motivate you to keep practising diligently.

DAILY MONITORING DIARY WEEK ENDING ___________________

Day	M	T	W	T	F	S	S
Overall Anxiety Rating for the day (0-10)							
1. EXERCISE							
How long?							
Anxiety level before (0-10)							
Anxiety level after (0-10)							
2. BREATHING							
How long?							
Anxiety level before (0-10)							
Anxiety level after (0-10)							
3. RELAXATION							
How long?							
Anxiety level before (0-10)							
Anxiety level after (0-10)							
4. PERVASIVE PESSIMISTIC THINKING							
How often this type of thought occurred							
Belief in thoughts before challenging (0-10)							
Belief in thoughts after challenging (0-10)							

Date: ______________

Anxiety Management Worksheet

The purpose of this worksheet is to help you to see every stressful event as an opportunity for
1. greater understanding of yourself, your anxiety and the people around you, and
2. practicing tools to manage your anxiety.

Step One: An Event

Briefly describe an event when you became anxious. Give such details as time, place and people involved, and end with "That's when I began to work myself up..."

____

____

____

____   Rate your anxiety on a scale of 0 to 100%: [   ] %

E

Step Two: The Working-Up Process

Learn about your working up process by identifying your thoughts, feelings, behaviours and bodily reactions during the event. Tick the ones that most resonate with you.

Undermining Beliefs

I fear that I have lost...
- ☐ approval
- ☐ control
- ☐ co-operation
- ☐ face
- ☐ respect
- ☐ success
- ☐ trust
- ☐ validation
- ☐ love

This event proves that I am...
- ☐ stupid
- ☐ abnormal
- ☐ incompetent
- ☐ lazy
- ☐ irresponsible
- ☐ a total failure
- ☐ undisciplined
- ☐ untogether
- ☐ useless

I worry that I will suffer...
- ☐ mental collapse
- ☐ illness
- ☐ financial hardship

What I want is...
- ☐ total control
- ☐ respect
- ☐ success
- ☐ perfection
- ☐ comfort
- ☐ fairness
- ☐ tranquility
- ☐ all the answers
- ☐ for life to go smoothly
- ☐ to be all things to all people

B

Self-destructive Behaviour

Active
- ☐ get violent
- ☐ swear
- ☐ slam doors
- ☐ run away
- ☐ overeat
- ☐ harm myself
- ☐ criticise

Passive
- ☐ take it too seriously
- ☐ give up
- ☐ wallow in self pity
- ☐ sulk
- ☐ space out
- ☐ procrastinate
- ☐ give in
- ☐ be controlled

Intense Feelings

Angry feelings
- ☐ hateful
- ☐ aggravated
- ☐ annoyed
- ☐ hostile
- ☐ outraged
- ☐ punitive
- ☐ resentful
- ☐ vengeful

Fearful feelings
- ☐ helpless
- ☐ hopeless
- ☐ disappointed
- ☐ sad

- ☐ attacked
- ☐ worn out
- ☐ rejected
- ☐ jealous
- ☐ afraid
- ☐ exploited
- ☐ lonely
- ☐ abandoned
- ☐ guilty
- ☐ insulted
- ☐ confused
- ☐ disillusioned
- ☐ misunderstood
- ☐ trapped

Bodily Reactions (limbic system)

I am uncomfortable because I am experiencing...
- ☐ tremors
- ☐ nausea
- ☐ sweaty palms
- ☐ stomach-ache
- ☐ pounding heart
- ☐ general tension
- ☐ fatigue
- ☐ imagination on fire
- ☐ headache
- ☐ dry mouth
- ☐ jaw clenching
- ☐ shortness of breath

Continued over

B   **F**   **L**

Step Three: The Working-Down Process

Begin with, "Suddenly I realised that I was anxious and that I had choices..." This is the step of self-leadership and trust in one's ability to handle the situation.

Choose helpful thoughts:

I choose to depersonalise
There is no intention to hurt me. He is doing the best he can with the tools he has at the moment.

I choose realism over romanticism
Life presents many obstacles. I lower or raise standards as needed.

There is no right or wrong
Unless it is a moral issue, I will see it simply as a difference of opinion and/or taste.

I choose the total view of positivity
Even though this event is negative, the total view of his behaviour is positive.

I surrender control
Since I cannot change this situation, I choose to let go of it.

I choose to put this event in perspective This event is not a catastrophe because it is not life threatening. It can be viewed as a trivial life event, a normal life problem that needs to be solved not dramatised.

I choose to view this event as average, falling within the normal range
This event is not exceptional; many people have gone through this.

It's temporary - "this too shall pass"
Life is constantly changing and moving through phases and this situation will also change.

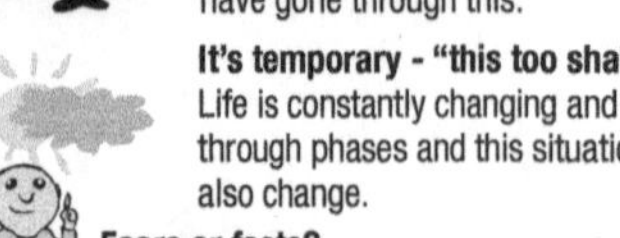

Fears or facts?
Why fear? It may not happen!

I choose to focus on this as a learning experience
Every problem that comes my way is an opportunity for me to learn about my strengths and weaknesses, others and life.

Feel soothing emotions:

I choose to feel warm, loving emotions. I do this by focusing on my heart and letting love, trust forgiveness, compassion, hope or gratitude fill my heart space.

Behave constructively:

I choose to work in part acts:
I will break the overwhelming job into manageable parts.

Do the difficult:
I will face what I fear and act with self-discipline.

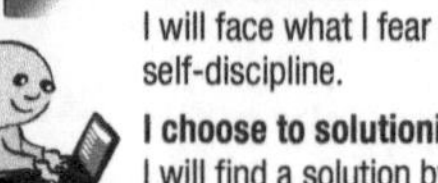

I choose to solutionise:
I will find a solution by taking advice or doing research.

Prioritise myself:
I will keep my life balanced by meeting friends, doing exercise or laughing.

Compartmentalise:
I will not let this event cloud my whole day; I will focus on something else now.

Utilise calming strategies:

When I:
- relax,
- breathe deeply,
- go for a run,
- shower,
- lie down,
- read,
- watch TV,
- climb into a mental helicopter,
- practice mindfulness/meditation,
  my mind and body calm down.

Step Four: The Self Motivation Process

Endorse yourself for any growth no matter how small.

In the past I would have...

____

____

But this time I...

____

____

Tick off the traits that you strengthened when you worked down your anxiety:

☐ generosity	☐ peacefulness
☐ kindness	☐ self-discipline
☐ compassion	☐ forgiveness
☐ consideration	☐ courage
☐ helpfulness	☐ responsibility
☐ respectfulness	☐ reliability
☐ honesty	☐ loyalty
☐ fairness	☐ love
☐ patience	☐ humility

Rate your anxiety on a scale of 0 to 100%:

☐ %

o

w

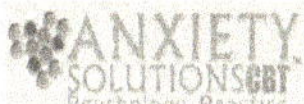

Anxiety Management Worksheet

The purpose of this worksheet is to help you to see every stressful event as an opportunity for
1. greater understanding of yourself, your anxiety and the people around you, and
2. practicing tools to manage your anxiety.

Step One: An Event

Briefly describe an event when you became anxious. Give such details as time, place and people involved, and end with "That's when I began to work myself up..."

____

____

____

____ Rate your anxiety on a scale of 0 to 100%: [   ] %

E

Step Two: The Working-Up Process

Learn about your working up process by identifying your thoughts, feelings, behaviours and bodily reactions during the event.
Tick the ones that most resonate with you.

Undermining Beliefs

B

I fear that I have lost...
- ☐ approval
- ☐ control
- ☐ co-operation
- ☐ face
- ☐ respect
- ☐ success
- ☐ trust
- ☐ validation
- ☐ love

This event proves that I am...
- ☐ stupid
- ☐ abnormal
- ☐ incompetent
- ☐ lazy
- ☐ irresponsible
- ☐ a total failure
- ☐ undisciplined
- ☐ untogether
- ☐ useless

I worry that I will suffer...
- ☐ mental collapse
- ☐ illness
- ☐ financial hardship

What I want is...
- ☐ total control
- ☐ respect
- ☐ success
- ☐ perfection
- ☐ comfort
- ☐ fairness
- ☐ tranquility
- ☐ all the answers
- ☐ for life to go smoothly
- ☐ to be all things to all people

Self-destructive Behaviour

Active
- ☐ get violent
- ☐ swear
- ☐ slam doors
- ☐ run away
- ☐ overeat
- ☐ harm myself
- ☐ criticise

Passive
- ☐ take it too seriously
- ☐ give up
- ☐ wallow in self pity
- ☐ sulk
- ☐ space out
- ☐ procrastinate
- ☐ give in
- ☐ be controlled

Intense Feelings

Angry feelings
- ☐ hateful
- ☐ aggravated
- ☐ annoyed
- ☐ hostile
- ☐ outraged
- ☐ punitive
- ☐ resentful
- ☐ vengeful
- ☐ attacked
- ☐ worn out
- ☐ rejected
- ☐ jealous
- ☐ afraid
- ☐ exploited
- ☐ lonely
- ☐ abandoned
- ☐ guilty
- ☐ insulted

Fearful feelings
- ☐ helpless
- ☐ hopeless
- ☐ disappointed
- ☐ sad
- ☐ confused
- ☐ disillusioned
- ☐ misunderstood
- ☐ trapped

Bodily Reactions (limbic system)

I am uncomfortable because I am experiencing...
- ☐ tremors
- ☐ nausea
- ☐ sweaty palms
- ☐ stomach-ache
- ☐ pounding heart
- ☐ general tension
- ☐ fatigue
- ☐ imagination on fire
- ☐ headache
- ☐ dry mouth
- ☐ jaw clenching
- ☐ shortness of breath

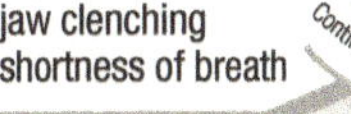

B   **F**   **L**

Step Three: The Working-Down Process

Begin with, "Suddenly I realised that I was anxious and that I had choices..." This is the step of self-leadership and trust in one's ability to handle the situation.

Choose helpful thoughts:

I choose to depersonalise
There is no intention to hurt me. He is doing the best he can with the tools he has at the moment.

I choose realism over romanticism
Life presents many obstacles. I lower or raise standards as needed.

There is no right or wrong
Unless it is a moral issue, I will see it simply as a difference of opinion and/or taste.

I choose the total view of positivity
Even though this event is negative, the total view of his behaviour is positive.

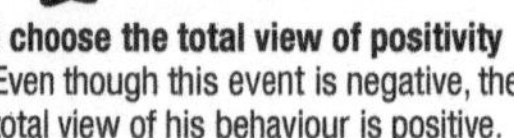

I surrender control
Since I cannot change this situation, I choose to let go of it.

I choose to put this event in perspective This event is not a catastrophe because it is not life threatening. It can be viewed as a trivial life event, a normal life problem that needs to be solved not dramatised.

I choose to view this event as average, falling within the normal range
This event is not exceptional; many people have gone through this.

It's temporary - "this too shall pass"
Life is constantly changing and moving through phases and this situation will also change.

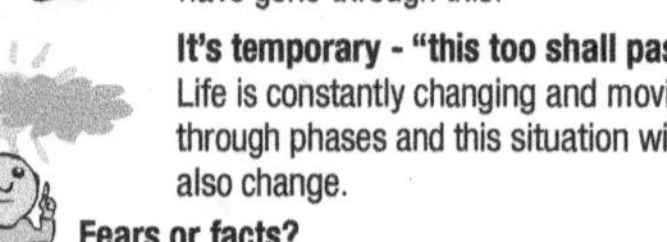

Fears or facts?
Why fear? It may not happen!

I choose to focus on this as a learning experience
Every problem that comes my way is an opportunity for me to learn about my strengths and weaknesses, others and life.

Feel soothing emotions:

I choose to feel warm, loving emotions. I do this by focusing on my heart and letting love, trust forgiveness, compassion, hope or gratitude fill my heart space.

Behave constructively:

I choose to work in part acts:
I will break the overwhelming job into manageable parts.

Do the difficult:
I will face what I fear and act with self-discipline.

I choose to solutionise:
I will find a solution by taking advice or doing research.

Prioritise myself:
I will keep my life balanced by meeting friends, doing exercise or laughing.

Compartmentalise:
I will not let this event cloud my whole day; I will focus on something else now.

Utilise calming strategies:

When I:
• relax,
• breathe deeply,
• go for a run,
• shower,
• lie down,
• read,
• watch TV,
• climb into a mental helicopter,
• practice mindfulness/meditation,
my mind and body calm down.

Step Four: The Self Motivation Process

Endorse yourself for any growth no matter how small.

In the past I would have...

____

____

But this time I...

____

____

Tick off the traits that you strengthened when you worked down your anxiety:

☐ generosity	☐ peacefulness	
☐ kindness	☐ self-discipline	
☐ compassion	☐ forgiveness	
☐ consideration	☐ courage	
☐ helpfulness	☐ responsibility	
☐ respectfulness	☐ reliability	
☐ honesty	☐ loyalty	
☐ fairness	☐ love	
☐ patience	☐ humility	

Rate your anxiety on a scale of 0 to 100%:

______ %

O

W

Date: ___________

Anxiety Management Worksheet

The purpose of this worksheet is to help you to see every stressful event as an opportunity for
1. greater understanding of yourself, your anxiety and the people around you, and
2. practicing tools to manage your anxiety.

Step One: An Event

Briefly describe an event when you became anxious. Give such details as time, place and people involved, and end with "That's when I began to work myself up..."

____

____   E

____

_______________________________________ Rate your anxiety on a scale of 0 to 100%: [   ] %

Step Two: The Working-Up Process

Learn about your working up process by identifying your thoughts, feelings, behaviours and bodily reactions during the event.
Tick the ones that most resonate with you.

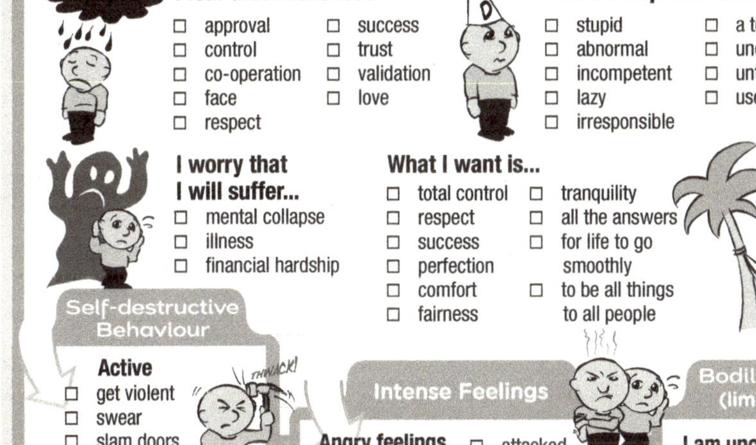

B

B   F   L

Step Three: The Working-Down Process

Begin with, "Suddenly I realised that I was anxious and that I had choices..." This is the step of self-leadership and trust in one's ability to handle the situation.

Choose helpful thoughts:

I choose to depersonalise
There is no intention to hurt me. He is doing the best he can with the tools he has at the moment.

I choose realism over romanticism
Life presents many obstacles. I lower or raise standards as needed.

There is no right or wrong
Unless it is a moral issue, I will see it simply as a difference of opinion and/or taste.

I choose the total view of positivity
Even though this event is negative, the total view of his behaviour is positive.

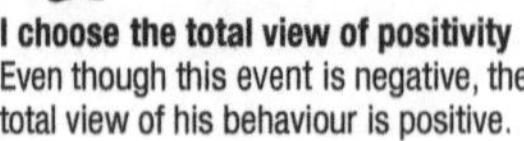

I surrender control
Since I cannot change this situation, I choose to let go of it.

I choose to put this event in perspective This event is not a catastrophe because it is not life threatening. It can be viewed as a trivial life event, a normal life problem that needs to be solved not dramatised.

I choose to view this event as average, falling within the normal range
This event is not exceptional; many people have gone through this.

It's temporary - "this too shall pass"
Life is constantly changing and moving through phases and this situation will also change.

Fears or facts?
Why fear? It may not happen!

I choose to focus on this as a learning experience
Every problem that comes my way is an opportunity for me to learn about my strengths and weaknesses, others and life.

Feel soothing emotions:

I choose to feel warm, loving emotions. I do this by focusing on my heart and letting love, trust forgiveness, compassion, hope or gratitude fill my heart space.

Behave constructively:

I choose to work in part acts:
I will break the overwhelming job into manageable parts.

Do the difficult:
I will face what I fear and act with self-discipline.

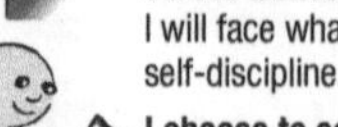

I choose to solutionise:
I will find a solution by taking advice or doing research.

Prioritise myself:
I will keep my life balanced by meeting friends, doing exercise or laughing.

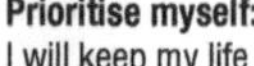

Compartmentalise:
I will not let this event cloud my whole day; I will focus on something else now.

Utilise calming strategies:

When I:
- relax,
- breathe deeply,
- go for a run,
- shower,
- lie down,
- read,
- watch TV,
- climb into a mental helicopter,
- practice mindfulness/meditation,

my mind and body calm down.

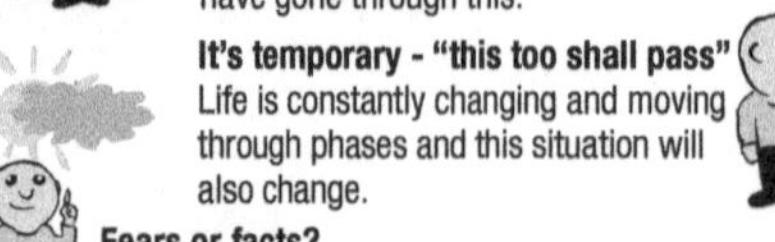

Step Four: The Self Motivation Process

Endorse yourself for any growth no matter how small.

In the past I would have...

____

____

But this time I...

____

____

Tick off the traits that you strengthened when you worked down your anxiety:

- ☐ generosity
- ☐ kindness
- ☐ compassion
- ☐ consideration
- ☐ helpfulness
- ☐ respectfulness
- ☐ honesty
- ☐ fairness
- ☐ patience
- ☐ peacefulness
- ☐ self-discipline
- ☐ forgiveness
- ☐ courage
- ☐ responsibility
- ☐ reliability
- ☐ loyalty
- ☐ love
- ☐ humility

Rate your anxiety on a scale of 0 to 100%:

☐ %

o

w

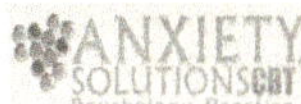

Anxiety Management Worksheet

The purpose of this worksheet is to help you to see every stressful event as an opportunity for
1. greater understanding of yourself, your anxiety and the people around you, and
2. practicing tools to manage your anxiety.

Step One: An Event

Briefly describe an event when you became anxious. Give such details as time, place and people involved, and end with "That's when I began to work myself up..."

____

____

____

____ Rate your anxiety on a scale of 0 to 100%: [   ] %

E

Step Two: The Working-Up Process

Learn about your working up process by identifying your thoughts, feelings, behaviours and bodily reactions during the event.
Tick the ones that most resonate with you.

Undermining Beliefs

B

I fear that I have lost...

- ☐ approval
- ☐ success
- ☐ control
- ☐ trust
- ☐ co-operation
- ☐ validation
- ☐ face
- ☐ love
- ☐ respect

This event proves that I am...

- ☐ stupid
- ☐ a total failure
- ☐ abnormal
- ☐ undisciplined
- ☐ incompetent
- ☐ untogether
- ☐ lazy
- ☐ useless
- ☐ irresponsible

I worry that I will suffer...

- ☐ mental collapse
- ☐ illness
- ☐ financial hardship

What I want is...

- ☐ total control
- ☐ tranquility
- ☐ respect
- ☐ all the answers
- ☐ success
- ☐ for life to go smoothly
- ☐ perfection
- ☐ comfort
- ☐ to be all things to all people
- ☐ fairness

Self-destructive Behaviour

Active

- ☐ get violent
- ☐ swear
- ☐ slam doors
- ☐ run away
- ☐ overeat
- ☐ harm myself
- ☐ criticise

Passive

- ☐ take it too seriously
- ☐ give up
- ☐ wallow in self pity
- ☐ sulk
- ☐ space out
- ☐ procrastinate
- ☐ give in
- ☐ be controlled

Intense Feelings

Angry feelings

- ☐ hateful
- ☐ attacked
- ☐ aggravated
- ☐ worn out
- ☐ annoyed
- ☐ rejected
- ☐ hostile
- ☐ jealous
- ☐ outraged
- ☐ afraid
- ☐ punitive
- ☐ exploited
- ☐ resentful
- ☐ lonely
- ☐ vengeful
- ☐ abandoned

Fearful feelings

- ☐ guilty
- ☐ helpless
- ☐ insulted
- ☐ hopeless
- ☐ confused
- ☐ disappointed
- ☐ disillusioned
- ☐ sad
- ☐ misunderstood
- ☐ trapped

Bodily Reactions (limbic system)

I am uncomfortable because I am experiencing...

- ☐ tremors
- ☐ nausea
- ☐ sweaty palms
- ☐ stomach-ache
- ☐ pounding heart
- ☐ general tension
- ☐ fatigue
- ☐ imagination on fire
- ☐ headache
- ☐ dry mouth
- ☐ jaw clenching
- ☐ shortness of breath

Continued over

B **F** **L**

Step Three: The Working-Down Process

Begin with, "Suddenly I realised that I was anxious and that I had choices..." This is the step of self-leadership and trust in one's ability to handle the situation.

Choose helpful thoughts:

I choose to depersonalise
There is no intention to hurt me. He is doing the best he can with the tools he has at the moment.

I choose realism over romanticism
Life presents many obstacles. I lower or raise standards as needed.

There is no right or wrong
Unless it is a moral issue, I will see it simply as a difference of opinion and/or taste.

I choose the total view of positivity
Even though this event is negative, the total view of his behaviour is positive.

I surrender control
Since I cannot change this situation, I choose to let go of it.

I choose to put this event in perspective This event is not a catastrophe because it is not life threatening. It can be viewed as a trivial life event, a normal life problem that needs to be solved not dramatised.

I choose to view this event as average, falling within the normal range
This event is not exceptional; many people have gone through this.

It's temporary - "this too shall pass"
Life is constantly changing and moving through phases and this situation will also change.

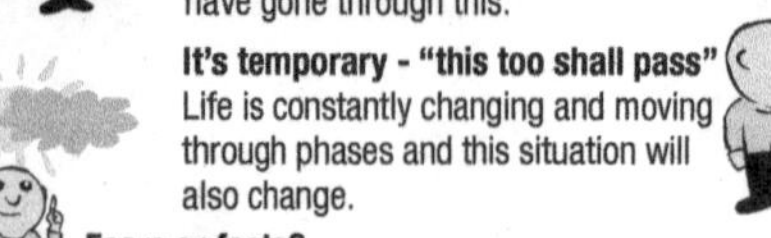

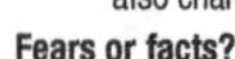

Fears or facts?
Why fear? It may not happen!

I choose to focus on this as a learning experience
Every problem that comes my way is an opportunity for me to learn about my strengths and weaknesses, others and life.

Feel soothing emotions:

I choose to feel warm, loving emotions. I do this by focusing on my heart and letting love, trust forgiveness, compassion, hope or gratitude fill my heart space.

Behave constructively:

I choose to work in part acts:
I will break the overwhelming job into manageable parts.

Do the difficult:
I will face what I fear and act with self-discipline.

I choose to solutionise:
I will find a solution by taking advice or doing research.

Prioritise myself:
I will keep my life balanced by meeting friends, doing exercise or laughing.

Compartmentalise:
I will not let this event cloud my whole day; I will focus on something else now.

Utilise calming strategies:

When I:
- relax,
- breathe deeply,
- go for a run,
- shower,
- lie down,
- read,
- watch TV,
- climb into a mental helicopter,
- practice mindfulness/meditation,
my mind and body calm down.

Step Four: The Self Motivation Process

Endorse yourself for any growth no matter how small.

In the past I would have...

____

____

But this time I...

____

____

Tick off the traits that you strengthened when you worked down your anxiety:

☐ generosity   ☐ peacefulness
☐ kindness   ☐ self-discipline
☐ compassion   ☐ forgiveness
☐ consideration   ☐ courage
☐ helpfulness   ☐ responsibility
☐ respectfulness   ☐ reliability
☐ honesty   ☐ loyalty
☐ fairness   ☐ love
☐ patience   ☐ humility

Rate your anxiety on a scale of 0 to 100%:

_______ %

O

W

Anxiety Management Worksheet

The purpose of this worksheet is to help you to see every stressful event as an opportunity for
1. greater understanding of yourself, your anxiety and the people around you, and
2. practicing tools to manage your anxiety.

Step One: An Event

Briefly describe an event when you became anxious. Give such details as time, place and people involved, and end with "That's when I began to work myself up..."

____

____   **E**

____

_______________________________   Rate your anxiety on a scale of 0 to 100%: [   ] **%**

Step Two: The Working-Up Process

Learn about your working up process by identifying your thoughts, feelings, behaviours and bodily reactions during the event. Tick the ones that most resonate with you.

Undermining Beliefs   **B**

I fear that I have lost...
- ☐ approval
- ☐ control
- ☐ co-operation
- ☐ face
- ☐ respect
- ☐ success
- ☐ trust
- ☐ validation
- ☐ love

This event proves that I am...
- ☐ stupid
- ☐ abnormal
- ☐ incompetent
- ☐ lazy
- ☐ irresponsible
- ☐ a total failure
- ☐ undisciplined
- ☐ untogether
- ☐ useless

I worry that I will suffer...
- ☐ mental collapse
- ☐ illness
- ☐ financial hardship

What I want is...
- ☐ total control
- ☐ respect
- ☐ success
- ☐ perfection
- ☐ comfort
- ☐ fairness
- ☐ tranquility
- ☐ all the answers
- ☐ for life to go smoothly
- ☐ to be all things to all people

Self-destructive Behaviour   **B**

Active
- ☐ get violent
- ☐ swear
- ☐ slam doors
- ☐ run away
- ☐ overeat
- ☐ harm myself
- ☐ criticise

Passive
- ☐ take it too seriously
- ☐ give up
- ☐ wallow in self pity
- ☐ sulk
- ☐ space out
- ☐ procrastinate
- ☐ give in
- ☐ be controlled

Intense Feelings   **F**

Angry feelings
- ☐ hateful
- ☐ aggravated
- ☐ annoyed
- ☐ hostile
- ☐ outraged
- ☐ punitive
- ☐ resentful
- ☐ vengeful

Fearful feelings
- ☐ helpless
- ☐ hopeless
- ☐ disappointed
- ☐ sad
- ☐ attacked
- ☐ worn out
- ☐ rejected
- ☐ jealous
- ☐ afraid
- ☐ exploited
- ☐ lonely
- ☐ abandoned
- ☐ guilty
- ☐ insulted
- ☐ confused
- ☐ disillusioned
- ☐ misunderstood
- ☐ trapped

Bodily Reactions (limbic system)   **L**

I am uncomfortable because I am experiencing...
- ☐ tremors
- ☐ nausea
- ☐ sweaty palms
- ☐ stomach-ache
- ☐ pounding heart
- ☐ general tension
- ☐ fatigue
- ☐ imagination on fire
- ☐ headache
- ☐ dry mouth
- ☐ jaw clenching
- ☐ shortness of breath

Continued over

Step Three: The Working-Down Process

Begin with, "Suddenly I realised that I was anxious and that I had choices…" This is the step of self-leadership and trust in one's ability to handle the situation.

Choose helpful thoughts:

I choose to depersonalise
There is no intention to hurt me. He is doing the best he can with the tools he has at the moment.

I choose realism over romanticism
Life presents many obstacles. I lower or raise standards as needed.

There is no right or wrong
Unless it is a moral issue, I will see it simply as a difference of opinion and/or taste.

I choose the total view of positivity
Even though this event is negative, the total view of his behaviour is positive.

I surrender control
Since I cannot change this situation, I choose to let go of it.

I choose to put this event in perspective This event is not a catastrophe because it is not life threatening. It can be viewed as a trivial life event, a normal life problem that needs to be solved not dramatised.

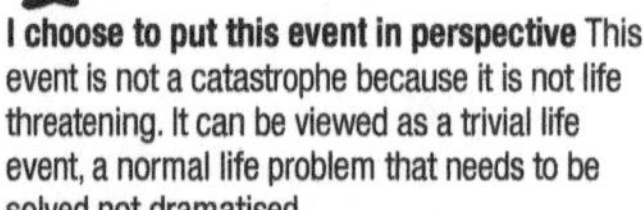

I choose to view this event as average, falling within the normal range
This event is not exceptional; many people have gone through this.

It's temporary - "this too shall pass"
Life is constantly changing and moving through phases and this situation will also change.

Fears or facts?
Why fear? It may not happen!

I choose to focus on this as a learning experience
Every problem that comes my way is an opportunity for me to learn about my strengths and weaknesses, others and life.

Feel soothing emotions:

I choose to feel warm, loving emotions. I do this by focusing on my heart and letting love, trust forgiveness, compassion, hope or gratitude fill my heart space.

Behave constructively:

I choose to work in part acts:
I will break the overwhelming job into manageable parts.

Do the difficult:
I will face what I fear and act with self-discipline.

I choose to solutionise:
I will find a solution by taking advice or doing research.

Prioritise myself:
I will keep my life balanced by meeting friends, doing exercise or laughing.

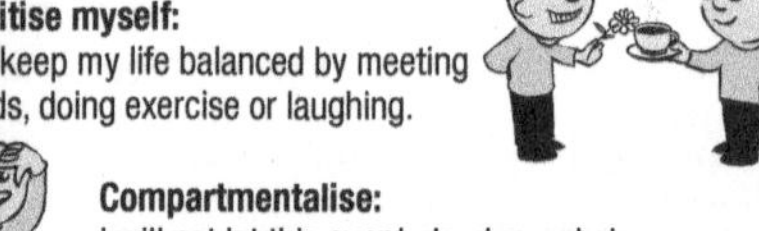

Compartmentalise:
I will not let this event cloud my whole day; I will focus on something else now.

Utilise calming strategies:

When I:
- relax,
- breathe deeply,
- go for a run,
- shower,
- lie down,
- read,
- watch TV,
- climb into a mental helicopter,
- practice mindfulness/meditation,

my mind and body calm down.

Step Four: The Self Motivation Process

Endorse yourself for any growth no matter how small.

In the past I would have...

____

____

But this time I...

____

____

Tick off the traits that you strengthened when you worked down your anxiety:

☐ generosity	☐ peacefulness
☐ kindness	☐ self-discipline
☐ compassion	☐ forgiveness
☐ consideration	☐ courage
☐ helpfulness	☐ responsibility
☐ respectfulness	☐ reliability
☐ honesty	☐ loyalty
☐ fairness	☐ love
☐ patience	☐ humility

Rate your anxiety on a scale of 0 to 100%:

[________] %

O

W

Date: ___________

Anxiety Management Worksheet

The purpose of this worksheet is to help you to see every stressful event as an opportunity for
1. greater understanding of yourself, your anxiety and the people around you, and
2. practicing tools to manage your anxiety.

Step One: An Event

Briefly describe an event when you became anxious. Give such details as time, place and people involved, and end with "That's when I began to work myself up…"

____

____

____

____ Rate your anxiety on a scale of 0 to 100%: [   ] %

E

Step Two: The Working-Up Process

Learn about your working up process by identifying your thoughts, feelings, behaviours and bodily reactions during the event. Tick the ones that most resonate with you.

Undermining Beliefs

B

I fear that I have lost...
- ☐ approval
- ☐ control
- ☐ co-operation
- ☐ face
- ☐ respect
- ☐ success
- ☐ trust
- ☐ validation
- ☐ love

This event proves that I am...
- ☐ stupid
- ☐ abnormal
- ☐ incompetent
- ☐ lazy
- ☐ irresponsible
- ☐ a total failure
- ☐ undisciplined
- ☐ untogether
- ☐ useless

I worry that I will suffer...
- ☐ mental collapse
- ☐ illness
- ☐ financial hardship

What I want is...
- ☐ total control
- ☐ respect
- ☐ success
- ☐ perfection
- ☐ comfort
- ☐ fairness
- ☐ tranquility
- ☐ all the answers
- ☐ for life to go smoothly
- ☐ to be all things to all people

Self-destructive Behaviour

Active
- ☐ get violent
- ☐ swear
- ☐ slam doors
- ☐ run away
- ☐ overeat
- ☐ harm myself
- ☐ criticise

Passive
- ☐ take it too seriously
- ☐ give up
- ☐ wallow in self pity
- ☐ sulk
- ☐ space out
- ☐ procrastinate
- ☐ give in
- ☐ be controlled

Intense Feelings

Angry feelings
- ☐ hateful
- ☐ aggravated
- ☐ annoyed
- ☐ hostile
- ☐ outraged
- ☐ punitive
- ☐ resentful
- ☐ vengeful
- ☐ attacked
- ☐ worn out
- ☐ rejected
- ☐ jealous
- ☐ afraid
- ☐ exploited
- ☐ lonely
- ☐ abandoned
- ☐ guilty

Fearful feelings
- ☐ helpless
- ☐ hopeless
- ☐ disappointed
- ☐ sad
- ☐ insulted
- ☐ confused
- ☐ disillusioned
- ☐ misunderstood
- ☐ trapped

Bodily Reactions (limbic system)

I am uncomfortable because I am experiencing...
- ☐ tremors
- ☐ nausea
- ☐ sweaty palms
- ☐ stomach-ache
- ☐ pounding heart
- ☐ general tension
- ☐ fatigue
- ☐ imagination on fire
- ☐ headache
- ☐ dry mouth
- ☐ jaw clenching
- ☐ shortness of breath

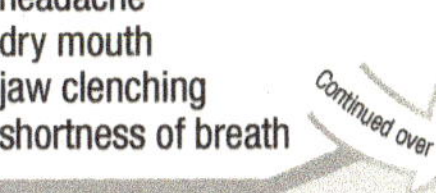

B   **F**   **L**

Step Three: The Working-Down Process

Begin with, "Suddenly I realised that I was anxious and that I had choices..." This is the step of self-leadership and trust in one's ability to handle the situation.

Choose helpful thoughts:

I choose to depersonalise
There is no intention to hurt me. He is doing the best he can with the tools he has at the moment.

I choose realism over romanticism
Life presents many obstacles. I lower or raise standards as needed.

There is no right or wrong
Unless it is a moral issue, I will see it simply as a difference of opinion and/or taste.

I choose the total view of positivity
Even though this event is negative, the total view of his behaviour is positive.

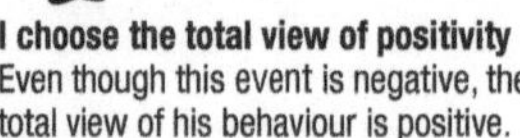

I surrender control
Since I cannot change this situation, I choose to let go of it.

I choose to put this event in perspective This event is not a catastrophe because it is not life threatening. It can be viewed as a trivial life event, a normal life problem that needs to be solved not dramatised.

I choose to view this event as average, falling within the normal range
This event is not exceptional; many people have gone through this.

It's temporary - "this too shall pass"
Life is constantly changing and moving through phases and this situation will also change.

Fears or facts?
Why fear? It may not happen!

I choose to focus on this as a learning experience
Every problem that comes my way is an opportunity for me to learn about my strengths and weaknesses, others and life.

Feel soothing emotions:

I choose to feel warm, loving emotions. I do this by focusing on my heart and letting love, trust forgiveness, compassion, hope or gratitude fill my heart space.

Behave constructively:

I choose to work in part acts:
I will break the overwhelming job into manageable parts.

Do the difficult:
I will face what I fear and act with self-discipline.

I choose to solutionise:
I will find a solution by taking advice or doing research.

Prioritise myself:
I will keep my life balanced by meeting friends, doing exercise or laughing.

Compartmentalise:
I will not let this event cloud my whole day; I will focus on something else now.

Utilise calming strategies:

When I:
- relax,
- breathe deeply,
- go for a run,
- shower,
- lie down,
- read,
- watch TV,
- climb into a mental helicopter,
- practice mindfulness/meditation,

my mind and body calm down.

Step Four: The Self Motivation Process

Endorse yourself for any growth no matter how small.

In the past I would have...

____

____

But this time I...

____

____

Tick off the traits that you strengthened when you worked down your anxiety:

☐	generosity	☐	peacefulness
☐	kindness	☐	self-discipline
☐	compassion	☐	forgiveness
☐	consideration	☐	courage
☐	helpfulness	☐	responsibility
☐	respectfulness	☐	reliability
☐	honesty	☐	loyalty
☐	fairness	☐	love
☐	patience	☐	humility

Rate your anxiety on a scale of 0 to 100%:

________ %

O   W

Date: ___________

Anxiety Management Worksheet

The purpose of this worksheet is to help you to see every stressful event as an opportunity for
1. greater understanding of yourself, your anxiety and the people around you, and
2. practicing tools to manage your anxiety.

Step One: An Event

Briefly describe an event when you became anxious. Give such details as time, place and people involved, and end with "That's when I began to work myself up…"

____

____

____

_______________________________ Rate your anxiety on a scale of 0 to 100%: [   ] %

E

Step Two: The Working-Up Process

Learn about your working up process by identifying your thoughts, feelings, behaviours and bodily reactions during the event. Tick the ones that most resonate with you.

Undermining Beliefs

B

I fear that I have lost...

- ☐ approval
- ☐ control
- ☐ co-operation
- ☐ face
- ☐ respect
- ☐ success
- ☐ trust
- ☐ validation
- ☐ love

This event proves that I am...

- ☐ stupid
- ☐ abnormal
- ☐ incompetent
- ☐ lazy
- ☐ irresponsible
- ☐ a total failure
- ☐ undisciplined
- ☐ untogether
- ☐ useless

I worry that I will suffer...

- ☐ mental collapse
- ☐ illness
- ☐ financial hardship

What I want is...

- ☐ total control
- ☐ respect
- ☐ success
- ☐ perfection
- ☐ comfort
- ☐ fairness
- ☐ tranquility
- ☐ all the answers
- ☐ for life to go smoothly
- ☐ to be all things to all people

Self-destructive Behaviour

Active

- ☐ get violent
- ☐ swear
- ☐ slam doors
- ☐ run away
- ☐ overeat
- ☐ harm myself
- ☐ criticise

Passive

- ☐ take it too seriously
- ☐ give up
- ☐ wallow in self pity
- ☐ sulk
- ☐ space out
- ☐ procrastinate
- ☐ give in
- ☐ be controlled

Intense Feelings

Angry feelings

- ☐ hateful
- ☐ aggravated
- ☐ annoyed
- ☐ hostile
- ☐ outraged
- ☐ punitive
- ☐ resentful
- ☐ vengeful
- ☐ attacked
- ☐ worn out
- ☐ rejected
- ☐ jealous
- ☐ afraid
- ☐ exploited
- ☐ lonely
- ☐ abandoned
- ☐ guilty

Fearful feelings

- ☐ helpless
- ☐ hopeless
- ☐ disappointed
- ☐ sad
- ☐ insulted
- ☐ confused
- ☐ disillusioned
- ☐ misunderstood
- ☐ trapped

Bodily Reactions (limbic system)

I am uncomfortable because I am experiencing...

- ☐ tremors
- ☐ nausea
- ☐ sweaty palms
- ☐ stomach-ache
- ☐ pounding heart
- ☐ general tension
- ☐ fatigue
- ☐ imagination on fire
- ☐ headache
- ☐ dry mouth
- ☐ jaw clenching
- ☐ shortness of breath

Continued over

B   **F**   **L**

Step Three: The Working-Down Process

Begin with, "Suddenly I realised that I was anxious and that I had choices..." This is the step of self-leadership and trust in one's ability to handle the situation.

Choose helpful thoughts:

I choose to depersonalise
There is no intention to hurt me. He is doing the best he can with the tools he has at the moment.

I choose realism over romanticism
Life presents many obstacles. I lower or raise standards as needed.

There is no right or wrong
Unless it is a moral issue, I will see it simply as a difference of opinion and/or taste.

I choose the total view of positivity
Even though this event is negative, the total view of his behaviour is positive.

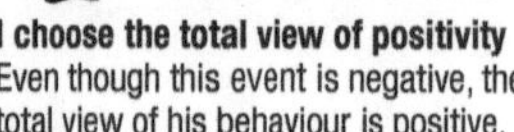

I surrender control
Since I cannot change this situation, I choose to let go of it.

I choose to put this event in perspective This event is not a catastrophe because it is not life threatening. It can be viewed as a trivial life event, a normal life problem that needs to be solved not dramatised.

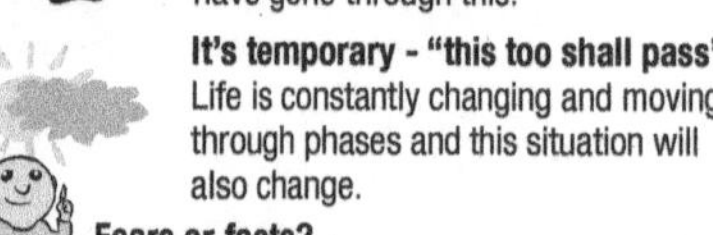

I choose to view this event as average, falling within the normal range
This event is not exceptional; many people have gone through this.

It's temporary - "this too shall pass"
Life is constantly changing and moving through phases and this situation will also change.

Fears or facts?
Why fear? It may not happen!

I choose to focus on this as a learning experience
Every problem that comes my way is an opportunity for me to learn about my strengths and weaknesses, others and life.

Feel soothing emotions:

I choose to feel warm, loving emotions. I do this by focusing on my heart and letting love, trust forgiveness, compassion, hope or gratitude fill my heart space.

Behave constructively:

I choose to work in part acts:
I will break the overwhelming job into manageable parts.

Do the difficult:
I will face what I fear and act with self-discipline.

I choose to solutionise:
I will find a solution by taking advice or doing research.

Prioritise myself:
I will keep my life balanced by meeting friends, doing exercise or laughing.

Compartmentalise:
I will not let this event cloud my whole day; I will focus on something else now.

Utilise calming strategies:

When I:
- relax,
- breathe deeply,
- go for a run,
- shower,
- lie down,
- read,
- watch TV,
- climb into a mental helicopter,
- practice mindfulness/meditation,

my mind and body calm down.

Step Four: The Self Motivation Process

Endorse yourself for any growth no matter how small.

In the past I would have...

____

____

But this time I...

____

____

Tick off the traits that you strengthened when you worked down your anxiety:

- ☐ generosity
- ☐ kindness
- ☐ compassion
- ☐ consideration
- ☐ helpfulness
- ☐ respectfulness
- ☐ honesty
- ☐ fairness
- ☐ patience
- ☐ peacefulness
- ☐ self-discipline
- ☐ forgiveness
- ☐ courage
- ☐ responsibility
- ☐ reliability
- ☐ loyalty
- ☐ love
- ☐ humility

Rate your anxiety on a scale of 0 to 100%:

________ %

O

W

Week 4

In segment four, we will be covering the following tools:

1. Perspective: thinking tool
2. Prioritise yourself: behavioural tool
3. Set your biological rhythms: behavioural tool
4. Feelings: feeling tool

Perspective: thinking tool

"I choose to put this incident in perspective. This event is not a catastrophe because it is not life-threatening. It can be viewed as a trivial life problem that needs to be solved not dramatised."

The word catastrophise refers to the process of taking an every-day event and turning it into a major catastrophe in your mind or with your words. This process may be conscious and deliberate, or unconscious. Either way, catastrophising will get your "fight or flight" responses going unnecessarily.

Our brains are programmed to understand what a catastrophe is and the need to respond to it with life-saving energy. But what exactly is a catastrophe?

The *Macquarie Dictionary* (16) defines a catastrophe as follows:

1. sudden disaster
2. disastrous event or end
3. sudden violent disturbance, esp. of the earth's surface; cataclysm

As you can see from this definition, a catastrophe is something major that causes real damage. Yet hundreds of people refer to everyday events as if they were real catastrophes.

Watch your language

Listen carefully to yourself and the people around you. Note the reaction to things such as:

> a burnt dinner
> not getting a job
> a mess on the floor
> a bad hairdo
> being held up in traffic
> a common headache

Many people would use catastrophic language to describe these events:

> "The dinner turned out to be a disaster!"
> "I did not get the job that I want, this will be my ruination!"
> "She spilled milk on the floor. What a calamity!"
> "My hair is too short, this is a crisis!"
> "This traffic jam is horrendous!"
> "I've got a killer headache! I probably have a tumour."

Other commonly used words indicating a catastrophe are tragedy, blow, shock, horror, abuse and trauma.

In summary, utilising catastrophic terms to describe everyday hassles puts your brain on the alert for danger. Therefore, it is important that you watch what you say. Use your words carefully and describe what you see in real terms.

> "Some of the food was burnt at dinner but we snacked on crackers and got through it ok."
> "I am so disappointed that I did not get the job I applied for. Luckily I have savings that will see me through."
> "No use crying over spilt milk. Better to clean it up so nobody slips."
> "My hair is too short, I hate it. I can't wait for it to grow out in three weeks."
> "This traffic jam is an inconvenience that will dissipate in the next few hours."
> "My headache is from bad posture. All I need to do is stretch to get relief."

Notice that you are not pretending that things are perfect. Nor are you trying to see a silver lining. Rather, you are describing realistically what happened instead of exaggerating negatively. Realistic assessments will activate coping mechanisms whereas catastrophic assessments will activate the "fight or flight" reaction.

Ruler

A very effective way to help you to see situations realistically is to utilise this ruler. (13)

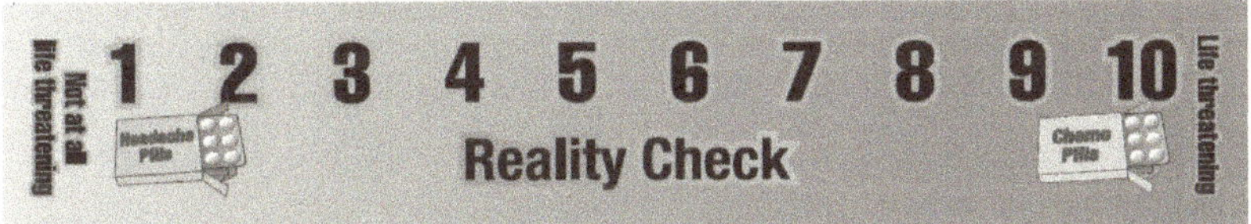

On one end of the ruler is number 1, which is the number depicting a situation that is not at all life-threatening. At the other end of the ruler is number 10, depicting situations which are life-threatening.

> Note: "Life-threatening" is an objective measure.

Life-threatening situations include: falling off a cliff, being caught in a rip in the ocean, being inside your house while it is on fire, or someone holding a knife to your throat. There are many events in life which may be major and incur a loss but they are still not life-threatening. When you are watching your house burn down, it is devastating but not life-threatening. When you fall, it may be painful but your life is not at risk. When a large wave knocks you over, it may be uncomfortable and you may need some assistance, but your life is not on the line.

Whenever a situation arises and you feel that you are becoming panicky, *as if you are in mortal danger*, use this tool. Ask yourself: "On a scale from 1 to 10, how life-threatening is this incident?"

What you will find is that very few situations, in fact, are life-threatening. As you "score" your event lower down on the scale, you will immediately feel your stress levels drop. The ruler enables you to "test out" whether or not your body is responding realistically. Are you looking at the facts?

Events that are not life-threatening are called "trivialities". (13) This does not mean that they are not important or that your worried feelings are not valid. It is just a way of forcing you to view the event with a more realistic perspective and help you become aware that, in the broader scheme of things, most issues that worry you are relatively trivial.

Let us say that you are irritated by the fact that a new neighbour talks loudly on the phone near your front door. You get worked up about it and, believing it will disturb your peaceful existence, even curse the man behind his back. Then you discover that a member of your family is dying. Suddenly the irritation is of no significance as your thoughts are totally consumed by the tragic news. The tragic news brought home to you that in the broader scheme of things (life and death situations), the irritation (a noisy neighbour) is a triviality.

However, this does not mean you have to put up with the new neighbour's noise and deny your irritation. It just means that you do not need to react as if you are about to die. Rather, you need to handle it as a problem that needs to be dealt with rationally, without all the emotionality.

Now that you understand how the ruler works and that it is useful to look at the facts of a situation, let's complete the following exercise.

EXERCISE 7

Fill out the columns below. Column 1 refers to past events in your life that have evoked catastrophic conclusions and major stress reactions. Column 2 refers to the point on the scale where you placed the events at the time. In column 3, write down how you would rate those same events at the present time. In column 4, write down the wording of your calming thought when you utilise this tool. (Writing things down repetitively helps you to develop a memory bank of how to rate events realistically).

Life event	Previous score	Current score	Calming thought
Example: *When I had my hair done for my engagement party, it looked awful and I had no time to correct it.*	10 I sobbed like a baby at first and then sulked all night ruining my party for myself.	1	This event was not life threatening. A bad hairdo is uncomfortable not disastrous.

Please note: When you are in the midst of catastrophising, you may not be able to utilise the ruler. However, once you have calmed down somewhat, it is still beneficial to use this tool as it will place the situation into perspective for you. Doing this after the fact will have a preventative effect in the future. Remember: This tool is only effective if the event is not really life-threatening. If an event is truly life-threatening, or cata- strophic, do not try and minimise it. Instead, look for a more appropriate tool to help you.

Daily monitoring diary

This week we focused on catastrophic thinking and language. If you become aware of when you utilise catastrophic thinking or language, note it in the daily monitoring diary. Moreover, from now on attempt to catch yourself having a catastrophic thought and then challenge it with the tool "**perspective**".

Prioritise yourself: behavioural tool

We live in a world where we have forgotten how to prioritise ourselves. In the Western world there is too much focus on success at work and material wealth. This usually translates into working long and hard while neglecting other parts of our life.

Over the years, I have said to clients that overwork: "No matter how important a situation is, your physical and mental health should take top priority."

One common response I get is: "Isn't it indulgent to put yourself first?"

Another common response is: "But I have to make a living and cannot take time off for myself."

The story of the woodcutter illustrates my point beautifully. (17) The woodcutter was in a large forest attempting to saw down a tree but not getting very far because his saw was blunt. An observant passer-by stopped to point out that the saw was blunt and needed sharpening. The woodcutter angrily replied "Do you think I am stupid? Do you think that I do not know that the saw is blunt? Can you see how large this forest is and how many trees I still have to cut? I simply do not have time to sharpen the saw!"

In the story, the saw is a metaphor for you. You may believe that you have so much to get through every day that you have no time to sharpen the saw, that is, to replenish yourself. This belief is foolhardy because a blunt saw is ineffective. If the woodcutter had taken the time to sharpen the saw, he would have completed his job in the forest much faster and more efficiently. Similarly, if you take the time to keep mentally and physically fit, you will achieve much more in the long-term. You would also feel less anxious.

To sharpen the saw, every week you need to "feed" the following five dimensions:

1. physical
2. spiritual
3. mental
4. social
5. emotional

Physical

This relates to eating, sleeping and exercise.

> Do you eat a healthy balanced diet? YES/NO
> Do you get enough sleep? YES/NO
> Do you exercise regularly? YES/NO

If you answered "no" to any of the above, please make a commitment to change here. Write down your plan of how you will make that change.

Spiritual

This relates to any religious or spiritual practice that "feeds your soul". It includes praying, participating at a house of worship, basking in nature, listening to music, meditating and yoga.

Do you practise any of the above in a consistent manner? YES/NO

If you answered "no," make a commitment here to bring a spiritual practice into your daily life. Write down your plan of how you will make that change.

Mental

The mental element refers to any activity which stimulates your brain but is different to your work. Even if you are a professor of maths, you need to do some pleasurable mental task that will activate other parts of your brain.

Some suggestions are reading non-fiction, playing cards, doing puzzles, learning to play a musical instrument or learning another language.

Do you enjoy stimulating mental activities outside of your work?

YES/NO

If you answered "no," commit now to incorporating some into your weekly schedule. Write down your plan of how you will make that change.

Social

Meeting with friends is very important. See the tool **"socialise"** on page 141.

Do you meet with any friends outside of work?   YES/NO

If you answered "no," make a commitment to start socialising more from today. Write down your plan of how you will make that change.

Emotional

Emotional "food" is a vital part of a stress free life. This means making time to share quality time with your partner and family. Sometimes it includes seeking help from a therapist.

> Do you have a regular date night with your partner?..YES/NO

> Do you make time for intimacy?   YES/NO

> Do you have quality time with your kids?   YES/NO

> Are you seeking emotional help if you are suffering from anxiety, depression or relationship issues?   YES/NO

If you said "no" to any of the above, please make a plan to do so right here and commit to starting right away. Write down your plan of how you will make that change.

Remember to prioritise your physical and mental health every single day. Do not let anyone or anything else convince you otherwise. When you feel well, healthy and energised, then the rest of your life is easier to deal with.

Set your biological rhythms: behavioural tool

Human beings have social and biological rhythms. This means we have a "body clock" that switches functions on and off at different times. When your life has a regular rhythm, your body clock will run efficiently and you will feel good.

Sleep is an excellent example of this. You have neurotransmitters that help you to fall asleep and others that help you to wake up and be alert. When you stick to regular bedtimes and wake up times, you will feel sleepy just before bedtime and be alert at wake up time. However, if you have no routine, your neurotransmitters have no idea what to do. Should they activate or de-activate? Are you expecting to be sleepy or to be alert? This confusion explains why sleeping in often results in you feeling groggy rather than awake.

Similarly, when you eat at regular times, your digestive system will become active just before a meal, preparing you for the meal. This is hunger. However, when you eat at random times, you may not be sure when you are hungry and you may crave food at odd times.

The Black Dog Institute discovered that when patients with mental health issues lived their lives according to regular routines, their moods tended to be more stable. In fact, overall feelings of well-being improved.

EXERCISE 8

The timetable below was compiled by The Black Dog Institute (18) to help patients decide on suitable routines and then monitor the benefits of sticking to the allocated time. Variations in mood frequently occur when routines are not consistent.

Please fill in the timetable below. Choose times that fit into your lifestyle and that you are most likely to maintain.

Social and biological rhythms monitoring timetable (adapted from Black Dog Institute)

		Mon	Tues	Wed	Thurs	Fri	Sat	Sun	
Bedtime	*earlier*								*Usual/ optimal time*
	later								
Main meal time	*earlier*								*Usual/ optimal time*
	later								
Socialising time	*earlier*								*Usual/ optimal time*
	later								
Exercise time	*earlier*								*Usual/ optimal time*
	later								

	Mon	Tues	Wed	Thurs	Fri	Sat	Sun	
Time of leaving home to go out	*earlier*							*Usual/ optimal time*
	later							
Waking up time	*earlier*							*Usual/ optimal time*
	later							
Anxiety level								

Choose an optimum time for each of the following:

> bedtime
> main meal time
> wake up time
> socialising time
> exercising time

This is how it will look when you fill it in.

	Mon	Tues	Wed	Thurs	Fri	Sat	Sun	
Bedtime 11.00pm	*earlier*							*Usual/ optimal time*
	X	X	X		X			
	later			X		X	X	
Main meal time 6.00pm	*earlier*							*Usual/ optimal time*
	X	X	X		X			
	later			X		X		
Socialising time 3.00pm	*earlier*				X	X		*Usual/ optimal time*
	X	X	X	X				
	later				X			
Exercise time 9.00am	*earlier*							*Usual/ optimal time*
	X		X		X			
	later				X			
Time of leaving home to go out 11.00am	*earlier*							*Usual/ optimal time*
	X	X	X	X	X			
	later					X		
Waking up time 7.00am	*earlier*							*Usual/ optimal time*
	X	X	X	X	X	X		
	later						X	
Anxiety level	1	3	1	4	3	7	8	

Begin following the timetable you have constructed and continue to rate your anxiety on a daily basis in the daily monitoring diary. Observe if, and how much, inconsistency exacerbates your anxiety. If after a month, you find no difference, then by all means drop the routine. However, most people find that their overall mood improves and their anxiety lessens with regular routines.

Feel soothing emotions: feeling tool

Just as you can only think one thought at a time, you can only feel one feeling at a time. When you substitute soothing emotions for distressing emotions, you will feel calmer. Intense negative feelings include angry feelings (fight) and fearful feelings (flight). Soothing emotions include love, trust, forgiveness, compassion and gratitude.

In order to move from distressing feelings to soothing feelings, you need to focus on the area where the emotion is felt. This area is called your *heart space* and it is located literally in your chest around your heart. (19)

You can fill your heart space with a positive feeling by imagining a positive interaction you have had — just like watching a video of a past event in your life.

EXERCISE 9

Let us say you are furious with your child. You want to become loving instead.

Take a minute and focus on the area around your heart. Now focus on your breathing and imagine you are breathing from your heart. Do this for five breaths. Think of a loving moment you had with your child in the past. Feel that love fill your heart space.

There is no room for any other emotion besides love when you do this. Your anger will dissipate. The more you do this the easier it becomes and the less angry you will be.

EXERCISE 10

Let us say you are fearful for the future. You are worried that you will not get a job. You would prefer to trust in the future.

Take a minute and focus on the area around your heart. Now focus on your breathing and imagine that you are breathing from your heart. Do this for five breaths. Think of previous times in your life when you found a job after a job loss. Let feelings of trust fill your heart space.

There is no room for any other emotion than trust when you do this. Your fear will decrease. Keep practising this to sustain the trust long-term.

EXERCISE 11

Let's imagine that you are not coping well at work because your mother is ill. At first you are critical of yourself, disappointed that you are not able to work perfectly all the time. Then you come to realise that rather than being so self-judgmental, you need to give yourself permission to feel compassion for your difficult circumstances.

Take a minute and focus on the area around your heart. Now focus on your breathing and imagine you are breathing from your heart. Do this for five breaths. Imagine a friend is in your exact position. You feel compassion for her because her life is tough right now. Her mother is sick and she needs to keep working. Experience compassion, fill your heart space. Then direct the compassion towards yourself.

There is no longer any room for criticism. All you feel is compassion.

DAILY MONITORING DIARY WEEK ENDING ....

Day	M	T	W	T	F	S	S
Overall Anxiety Rating for the day (0-10)							
1. EXERCISE							
How long?							
Anxiety level before (0-10)							
Anxiety level after (0-10)							
2. BREATHING							
How long?							
Anxiety level before (0-10)							
Anxiety level after (0-10)							
3. RELAXATION							
How long?							
Anxiety level before (0-10)							
Anxiety level after (0-10)							
4. PERVASIVE PESSIMISTIC THINKING							
How often this type of thought occurred							
Belief in thoughts before challenging (0-10)							
Belief in thoughts after challenging (0-10)							

Day	M	T	W	T	F	S	S
5. CATASTROPHIC THINKING							
How often this type of thought occurred							
Belief in thoughts before challenging (0-10)							
Belief in thoughts after challenging (0-10)							

Date: ___________

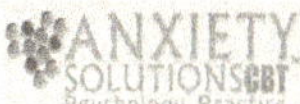

Anxiety Management Worksheet

The purpose of this worksheet is to help you to see every stressful event as an opportunity for
1. greater understanding of yourself, your anxiety and the people around you, and
2. practicing tools to manage your anxiety.

Step One: An Event

Briefly describe an event when you became anxious. Give such details as time, place and people involved, and end with "That's when I began to work myself up…"

____

____

____

_______________________________ Rate your anxiety on a scale of 0 to 100%: [   ] %

E

Step Two: The Working-Up Process

Learn about your working up process by identifying your thoughts, feelings, behaviours and bodily reactions during the event.
Tick the ones that most resonate with you.

Undermining Beliefs

B

I fear that I have lost...

- approval
- control
- co-operation
- face
- respect
- success
- trust
- validation
- love

This event proves that I am...

- stupid
- abnormal
- incompetent
- lazy
- irresponsible
- a total failure
- undisciplined
- untogether
- useless

I worry that I will suffer...

- mental collapse
- illness
- financial hardship

What I want is...

- total control
- respect
- success
- perfection
- comfort
- fairness
- tranquility
- all the answers
- for life to go smoothly
- to be all things to all people

Self-destructive Behaviour

Active

- get violent
- swear
- slam doors
- run away
- overeat
- harm myself
- criticise

Passive

- take it too seriously
- give up
- wallow in self pity
- sulk
- space out
- procrastinate
- give in
- be controlled

Intense Feelings

Angry feelings

- hateful
- aggravated
- annoyed
- hostile
- outraged
- punitive
- resentful
- vengeful

Fearful feelings

- helpless
- hopeless
- disappointed
- sad
- attacked
- worn out
- rejected
- jealous
- afraid
- exploited
- lonely
- abandoned
- guilty
- insulted
- confused
- disillusioned
- misunderstood
- trapped

Bodily Reactions (limbic system)

I am uncomfortable because I am experiencing...

- tremors
- nausea
- sweaty palms
- stomach-ache
- pounding heart
- general tension
- fatigue
- imagination on fire
- headache
- dry mouth
- jaw clenching
- shortness of breath

Continued over

B   **F**   **L**

Step Three: The Working-Down Process

Begin with, "Suddenly I realised that I was anxious and that I had choices..." This is the step of self-leadership and trust in one's ability to handle the situation.

Choose helpful thoughts:

I choose to depersonalise
There is no intention to hurt me. He is doing the best he can with the tools he has at the moment.

I choose realism over romanticism
Life presents many obstacles. I lower or raise standards as needed.

There is no right or wrong
Unless it is a moral issue, I will see it simply as a difference of opinion and/or taste.

I choose the total view of positivity
Even though this event is negative, the total view of his behaviour is positive.

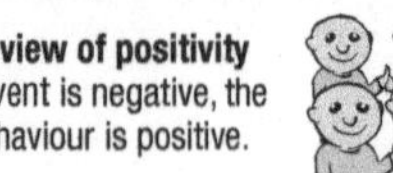

I surrender control
Since I cannot change this situation, I choose to let go of it.

I choose to put this event in perspective
This event is not a catastrophe because it is not life threatening. It can be viewed as a trivial life event, a normal life problem that needs to be solved not dramatised.

I choose to view this event as average, falling within the normal range
This event is not exceptional; many people have gone through this.

It's temporary - "this too shall pass"
Life is constantly changing and moving through phases and this situation will also change.

Fears or facts?
Why fear? It may not happen!

I choose to focus on this as a learning experience
Every problem that comes my way is an opportunity for me to learn about my strengths and weaknesses, others and life.

Feel soothing emotions:

I choose to feel warm, loving emotions. I do this by focusing on my heart and letting love, trust forgiveness, compassion, hope or gratitude fill my heart space.

Behave constructively:

I choose to work in part acts:
I will break the overwhelming job into manageable parts.

Do the difficult:
I will face what I fear and act with self-discipline.

I choose to solutionise:
I will find a solution by taking advice or doing research.

Prioritise myself:
I will keep my life balanced by meeting friends, doing exercise or laughing.

Compartmentalise:
I will not let this event cloud my whole day; I will focus on something else now.

Utilise calming strategies:

When I:
- relax,
- breathe deeply,
- go for a run,
- shower,
- lie down,
- read,
- watch TV,
- climb into a mental helicopter,
- practice mindfulness/meditation,

my mind and body calm down.

Step Four: The Self Motivation Process

Endorse yourself for any growth no matter how small.

In the past I would have...

____

____

But this time I...

____

____

Tick off the traits that you strengthened when you worked down your anxiety:

☐ generosity	☐ peacefulness
☐ kindness	☐ self-discipline
☐ compassion	☐ forgiveness
☐ consideration	☐ courage
☐ helpfulness	☐ responsibility
☐ respectfulness	☐ reliability
☐ honesty	☐ loyalty
☐ fairness	☐ love
☐ patience	☐ humility

Rate your anxiety on a scale of 0 to 100%:

[______] %

O

W

Date: ___________

Anxiety Management Worksheet

The purpose of this worksheet is to help you to see every stressful event as an opportunity for
1. greater understanding of yourself, your anxiety and the people around you, and
2. practicing tools to manage your anxiety.

Step One: An Event

Briefly describe an event when you became anxious. Give such details as time, place and people involved, and end with "That's when I began to work myself up…"

____

____

____

____ Rate your anxiety on a scale of 0 to 100%: [   ] %

E

Step Two: The Working-Up Process

Learn about your working up process by identifying your thoughts, feelings, behaviours and bodily reactions during the event.
Tick the ones that most resonate with you.

Undermining Beliefs

B

I fear that I have lost...

- ☐ approval
- ☐ control
- ☐ co-operation
- ☐ face
- ☐ respect
- ☐ success
- ☐ trust
- ☐ validation
- ☐ love

This event proves that I am...

- ☐ stupid
- ☐ abnormal
- ☐ incompetent
- ☐ lazy
- ☐ irresponsible
- ☐ a total failure
- ☐ undisciplined
- ☐ untogether
- ☐ useless

I worry that I will suffer...

- ☐ mental collapse
- ☐ illness
- ☐ financial hardship

What I want is...

- ☐ total control
- ☐ respect
- ☐ success
- ☐ perfection
- ☐ comfort
- ☐ fairness
- ☐ tranquility
- ☐ all the answers
- ☐ for life to go smoothly
- ☐ to be all things to all people

Self-destructive Behaviour

Active
- ☐ get violent
- ☐ swear
- ☐ slam doors
- ☐ run away
- ☐ overeat
- ☐ harm myself
- ☐ criticise

Passive
- ☐ take it too seriously
- ☐ give up
- ☐ wallow in self pity
- ☐ sulk
- ☐ space out
- ☐ procrastinate
- ☐ give in
- ☐ be controlled

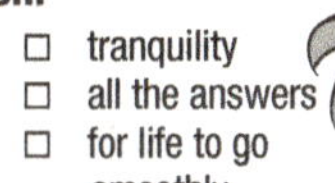

Intense Feelings

Angry feelings
- ☐ hateful
- ☐ aggravated
- ☐ annoyed
- ☐ hostile
- ☐ outraged
- ☐ punitive
- ☐ resentful
- ☐ vengeful

Fearful feelings
- ☐ helpless
- ☐ hopeless
- ☐ disappointed
- ☐ sad

- ☐ attacked
- ☐ worn out
- ☐ rejected
- ☐ jealous
- ☐ afraid
- ☐ exploited
- ☐ lonely
- ☐ abandoned
- ☐ guilty
- ☐ insulted
- ☐ confused
- ☐ disillusioned
- ☐ misunderstood
- ☐ trapped

Bodily Reactions (limbic system)

I am uncomfortable because I am experiencing...

- ☐ tremors
- ☐ nausea
- ☐ sweaty palms
- ☐ stomach-ache
- ☐ pounding heart
- ☐ general tension
- ☐ fatigue
- ☐ imagination on fire
- ☐ headache
- ☐ dry mouth
- ☐ jaw clenching
- ☐ shortness of breath

Continued over

B   **F**   **L**

Step Three: The Working-Down Process

Begin with, "Suddenly I realised that I was anxious and that I had choices..." This is the step of self-leadership and trust in one's ability to handle the situation.

Choose helpful thoughts:

I choose to depersonalise
There is no intention to hurt me. He is doing the best he can with the tools he has at the moment.

I choose realism over romanticism
Life presents many obstacles. I lower or raise standards as needed.

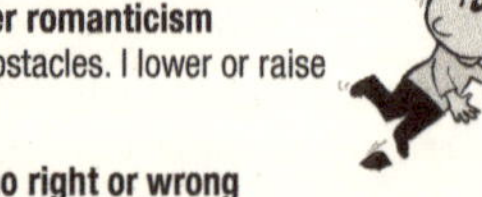

There is no right or wrong
Unless it is a moral issue, I will see it simply as a difference of opinion and/or taste.

I choose the total view of positivity
Even though this event is negative, the total view of his behaviour is positive.

I surrender control
Since I cannot change this situation, I choose to let go of it.

I choose to put this event in perspective This event is not a catastrophe because it is not life threatening. It can be viewed as a trivial life event, a normal life problem that needs to be solved not dramatised.

I choose to view this event as average, falling within the normal range
This event is not exceptional; many people have gone through this.

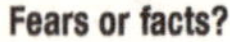

It's temporary - "this too shall pass"
Life is constantly changing and moving through phases and this situation will also change.

Fears or facts?
Why fear? It may not happen!

I choose to focus on this as a learning experience
Every problem that comes my way is an opportunity for me to learn about my strengths and weaknesses, others and life.

Feel soothing emotions:

I choose to feel warm, loving emotions. I do this by focusing on my heart and letting love, trust forgiveness, compassion, hope or gratitude fill my heart space.

Behave constructively:

I choose to work in part acts:
I will break the overwhelming job into manageable parts.

Do the difficult:
I will face what I fear and act with self-discipline.

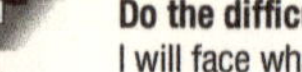

I choose to solutionise:
I will find a solution by taking advice or doing research.

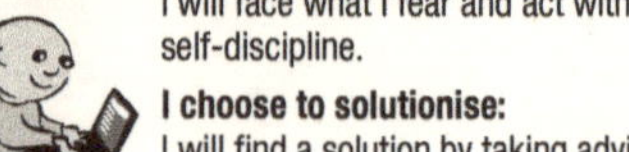

Prioritise myself:
I will keep my life balanced by meeting friends, doing exercise or laughing.

Compartmentalise:
I will not let this event cloud my whole day; I will focus on something else now.

Utilise calming strategies:

When I:
- relax,
- breathe deeply,
- go for a run,
- shower,
- lie down,
- read,
- watch TV,
- climb into a mental helicopter,
- practice mindfulness/meditation,

my mind and body calm down.

Step Four: The Self Motivation Process

Endorse yourself for any growth no matter how small.

In the past I would have...

____

____

But this time I...

____

____

Tick off the traits that you strengthened when you worked down your anxiety:

☐ generosity ☐ peacefulness
☐ kindness ☐ self-discipline
☐ compassion ☐ forgiveness
☐ consideration ☐ courage
☐ helpfulness ☐ responsibility
☐ respectfulness ☐ reliability
☐ honesty ☐ loyalty
☐ fairness ☐ love
☐ patience ☐ humility

Rate your anxiety on a scale of 0 to 100%:

_______ %

o

w

Date: ___________

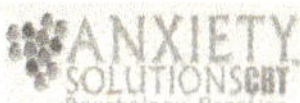

Anxiety Management Worksheet

The purpose of this worksheet is to help you to see every stressful event as an opportunity for
1. greater understanding of yourself, your anxiety and the people around you, and
2. practicing tools to manage your anxiety.

Step One: An Event

Briefly describe an event when you became anxious. Give such details as time, place and people involved, and end with "That's when I began to work myself up..."

____

____

____

_______________________________________ Rate your anxiety on a scale of 0 to 100%: [   ] %

E

Step Two: The Working-Up Process

Learn about your working up process by identifying your thoughts, feelings, behaviours and bodily reactions during the event.
Tick the ones that most resonate with you.

Undermining Beliefs

B

I fear that I have lost...

☐ approval   ☐ success
☐ control   ☐ trust
☐ co-operation ☐ validation
☐ face   ☐ love
☐ respect

This event proves that I am...

☐ stupid   ☐ a total failure
☐ abnormal   ☐ undisciplined
☐ incompetent   ☐ untogether
☐ lazy   ☐ useless
☐ irresponsible

I worry that I will suffer...

☐ mental collapse
☐ illness
☐ financial hardship

What I want is...

☐ total control   ☐ tranquility
☐ respect   ☐ all the answers
☐ success   ☐ for life to go
☐ perfection   smoothly
☐ comfort   ☐ to be all things
☐ fairness   to all people

Self-destructive Behaviour

Active

☐ get violent
☐ swear
☐ slam doors
☐ run away
☐ overeat
☐ harm myself
☐ criticise

Passive

☐ take it too seriously
☐ give up
☐ wallow in self pity
☐ sulk
☐ space out
☐ procrastinate
☐ give in
☐ be controlled

Intense Feelings

Angry feelings

☐ hateful   ☐ attacked
☐ aggravated   ☐ worn out
☐ annoyed   ☐ rejected
☐ hostile   ☐ jealous
☐ outraged   ☐ afraid
☐ punitive   ☐ exploited
☐ resentful   ☐ lonely
☐ vengeful   ☐ abandoned
                ☐ guilty

Fearful feelings   ☐ insulted

☐ helpless   ☐ confused
☐ hopeless   ☐ disillusioned
☐ disappointed ☐ misunderstood
☐ sad   ☐ trapped

Bodily Reactions (limbic system)

I am uncomfortable because I am experiencing...

☐ tremors
☐ nausea
☐ sweaty palms
☐ stomach-ache
☐ pounding heart
☐ general tension
☐ fatigue
☐ imagination on fire
☐ headache
☐ dry mouth
☐ jaw clenching
☐ shortness of breath

Continued over

B   **F**   **L**

Step Three: The Working-Down Process

Begin with, "Suddenly I realised that I was anxious and that I had choices..." This is the step of self-leadership and trust in one's ability to handle the situation.

Choose helpful thoughts:

I choose to depersonalise
There is no intention to hurt me. He is doing the best he can with the tools he has at the moment.

I choose realism over romanticism
Life presents many obstacles. I lower or raise standards as needed.

There is no right or wrong
Unless it is a moral issue, I will see it simply as a difference of opinion and/or taste.

I choose the total view of positivity
Even though this event is negative, the total view of his behaviour is positive.

I surrender control
Since I cannot change this situation, I choose to let go of it.

I choose to put this event in perspective This event is not a catastrophe because it is not life threatening. It can be viewed as a trivial life event, a normal life problem that needs to be solved not dramatised.

I choose to view this event as average, falling within the normal range
This event is not exceptional; many people have gone through this.

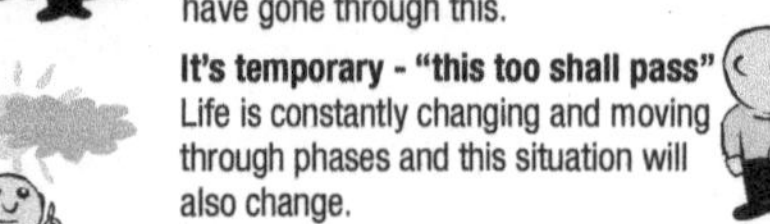

It's temporary - "this too shall pass"
Life is constantly changing and moving through phases and this situation will also change.

Fears or facts?
Why fear? It may not happen!

I choose to focus on this as a learning experience
Every problem that comes my way is an opportunity for me to learn about my strengths and weaknesses, others and life.

Feel soothing emotions:

I choose to feel warm, loving emotions. I do this by focusing on my heart and letting love, trust forgiveness, compassion, hope or gratitude fill my heart space.

Behave constructively:

I choose to work in part acts:
I will break the overwhelming job into manageable parts.

Do the difficult:
I will face what I fear and act with self-discipline.

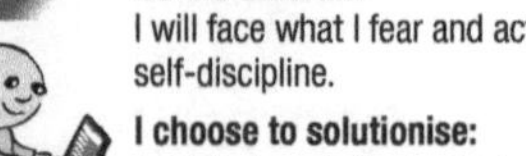

I choose to solutionise:
I will find a solution by taking advice or doing research.

Prioritise myself:
I will keep my life balanced by meeting friends, doing exercise or laughing.

Compartmentalise:
I will not let this event cloud my whole day; I will focus on something else now.

Utilise calming strategies:

When I:
- relax,
- breathe deeply,
- go for a run,
- shower,
- lie down,
- read,
- watch TV,
- climb into a mental helicopter,
- practice mindfulness/meditation,

my mind and body calm down.

Step Four: The Self Motivation Process

Endorse yourself for any growth no matter how small.

In the past I would have...

____

____

But this time I...

____

____

Tick off the traits that you strengthened when you worked down your anxiety:

☐ generosity	☐ peacefulness
☐ kindness	☐ self-discipline
☐ compassion	☐ forgiveness
☐ consideration	☐ courage
☐ helpfulness	☐ responsibility
☐ respectfulness	☐ reliability
☐ honesty	☐ loyalty
☐ fairness	☐ love
☐ patience	☐ humility

Rate your anxiety on a scale of 0 to 100%:

_______ %

O

W

Date: _______________

Anxiety Management Worksheet

The purpose of this worksheet is to help you to see every stressful event as an opportunity for
1. greater understanding of yourself, your anxiety and the people around you, and
2. practicing tools to manage your anxiety.

Step One: An Event

Briefly describe an event when you became anxious. Give such details as time, place and people involved, and end with "That's when I began to work myself up..."

____

____   **E**

____

________________________________ Rate your anxiety on a scale of 0 to 100%: [   ] %

Step Two: The Working-Up Process

Learn about your working up process by identifying your thoughts, feelings, behaviours and bodily reactions during the event.
Tick the ones that most resonate with you.

Undermining Beliefs

B

I fear that I have lost...

- ☐ approval
- ☐ control
- ☐ co-operation
- ☐ face
- ☐ respect
- ☐ success
- ☐ trust
- ☐ validation
- ☐ love

This event proves that I am...

- ☐ stupid
- ☐ abnormal
- ☐ incompetent
- ☐ lazy
- ☐ irresponsible
- ☐ a total failure
- ☐ undisciplined
- ☐ untogether
- ☐ useless

I worry that I will suffer...

- ☐ mental collapse
- ☐ illness
- ☐ financial hardship

What I want is...

- ☐ total control
- ☐ respect
- ☐ success
- ☐ perfection
- ☐ comfort
- ☐ fairness
- ☐ tranquility
- ☐ all the answers
- ☐ for life to go smoothly
- ☐ to be all things to all people

Self-destructive Behaviour

Active

- ☐ get violent
- ☐ swear
- ☐ slam doors
- ☐ run away
- ☐ overeat
- ☐ harm myself
- ☐ criticise

Passive

- ☐ take it too seriously
- ☐ give up
- ☐ wallow in self pity
- ☐ sulk
- ☐ space out
- ☐ procrastinate
- ☐ give in
- ☐ be controlled

Intense Feelings

Angry feelings

- ☐ hateful
- ☐ aggravated
- ☐ annoyed
- ☐ hostile
- ☐ outraged
- ☐ punitive
- ☐ resentful
- ☐ vengeful

Fearful feelings

- ☐ helpless
- ☐ hopeless
- ☐ disappointed
- ☐ sad
- ☐ attacked
- ☐ worn out
- ☐ rejected
- ☐ jealous
- ☐ afraid
- ☐ exploited
- ☐ lonely
- ☐ abandoned
- ☐ guilty
- ☐ insulted
- ☐ confused
- ☐ disillusioned
- ☐ misunderstood
- ☐ trapped

Bodily Reactions (limbic system)

I am uncomfortable because I am experiencing...

- ☐ tremors
- ☐ nausea
- ☐ sweaty palms
- ☐ stomach-ache
- ☐ pounding heart
- ☐ general tension
- ☐ fatigue
- ☐ imagination on fire
- ☐ headache
- ☐ dry mouth
- ☐ jaw clenching
- ☐ shortness of breath

Continued over

B   **F**   **L**

Step Three: The Working-Down Process

Begin with, "Suddenly I realised that I was anxious and that I had choices..." This is the step of self-leadership and trust in one's ability to handle the situation.

Choose helpful thoughts:

I choose to depersonalise
There is no intention to hurt me. He is doing the best he can with the tools he has at the moment.

I choose realism over romanticism
Life presents many obstacles. I lower or raise standards as needed.

There is no right or wrong
Unless it is a moral issue, I will see it simply as a difference of opinion and/or taste.

I choose the total view of positivity
Even though this event is negative, the total view of his behaviour is positive.

I surrender control
Since I cannot change this situation, I choose to let go of it.

I choose to put this event in perspective This event is not a catastrophe because it is not life threatening. It can be viewed as a trivial life event, a normal life problem that needs to be solved not dramatised.

I choose to view this event as average, falling within the normal range
This event is not exceptional; many people have gone through this.

It's temporary - "this too shall pass"
Life is constantly changing and moving through phases and this situation will also change.

Fears or facts?
Why fear? It may not happen!

I choose to focus on this as a learning experience
Every problem that comes my way is an opportunity for me to learn about my strengths and weaknesses, others and life.

Feel soothing emotions:

I choose to feel warm, loving emotions. I do this by focusing on my heart and letting love, trust forgiveness, compassion, hope or gratitude fill my heart space.

Behave constructively:

I choose to work in part acts:
I will break the overwhelming job into manageable parts.

Do the difficult:
I will face what I fear and act with self-discipline.

I choose to solutionise:
I will find a solution by taking advice or doing research.

Prioritise myself:
I will keep my life balanced by meeting friends, doing exercise or laughing.

Compartmentalise:
I will not let this event cloud my whole day; I will focus on something else now.

Utilise calming strategies:

When I:
- relax,
- breathe deeply,
- go for a run,
- shower,
- lie down,
- read,
- watch TV,
- climb into a mental helicopter,
- practice mindfulness/meditation,

my mind and body calm down.

Step Four: The Self Motivation Process

Endorse yourself for any growth no matter how small.

In the past I would have...

____

____

But this time I...

____

____

Tick off the traits that you strengthened when you worked down your anxiety:

☐ generosity	☐ peacefulness
☐ kindness	☐ self-discipline
☐ compassion	☐ forgiveness
☐ consideration	☐ courage
☐ helpfulness	☐ responsibility
☐ respectfulness	☐ reliability
☐ honesty	☐ loyalty
☐ fairness	☐ love
☐ patience	☐ humility

Rate your anxiety on a scale of 0 to 100%:

________ %

o

w

Date: ___________

Anxiety Management Worksheet

The purpose of this worksheet is to help you to see every stressful event as an opportunity for
1. greater understanding of yourself, your anxiety and the people around you, and
2. practicing tools to manage your anxiety.

Step One: An Event

Briefly describe an event when you became anxious. Give such details as time, place and people involved, and end with "That's when I began to work myself up..."

____

____

____

__________________________________ Rate your anxiety on a scale of 0 to 100%: [   ] %

E

Step Two: The Working-Up Process

Learn about your working up process by identifying your thoughts, feelings, behaviours and bodily reactions during the event. Tick the ones that most resonate with you.

Undermining Beliefs

B

I fear that I have lost...

- ☐ approval
- ☐ control
- ☐ co-operation
- ☐ face
- ☐ respect
- ☐ success
- ☐ trust
- ☐ validation
- ☐ love

This event proves that I am...

- ☐ stupid
- ☐ abnormal
- ☐ incompetent
- ☐ lazy
- ☐ irresponsible
- ☐ a total failure
- ☐ undisciplined
- ☐ untogether
- ☐ useless

I worry that I will suffer...

- ☐ mental collapse
- ☐ illness
- ☐ financial hardship

What I want is...

- ☐ total control
- ☐ respect
- ☐ success
- ☐ perfection
- ☐ comfort
- ☐ fairness
- ☐ tranquility
- ☐ all the answers
- ☐ for life to go smoothly
- ☐ to be all things to all people

Self-destructive Behaviour

Active
- ☐ get violent
- ☐ swear
- ☐ slam doors
- ☐ run away
- ☐ overeat
- ☐ harm myself
- ☐ criticise

Passive
- ☐ take it too seriously
- ☐ give up
- ☐ wallow in self pity
- ☐ sulk
- ☐ space out
- ☐ procrastinate
- ☐ give in
- ☐ be controlled

Intense Feelings

Angry feelings
- ☐ hateful
- ☐ aggravated
- ☐ annoyed
- ☐ hostile
- ☐ outraged
- ☐ punitive
- ☐ resentful
- ☐ vengeful

Fearful feelings
- ☐ helpless
- ☐ hopeless
- ☐ disappointed
- ☐ sad
- ☐ attacked
- ☐ worn out
- ☐ rejected
- ☐ jealous
- ☐ afraid
- ☐ exploited
- ☐ lonely
- ☐ abandoned
- ☐ guilty
- ☐ insulted
- ☐ confused
- ☐ disillusioned
- ☐ misunderstood
- ☐ trapped

Bodily Reactions (limbic system)

I am uncomfortable because I am experiencing...
- ☐ tremors
- ☐ nausea
- ☐ sweaty palms
- ☐ stomach-ache
- ☐ pounding heart
- ☐ general tension
- ☐ fatigue
- ☐ imagination on fire
- ☐ headache
- ☐ dry mouth
- ☐ jaw clenching
- ☐ shortness of breath

Continued over

B   **F**   **L**

Step Three: The Working-Down Process

Begin with, "Suddenly I realised that I was anxious and that I had choices…" This is the step of self-leadership and trust in one's ability to handle the situation.

Choose helpful thoughts:

I choose to depersonalise
There is no intention to hurt me. He is doing the best he can with the tools he has at the moment.

I choose realism over romanticism
Life presents many obstacles. I lower or raise standards as needed.

There is no right or wrong
Unless it is a moral issue, I will see it simply as a difference of opinion and/or taste.

I choose the total view of positivity
Even though this event is negative, the total view of his behaviour is positive.

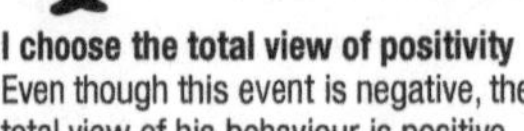

I surrender control
Since I cannot change this situation, I choose to let go of it.

I choose to put this event in perspective This event is not a catastrophe because it is not life threatening. It can be viewed as a trivial life event, a normal life problem that needs to be solved not dramatised.

I choose to view this event as average, falling within the normal range
This event is not exceptional; many people have gone through this.

It's temporary - "this too shall pass"
Life is constantly changing and moving through phases and this situation will also change.

Fears or facts?
Why fear? It may not happen!

I choose to focus on this as a learning experience
Every problem that comes my way is an opportunity for me to learn about my strengths and weaknesses, others and life.

Feel soothing emotions:

I choose to feel warm, loving emotions. I do this by focusing on my heart and letting love, trust forgiveness, compassion, hope or gratitude fill my heart space.

Behave constructively:

I choose to work in part acts:
I will break the overwhelming job into manageable parts.

Do the difficult:
I will face what I fear and act with self-discipline.

I choose to solutionise:
I will find a solution by taking advice or doing research.

Prioritise myself:
I will keep my life balanced by meeting friends, doing exercise or laughing.

Compartmentalise:
I will not let this event cloud my whole day; I will focus on something else now.

Utilise calming strategies:

When I:
- relax,
- breathe deeply,
- go for a run,
- shower,
- lie down,
- read,
- watch TV,
- climb into a mental helicopter,
- practice mindfulness/meditation,

my mind and body calm down.

Step Four: The Self Motivation Process

Endorse yourself for any growth no matter how small.

In the past I would have…

____

____

But this time I…

____

____

Tick off the traits that you strengthened when you worked down your anxiety:

☐ generosity	☐ peacefulness
☐ kindness	☐ self-discipline
☐ compassion	☐ forgiveness
☐ consideration	☐ courage
☐ helpfulness	☐ responsibility
☐ respectfulness	☐ reliability
☐ honesty	☐ loyalty
☐ fairness	☐ love
☐ patience	☐ humility

Rate your anxiety on a scale of 0 to 100%:

________ %

O

W

Date: ___________

Anxiety Management Worksheet

The purpose of this worksheet is to help you to see every stressful event as an opportunity for
1. greater understanding of yourself, your anxiety and the people around you, and
2. practicing tools to manage your anxiety.

Step One: An Event

Briefly describe an event when you became anxious. Give such details as time, place and people involved, and end with "That's when I began to work myself up..."

____

____

____

_______________________________ Rate your anxiety on a scale of 0 to 100%: [   ] %

E

Step Two: The Working-Up Process

Learn about your working up process by identifying your thoughts, feelings, behaviours and bodily reactions during the event.
Tick the ones that most resonate with you.

Undermining Beliefs

B

I fear that I have lost...

- ☐ approval
- ☐ control
- ☐ co-operation
- ☐ face
- ☐ respect
- ☐ success
- ☐ trust
- ☐ validation
- ☐ love

This event proves that I am...

- ☐ stupid
- ☐ abnormal
- ☐ incompetent
- ☐ lazy
- ☐ irresponsible
- ☐ a total failure
- ☐ undisciplined
- ☐ untogether
- ☐ useless

I worry that I will suffer...

- ☐ mental collapse
- ☐ illness
- ☐ financial hardship

What I want is...

- ☐ total control
- ☐ respect
- ☐ success
- ☐ perfection
- ☐ comfort
- ☐ fairness
- ☐ tranquility
- ☐ all the answers
- ☐ for life to go smoothly
- ☐ to be all things to all people

Self-destructive Behaviour

Active 
- ☐ get violent
- ☐ swear
- ☐ slam doors
- ☐ run away
- ☐ overeat
- ☐ harm myself
- ☐ criticise

Passive
- ☐ take it too seriously
- ☐ give up
- ☐ wallow in self pity
- ☐ sulk
- ☐ space out
- ☐ procrastinate
- ☐ give in
- ☐ be controlled

Intense Feelings

Angry feelings
- ☐ hateful
- ☐ aggravated
- ☐ annoyed
- ☐ hostile
- ☐ outraged
- ☐ punitive
- ☐ resentful
- ☐ vengeful

Fearful feelings
- ☐ helpless
- ☐ hopeless
- ☐ disappointed
- ☐ sad
- ☐ attacked
- ☐ worn out
- ☐ rejected
- ☐ jealous
- ☐ afraid
- ☐ exploited
- ☐ lonely
- ☐ abandoned
- ☐ guilty
- ☐ insulted
- ☐ confused
- ☐ disillusioned
- ☐ misunderstood
- ☐ trapped

Bodily Reactions (limbic system)

I am uncomfortable because I am experiencing... 
- ☐ tremors
- ☐ nausea
- ☐ sweaty palms
- ☐ stomach-ache
- ☐ pounding heart
- ☐ general tension
- ☐ fatigue
- ☐ imagination on fire
- ☐ headache
- ☐ dry mouth
- ☐ jaw clenching
- ☐ shortness of breath

Continued over

B   **F**   **L**

Step Three: The Working-Down Process

Begin with, "Suddenly I realised that I was anxious and that I had choices..." This is the step of self-leadership and trust in one's ability to handle the situation.

Choose helpful thoughts:

I choose to depersonalise
There is no intention to hurt me. He is doing the best he can with the tools he has at the moment.

I choose realism over romanticism
Life presents many obstacles. I lower or raise standards as needed.

There is no right or wrong
Unless it is a moral issue, I will see it simply as a difference of opinion and/or taste.

I choose the total view of positivity
Even though this event is negative, the total view of his behaviour is positive.

I surrender control
Since I cannot change this situation, I choose to let go of it.

I choose to put this event in perspective This event is not a catastrophe because it is not life threatening. It can be viewed as a trivial life event, a normal life problem that needs to be solved not dramatised.

I choose to view this event as average, falling within the normal range
This event is not exceptional; many people have gone through this.

It's temporary - "this too shall pass"
Life is constantly changing and moving through phases and this situation will also change.

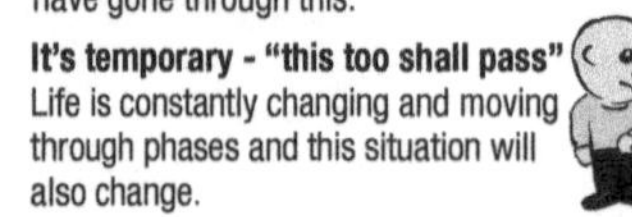

Fears or facts?
Why fear? It may not happen!

I choose to focus on this as a learning experience
Every problem that comes my way is an opportunity for me to learn about my strengths and weaknesses, others and life.

Feel soothing emotions:

I choose to feel warm, loving emotions. I do this by focusing on my heart and letting love, trust forgiveness, compassion, hope or gratitude fill my heart space.

Behave constructively:

I choose to work in part acts:
I will break the overwhelming job into manageable parts.

Do the difficult:
I will face what I fear and act with self-discipline.

I choose to solutionise:
I will find a solution by taking advice or doing research.

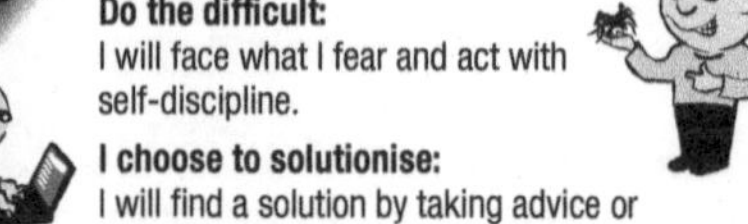

Prioritise myself:
I will keep my life balanced by meeting friends, doing exercise or laughing.

Compartmentalise:
I will not let this event cloud my whole day; I will focus on something else now.

Utilise calming strategies:

When I:
- relax,
- breathe deeply,
- go for a run,
- shower,
- lie down,
- read,
- watch TV,
- climb into a mental helicopter,
- practice mindfulness/meditation,

my mind and body calm down.

Step Four: The Self Motivation Process

Endorse yourself for any growth no matter how small.

In the past I would have...

____

____

But this time I...

____

____

Tick off the traits that you strengthened when you worked down your anxiety:

☐ generosity	☐ peacefulness
☐ kindness	☐ self-discipline
☐ compassion	☐ forgiveness
☐ consideration	☐ courage
☐ helpfulness	☐ responsibility
☐ respectfulness	☐ reliability
☐ honesty	☐ loyalty
☐ fairness	☐ love
☐ patience	☐ humility

Rate your anxiety on a scale of 0 to 100%:

_______ %

O

W

Date: _______________

Anxiety Management Worksheet

The purpose of this worksheet is to help you to see every stressful event as an opportunity for
1. greater understanding of yourself, your anxiety and the people around you, and
2. practicing tools to manage your anxiety.

Step One: An Event

Briefly describe an event when you became anxious. Give such details as time, place and people involved, and end with "That's when I began to work myself up…"

____

____

____

____ Rate your anxiety on a scale of 0 to 100%: [   ] %

E

Step Two: The Working-Up Process

Learn about your working up process by identifying your thoughts, feelings, behaviours and bodily reactions during the event. Tick the ones that most resonate with you.

Undermining Beliefs

B

I fear that I have lost…

- ☐ approval
- ☐ control
- ☐ co-operation
- ☐ face
- ☐ respect
- ☐ success
- ☐ trust
- ☐ validation
- ☐ love

This event proves that I am…

- ☐ stupid
- ☐ abnormal
- ☐ incompetent
- ☐ lazy
- ☐ irresponsible
- ☐ a total failure
- ☐ undisciplined
- ☐ untogether
- ☐ useless

I worry that I will suffer…

- ☐ mental collapse
- ☐ illness
- ☐ financial hardship

What I want is…

- ☐ total control
- ☐ respect
- ☐ success
- ☐ perfection
- ☐ comfort
- ☐ fairness
- ☐ tranquility
- ☐ all the answers
- ☐ for life to go smoothly
- ☐ to be all things to all people

Self-destructive Behaviour

Active

- ☐ get violent
- ☐ swear
- ☐ slam doors
- ☐ run away
- ☐ overeat
- ☐ harm myself
- ☐ criticise

Passive

- ☐ take it too seriously
- ☐ give up
- ☐ wallow in self pity
- ☐ sulk
- ☐ space out
- ☐ procrastinate
- ☐ give in
- ☐ be controlled

Intense Feelings

Angry feelings

- ☐ hateful
- ☐ aggravated
- ☐ annoyed
- ☐ hostile
- ☐ outraged
- ☐ punitive
- ☐ resentful
- ☐ vengeful

Fearful feelings

- ☐ helpless
- ☐ hopeless
- ☐ disappointed
- ☐ sad
- ☐ attacked
- ☐ worn out
- ☐ rejected
- ☐ jealous
- ☐ afraid
- ☐ exploited
- ☐ lonely
- ☐ abandoned
- ☐ guilty
- ☐ insulted
- ☐ confused
- ☐ disillusioned
- ☐ misunderstood
- ☐ trapped

Bodily Reactions (limbic system)

I am uncomfortable because I am experiencing…

- ☐ tremors
- ☐ nausea
- ☐ sweaty palms
- ☐ stomach-ache
- ☐ pounding heart
- ☐ general tension
- ☐ fatigue
- ☐ imagination on fire
- ☐ headache
- ☐ dry mouth
- ☐ jaw clenching
- ☐ shortness of breath

Continued over

B   **F**   **L**

Step Three: The Working-Down Process

Begin with, "Suddenly I realised that I was anxious and that I had choices..." This is the step of self-leadership and trust in one's ability to handle the situation.

Choose helpful thoughts:

I choose to depersonalise
There is no intention to hurt me. He is doing the best he can with the tools he has at the moment.

I choose realism over romanticism
Life presents many obstacles. I lower or raise standards as needed.

There is no right or wrong
Unless it is a moral issue, I will see it simply as a difference of opinion and/or taste.

I choose the total view of positivity
Even though this event is negative, the total view of his behaviour is positive.

I surrender control
Since I cannot change this situation, I choose to let go of it.

I choose to put this event in perspective This event is not a catastrophe because it is not life threatening. It can be viewed as a trivial life event, a normal life problem that needs to be solved not dramatised.

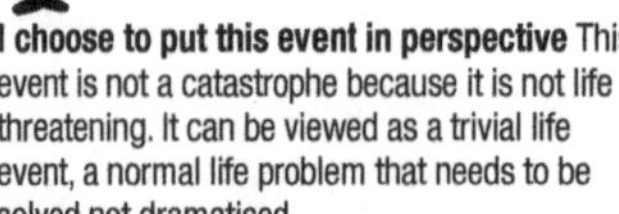

I choose to view this event as average, falling within the normal range
This event is not exceptional; many people have gone through this.

It's temporary - "this too shall pass"
Life is constantly changing and moving through phases and this situation will also change.

Fears or facts?
Why fear? It may not happen!

I choose to focus on this as a learning experience
Every problem that comes my way is an opportunity for me to learn about my strengths and weaknesses, others and life.

Feel soothing emotions:

I choose to feel warm, loving emotions. I do this by focusing on my heart and letting love, trust forgiveness, compassion, hope or gratitude fill my heart space.

Behave constructively:

I choose to work in part acts:
I will break the overwhelming job into manageable parts.

Do the difficult:
I will face what I fear and act with self-discipline.

I choose to solutionise:
I will find a solution by taking advice or doing research.

Prioritise myself:
I will keep my life balanced by meeting friends, doing exercise or laughing.

Compartmentalise:
I will not let this event cloud my whole day; I will focus on something else now.

Utilise calming strategies:

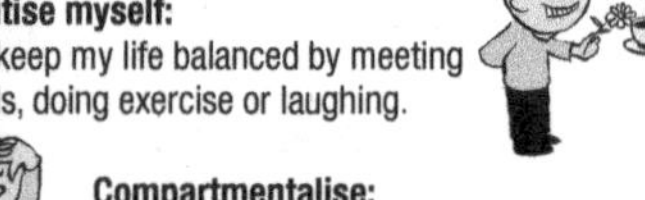

When I:
- relax,
- breathe deeply,
- go for a run,
- shower,
- lie down,
- read,
- watch TV,
- climb into a mental helicopter,
- practice mindfulness/meditation,

my mind and body calm down.

Step Four: The Self Motivation Process

Endorse yourself for any growth no matter how small.

In the past I would have...

____

____

But this time I...

____

____

Tick off the traits that you strengthened when you worked down your anxiety:

☐ generosity	☐ peacefulness
☐ kindness	☐ self-discipline
☐ compassion	☐ forgiveness
☐ consideration	☐ courage
☐ helpfulness	☐ responsibility
☐ respectfulness	☐ reliability
☐ honesty	☐ loyalty
☐ fairness	☐ love
☐ patience	☐ humility

Rate your anxiety on a scale of 0 to 100%:

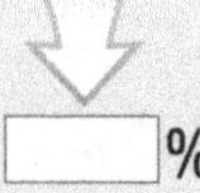

______%

Week 5

By week five, you should have better order and structure to your day. Hopefully you are practising relaxation and breathing on a daily basis plus exercising regularly. These tools were placed first so that you could begin working them into your daily schedule as soon as possible. The daily repetition and monitoring will be of huge benefit as the weeks move on.

In week five, the tools we will cover are:

1. Temporary: thinking tool
2. Socialise: behavioural tool
3. Mindfulness: calming tool

Temporary: thinking tool

"It's temporary. This too shall pass. Life is constantly changing and moving through phases and this situation will also change."

Much of the stress we experience in a situation derives from a feeling that the stressful situation will last forever. This is another manner of pessimistic thinking described by Martin Seligman (15) who calls it *permanent pessimistic thinking*. When you believe that something negative is not going to change and will stay that way forever, you will feel demotivated and maybe even depressed.

Managing physical pain illustrates this perfectly. It has been found that when a patient is told that their surgery will result in excruciating pain for three days, they usually cope well with the pain. However, when a patient with moderate pain is told that their pain could go on indefinitely, they can struggle much more to cope even though the degree of pain is less. Not knowing when the pain will end increases stress and maintains focus on the pain. (14)

Put simply, if a person knows that their pain will be short lived they will grit their teeth (figuratively and maybe literally) and get through it. However, when there is no end in sight, the suffering becomes difficult to endure.

Watch your language

Using words like "always" and "never" suggests a permanent situation. Therefore, when you say, "It will never get better," or "it will always be uncomfortable," your stress levels will rise. You may even feel hopeless and give up on things. (14) This is why it is important to be very specific about situations and to speak in temporary rather than permanent terms.

Here are some common situations where your use of language could lower your stress:

> You yell at your husband, "You never take out the garbage!"

- Is that true? Has he never, ever taken out the garbage? If the reality is that he forgot to take out the garbage two weeks in a row, then say that. "You have not taken out the garbage for two weeks in a row." When you modify your words, you will experience your stress levels reducing.

> Your friend does not invite you out for drinks. You think to yourself, "She never invites me out for a drink."

Is that true? Or does she invite you occasionally but not every time? If it is the latter, describe the situation factually and you will feel less hurt.

> Your child has not made his bed. You become furious saying "You always leave your bed unmade. Are you expecting me to make it? When will you do it yourself? "

Is this factual? Does your child always leave the bed unmade, or is it only on school days? Or when they are late for school? State the facts and watch your anger subside.

Words and phrases that indicate you might be over-generalising and applying a permanent pessimistic thinking style include:

> "(this is) how things always are"
> "everyone's always like that"
> "things never turn out well for me"

EXERCISE 12

Write down three occasions in your life when you thought things would never get better but they did. This will build up a memory bank that you can draw on in the future. There will come a time when you will feel hopeless again. When this happens, dip into this memory bank to reassure yourself that just as in these examples, the situation you are currently in will prove to be temporary, and will not stay the same.

For example:

I felt hopeless when I lost my job in 1975. After eight weeks of looking, I believed that I would never find another job. Luckily it did not stay the same. After six months, I found another job and it proved to be better paid than the previous one.

1

2

3

EXERCISE 13

Circle one response for each of the scenarios below.

1. Your friend forgets your birthday. You think:
   a) He always forgets my birthday.
   b) He forgot my birthday this year.

2. You are penalised for not returning your income-tax forms on time. You think:
   a) I never get things right.
   b) I was lazy about getting my taxes done this year.

3. You perform particularly badly in a job interview. You think:
   a) I never perform well in job interviews.
   b) I was nervous for this job interview.

4. You lose your temper with a friend. You think:
   a) I am always out of control.
   b) I am in a hostile mood right now.

5. You've been feeling run down lately. You think:
   a) I never get a chance to relax.
   b) I was exceptionally busy this week.

6. Your partner says something that hurts your feelings. You think:
   a) She/he always blurts things out without thinking of others.
   b) She/he was in a bad mood today and momentarily lost control.

7. You gained weight over the holidays and now you are struggling to lose it. You think:
   a) Diets do not work.
   b) The diet I tried did not work.

8. You struggle to get through your first exercise routine. You think:
   a) Exercising is difficult.
   b) My body needs to get used to this.

How many a)'s did you score?
How many b)'s did you score?

In the scenarios of the above exercise: a) responses are indicative of permanent, pessimistic thinking while b) responses indicate time limited, realistic descriptions of situations.

Put another way, when you think, "I always put off doing my taxes," you are basically saying that you permanently and at all times put off doing your taxes. However, when you say, "I was lazy about getting my taxes done this year," you are saying that perhaps on this occasion you did not get your taxes done on time but it is not necessarily a permanent condition. The condition (laziness) is temporary, and next time around you could perform differently.

In sum, when you believe that things will stay the same indefinitely, you will feel hopeless and therefore demotivated. However, when you believe that the situation is a momentary lapse or a temporary aberration, you will feel able to overcome it and persevere.

Anecdotes

Below are some situations where this tool can be very useful:

> You are sitting on a plane next to a noisy child. Tell yourself, "This discomfort is not forever. In five hours it will be over. I will walk off the plane into a large airport with plenty of space."

> It is the end of the day, "happy hour." Your kids are acting up and you are becoming infuriated. Tell yourself, "This will come to an end soon. Only 30 minutes to go until bed time. Soon the kids will be in bed and I will be able to relax."

> You are extremely busy at work needing to complete a project before a deadline. Tell yourself, "The deadline is in three weeks by which time the project has to be completed. In three weeks, I will be able to slow down and resume my normal work pace."

Daily monitoring diary

You will find a category devoted to permanent pessimistic thinking on your daily monitoring diary for this week. Notice if, and when, you think in permanent terms. Rate your anxiety and then challenge the thinking with the tool "**temporary**".

Socialise: behavioural tool

Socialising with others is a very important tool. (14) Mental health professionals recognise that social interactions are central to the treatment of anxiety and depression. The Black Dog Institute (18) lists "socialising time" as a category on its social and biological rhythms monitoring timetable, (on page 113) on a par with bedtime and exercise.

The benefits of socialising include:

> Socialising with others serves as a distraction. When you are busy chatting to friends, you forget your woes and can be quite animated.

> Socialising can force you to leave home and venture out to a different venue. This is therapeutic.

> Mixing with friends serves to help you to feel better about yourself. When you are anxious, you can be consumed with devaluing, negative self-talk. Your friends will remind you that you are a lovable human being.

> Friends understand us in a way that parents, siblings and family members' cannot. We choose our friends and they choose us. They see value in us even when we mess up. We share good times and bad, and there is a wonderful acceptance of each other.

> Socialising is affirming because it reminds you that you do not only have a fearful, anxious side. You have many different facets. Your whole worth, therefore, cannot be measured by your anxious habits and thoughts.

> Much of anxiety centres on fear. Being with friends can reduce the fear. You do not feel alone in facing your problems. You receive support, advice, help and comfort.

In order to gain the maximum benefit from this tool, socialising needs to be built into the fabric of your life and seen as valuable for your mental wellbeing. Do not wait for plans to be made spontaneously. Make plans conscientiously every week. Filling in the social and biological rhythms monitoring timetable will help you to do this. Do not rely on others to take the lead. Be proactive and ensure that you are creating situations that will benefit you.

On those occasions that you do not feel like mixing with others, just DO IT anyway. Force yourself, drag yourself, do whatever it takes to get to the meeting point. After a few minutes, you will be so glad that you did. You will discover that socialising is much better than moping about alone in your river of anxieties at home.

> Jo was feeling very anxious and just wanted to be left alone. When her friend Daisy called, and insisted Jo join her for a coffee with friends, it was the last thing Jo felt like doing. However, she forced herself to go because she did not want Daisy to know how awful she felt. Once she arrived however, and got caught up in the camaraderie, Jo's mood lifted. Her anxiety symptoms faded and she felt great.

EXERCISE 14

Would you describe yourself as a loner?   YES/NO

If no, do you prioritise your social life?   YES/NO

If not, why not?

How could you improve your social life?

Name those friends that are fun to hang out with.

Name those friends that you can confide in and ask for support.

Do you feel that anxiety has interfered with your social life? If so, how could you remedy that? (This is not referring to social anxiety. This refers to anxiety about other things that interfere with you being social).

Unless you are a true loner, a person who has no need for others, then socialising is vital for your mental health. Getting out of the house and mixing with others is part of your treatment.

Just as you plan to exercise and have meals, you need to plan to socialise.

Social anxiety

It is common for individuals suffering from generalised anxiety or phobias to reduce their socialising because they do not feel good about themselves. However, it is an entirely different thing if you suffer from social anxiety. Social anxiety is when the source of your fear is mixing with others.

Do you suffer from social anxiety?   YES/NO

If you answered "yes," then it will be difficult to prioritise your social life until that anxiety is managed. The most effective way of doing it is to *gradually* expose yourself to social situations. This method of reducing anxiety levels is explained in detail in "**do the difficult**" (page 197).

Mindfulness: calming tool

Being mindful is not the same as actively practising relaxation skills because mindfulness does not require stilling your mind and calming your muscles. Mindfulness is all about being present in the moment. Having said that, a natural consequence of mindfulness is calmness, because mindfulness ensures that you are not worrying about the future or agonising about the past.

The core features of mindfulness are:

> Observe: Observe your experience without being analytical. Try to directly experience your experience rather than thinking about it. Observe your thoughts, feelings and bodily sensations with a kind and gentle curiosity.

> Describe: Notice the fine details of what you are observing in a very descriptive, observational manner rather than placing subjective valuations upon it.

> Participate fully: Allow yourself to consider your whole experience, paying full care and attention.

> Be non-judgmental: This helps to reduce emotional distress usually related to attempting to avoid or control your experience. Practise accepting the whole experience without judging it as good, bad, right or wrong.

> Focus on one thing at a time: The art of "being present" is to develop the skill of paying attention to only one thing at a time, from moment to moment. By focusing your awareness to mindfully experiencing each moment you can reduce

your need to follow distracting thoughts or feelings that pop up, and more easily bring your focus to the now.

Different ways of practising mindfulness

There are a number of ways to practise mindfulness which will assist you to focus on the present moment:

> formal mindfulness practice
> informal mindfulness practice
> grounding
> slowing down and being present

Later we will discuss different types of mindfulness during different weekly segments. You may find one method that you love and stick to or you may mix and match depending on your mood and other factors. It does not matter how you go about it. The essential thing is that you keep practising mindfulness every day. The more you incorporate these various types of mindfulness into your day-to-day life, the calmer you will feel.

Daily monitoring diary

From this week onwards there is a section in the daily monitoring diary which is devoted to mindfulness. Whichever form you use, rate your anxiety before and after practising mindfulness. Over the weeks ahead, notice which type of mindfulness you prefer and which you tend to practise more than the others. Work to your strengths and, to ensure continuity, utilise the method you like the most and will most likely practise.

DAILY MONITORING DIARY WEEK ENDING _______________

Day	M	T	W	T	F	S	S
Overall Anxiety Rating for the day (0-10)							
1. EXERCISE							
How long?							
Anxiety level before (0-10)							
Anxiety level after (0-10)							
2. BREATHING							
How long?							
Anxiety level before (0-10)							
Anxiety level after (0-10)							
3. RELAXATION							
How long?							
Anxiety level before (0-10)							
Anxiety level after (0-10)							
4. PERVASIVE PESSIMISTIC THINKING							
How often this type of thought occurred							
Belief in thoughts before challenging (0-10)							
Belief in thoughts after challenging (0-10)							
5. CATASTROPHIC THINKING							
How often this type of thought occurred							
Belief in thoughts before challenging (0-10)							
Belief in thoughts after challenging (0-10)							

Day	M	T	W	T	F	S	S
6. PERMANENT PESSIMISTIC THINKING							
How often this type of thought occurred							
Belief in thoughts before challenging (0-10)							
Belief in thoughts after challenging (0-10)							
7. MINDFULNESS **(FORMAL, GROUNDING, INFORMAL MINDFULNESS)**							
How long?							
Anxiety level before (0-10)							
Anxiety level after (0-10)							

Date: ___________

Anxiety Management Worksheet

The purpose of this worksheet is to help you to see every stressful event as an opportunity for
1. greater understanding of yourself, your anxiety and the people around you, and
2. practicing tools to manage your anxiety.

Step One: An Event

Briefly describe an event when you became anxious. Give such details as time, place and people involved, and end with "That's when I began to work myself up…"

____

____

____

____ Rate your anxiety on a scale of 0 to 100%: [   ] %

E

Step Two: The Working-Up Process

Learn about your working up process by identifying your thoughts, feelings, behaviours and bodily reactions during the event.

Tick the ones that most resonate with you.

Undermining Beliefs

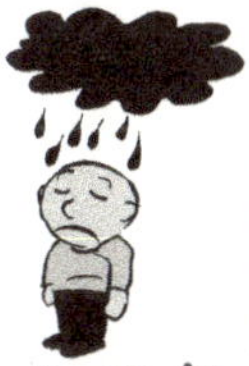

B

I fear that I have lost…

- ☐ approval
- ☐ control
- ☐ co-operation
- ☐ face
- ☐ respect
- ☐ success
- ☐ trust
- ☐ validation
- ☐ love

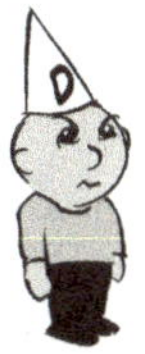

This event proves that I am…

- ☐ stupid
- ☐ abnormal
- ☐ incompetent
- ☐ lazy
- ☐ irresponsible
- ☐ a total failure
- ☐ undisciplined
- ☐ untogether
- ☐ useless

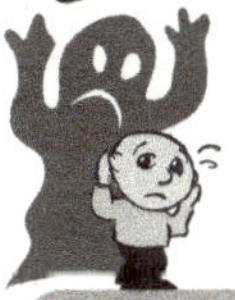

I worry that I will suffer…

- ☐ mental collapse
- ☐ illness
- ☐ financial hardship

What I want is…

- ☐ total control
- ☐ respect
- ☐ success
- ☐ perfection
- ☐ comfort
- ☐ fairness
- ☐ tranquility
- ☐ all the answers
- ☐ for life to go smoothly
- ☐ to be all things to all people

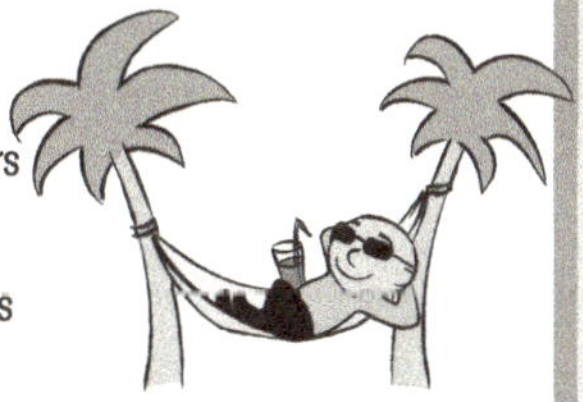

Self-destructive Behaviour

Active

- ☐ get violent
- ☐ swear
- ☐ slam doors
- ☐ run away
- ☐ overeat
- ☐ harm myself
- ☐ criticise

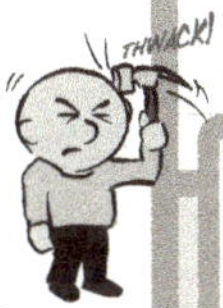

Passive

- ☐ take it too seriously
- ☐ give up
- ☐ wallow in self pity
- ☐ sulk
- ☐ space out
- ☐ procrastinate
- ☐ give in
- ☐ be controlled

Intense Feelings

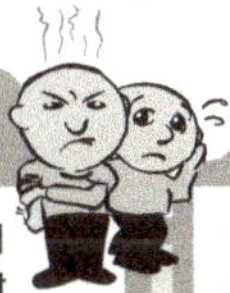

Angry feelings

- ☐ hateful
- ☐ aggravated
- ☐ annoyed
- ☐ hostile
- ☐ outraged
- ☐ punitive
- ☐ resentful
- ☐ vengeful
- ☐ attacked
- ☐ worn out
- ☐ rejected
- ☐ jealous
- ☐ afraid
- ☐ exploited
- ☐ lonely
- ☐ abandoned
- ☐ guilty

Fearful feelings

- ☐ helpless
- ☐ hopeless
- ☐ disappointed
- ☐ sad
- ☐ insulted
- ☐ confused
- ☐ disillusioned
- ☐ misunderstood
- ☐ trapped

Bodily Reactions (limbic system)

I am uncomfortable because I am experiencing…

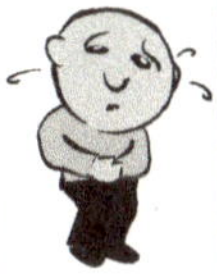

- ☐ tremors
- ☐ nausea
- ☐ sweaty palms
- ☐ stomach-ache
- ☐ pounding heart
- ☐ general tension
- ☐ fatigue
- ☐ imagination on fire
- ☐ headache
- ☐ dry mouth
- ☐ jaw clenching
- ☐ shortness of breath

Continued over

B   **F**   **L**

Step Three: The Working-Down Process

Begin with, "Suddenly I realised that I was anxious and that I had choices..." This is the step of self-leadership and trust in one's ability to handle the situation.

Choose helpful thoughts:

I choose to depersonalise
There is no intention to hurt me. He is doing the best he can with the tools he has at the moment.

I choose realism over romanticism
Life presents many obstacles. I lower or raise standards as needed.

There is no right or wrong
Unless it is a moral issue, I will see it simply as a difference of opinion and/or taste.

I choose the total view of positivity
Even though this event is negative, the total view of his behaviour is positive.

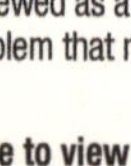

I surrender control
Since I cannot change this situation, I choose to let go of it.

I choose to put this event in perspective This event is not a catastrophe because it is not life threatening. It can be viewed as a trivial life event, a normal life problem that needs to be solved not dramatised.

I choose to view this event as average, falling within the normal range
This event is not exceptional; many people have gone through this.

It's temporary - "this too shall pass"
Life is constantly changing and moving through phases and this situation will also change.

Fears or facts?
Why fear? It may not happen!

I choose to focus on this as a learning experience
Every problem that comes my way is an opportunity for me to learn about my strengths and weaknesses, others and life.

Feel soothing emotions:

I choose to feel warm, loving emotions. I do this by focusing on my heart and letting love, trust forgiveness, compassion, hope or gratitude fill my heart space.

Behave constructively:

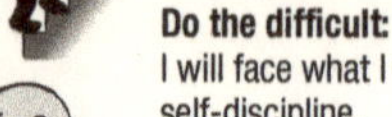

I choose to work in part acts:
I will break the overwhelming job into manageable parts.

Do the difficult:
I will face what I fear and act with self-discipline.

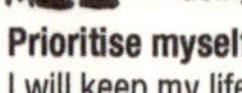

I choose to solutionise:
I will find a solution by taking advice or doing research.

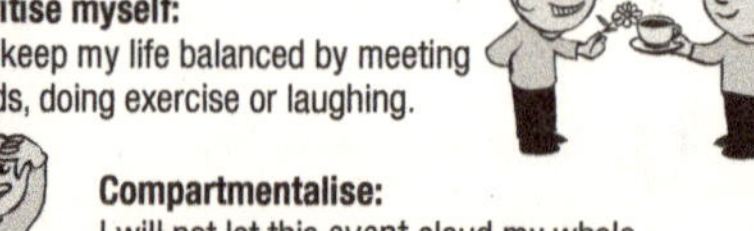

Prioritise myself:
I will keep my life balanced by meeting friends, doing exercise or laughing.

Compartmentalise:
I will not let this event cloud my whole day; I will focus on something else now.

Utilise calming strategies:

When I:
- relax,
- breathe deeply,
- go for a run,
- shower,
- lie down,
- read,
- watch TV,
- climb into a mental helicopter,
- practice mindfulness/meditation,
  my mind and body calm down.

Step Four: The Self Motivation Process

Endorse yourself for any growth no matter how small.

In the past I would have...

____

____

But this time I...

____

____

Tick off the traits that you strengthened when you worked down your anxiety:

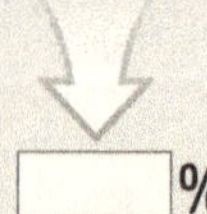

- ☐ generosity
- ☐ kindness
- ☐ compassion
- ☐ consideration
- ☐ helpfulness
- ☐ respectfulness
- ☐ honesty
- ☐ fairness
- ☐ patience
- ☐ peacefulness
- ☐ self-discipline
- ☐ forgiveness
- ☐ courage
- ☐ responsibility
- ☐ reliability
- ☐ loyalty
- ☐ love
- ☐ humility

Rate your anxiety on a scale of 0 to 100%:

☐ %

O   W

Date: _______________

Anxiety Management Worksheet

The purpose of this worksheet is to help you to see every stressful event as an opportunity for
1. greater understanding of yourself, your anxiety and the people around you, and
2. practicing tools to manage your anxiety.

Step One: An Event

Briefly describe an event when you became anxious. Give such details as time, place and people involved, and end with "That's when I began to work myself up..."

____

____

____

_______________________________________ Rate your anxiety on a scale of 0 to 100%: [   ] %

E

Step Two: The Working-Up Process

Learn about your working up process by identifying your thoughts, feelings, behaviours and bodily reactions during the event. Tick the ones that most resonate with you.

Undermining Beliefs

B

I fear that I have lost...

- ☐ approval
- ☐ control
- ☐ co-operation
- ☐ face
- ☐ respect
- ☐ success
- ☐ trust
- ☐ validation
- ☐ love

This event proves that I am...

- ☐ stupid
- ☐ abnormal
- ☐ incompetent
- ☐ lazy
- ☐ irresponsible
- ☐ a total failure
- ☐ undisciplined
- ☐ untogether
- ☐ useless

I worry that I will suffer...

- ☐ mental collapse
- ☐ illness
- ☐ financial hardship

What I want is...

- ☐ total control
- ☐ respect
- ☐ success
- ☐ perfection
- ☐ comfort
- ☐ fairness
- ☐ tranquility
- ☐ all the answers
- ☐ for life to go smoothly
- ☐ to be all things to all people

Self-destructive Behaviour

Active
- ☐ get violent
- ☐ swear
- ☐ slam doors
- ☐ run away
- ☐ overeat
- ☐ harm myself
- ☐ criticise

Passive
- ☐ take it too seriously
- ☐ give up
- ☐ wallow in self pity
- ☐ sulk
- ☐ space out
- ☐ procrastinate
- ☐ give in
- ☐ be controlled

Intense Feelings

Angry feelings
- ☐ hateful
- ☐ aggravated
- ☐ annoyed
- ☐ hostile
- ☐ outraged
- ☐ punitive
- ☐ resentful
- ☐ vengeful

Fearful feelings
- ☐ helpless
- ☐ hopeless
- ☐ disappointed
- ☐ sad
- ☐ attacked
- ☐ worn out
- ☐ rejected
- ☐ jealous
- ☐ afraid
- ☐ exploited
- ☐ lonely
- ☐ abandoned
- ☐ guilty
- ☐ insulted
- ☐ confused
- ☐ disillusioned
- ☐ misunderstood
- ☐ trapped

Bodily Reactions (limbic system)

I am uncomfortable because I am experiencing...
- ☐ tremors
- ☐ nausea
- ☐ sweaty palms
- ☐ stomach-ache
- ☐ pounding heart
- ☐ general tension
- ☐ fatigue
- ☐ imagination on fire
- ☐ headache
- ☐ dry mouth
- ☐ jaw clenching
- ☐ shortness of breath

Continued over

B   **F**   **L**

Step Three: The Working-Down Process

Begin with, "Suddenly I realised that I was anxious and that I had choices..." This is the step of self-leadership and trust in one's ability to handle the situation.

Choose helpful thoughts:

I choose to depersonalise
There is no intention to hurt me. He is doing the best he can with the tools he has at the moment.

I choose realism over romanticism
Life presents many obstacles. I lower or raise standards as needed.

There is no right or wrong
Unless it is a moral issue, I will see it simply as a difference of opinion and/or taste.

I choose the total view of positivity
Even though this event is negative, the total view of his behaviour is positive.

I surrender control
Since I cannot change this situation, I choose to let go of it.

I choose to put this event in perspective This event is not a catastrophe because it is not life threatening. It can be viewed as a trivial life event, a normal life problem that needs to be solved not dramatised.

I choose to view this event as average, falling within the normal range
This event is not exceptional; many people have gone through this.

It's temporary - "this too shall pass"
Life is constantly changing and moving through phases and this situation will also change.

Fears or facts?
Why fear? It may not happen!

I choose to focus on this as a learning experience
Every problem that comes my way is an opportunity for me to learn about my strengths and weaknesses, others and life.

Feel soothing emotions:

I choose to feel warm, loving emotions. I do this by focusing on my heart and letting love, trust forgiveness, compassion, hope or gratitude fill my heart space.

Behave constructively:

I choose to work in part acts:
I will break the overwhelming job into manageable parts.

Do the difficult:
I will face what I fear and act with self-discipline.

I choose to solutionise:
I will find a solution by taking advice or doing research.

Prioritise myself:
I will keep my life balanced by meeting friends, doing exercise or laughing.

Compartmentalise:
I will not let this event cloud my whole day; I will focus on something else now.

Utilise calming strategies:

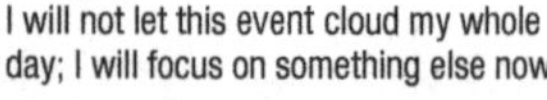

When I:
- relax,
- breathe deeply,
- go for a run,
- shower,
- lie down,
- read,
- watch TV,
- climb into a mental helicopter,
- practice mindfulness/meditation,

my mind and body calm down.

Step Four: The Self Motivation Process

Endorse yourself for any growth no matter how small.

In the past I would have...

____

____

But this time I...

____

____

Tick off the traits that you strengthened when you worked down your anxiety:

☐ generosity	☐ peacefulness
☐ kindness	☐ self-discipline
☐ compassion	☐ forgiveness
☐ consideration	☐ courage
☐ helpfulness	☐ responsibility
☐ respectfulness	☐ reliability
☐ honesty	☐ loyalty
☐ fairness	☐ love
☐ patience	☐ humility

Rate your anxiety on a scale of 0 to 100%:

⬇

___________ %

O

W

Date: ___________

Anxiety Management Worksheet

The purpose of this worksheet is to help you to see every stressful event as an opportunity for
1. greater understanding of yourself, your anxiety and the people around you, and
2. practicing tools to manage your anxiety.

Step One: An Event

Briefly describe an event when you became anxious. Give such details as time, place and people involved, and end with "That's when I began to work myself up..."

____

____

____

____ Rate your anxiety on a scale of 0 to 100%: [   ] %

E

Step Two: The Working-Up Process

Learn about your working up process by identifying your thoughts, feelings, behaviours and bodily reactions during the event. Tick the ones that most resonate with you.

Undermining Beliefs

B

I fear that I have lost...
- ☐ approval
- ☐ control
- ☐ co-operation
- ☐ face
- ☐ respect
- ☐ success
- ☐ trust
- ☐ validation
- ☐ love

This event proves that I am...
- ☐ stupid
- ☐ abnormal
- ☐ incompetent
- ☐ lazy
- ☐ irresponsible
- ☐ a total failure
- ☐ undisciplined
- ☐ untogether
- ☐ useless

I worry that I will suffer...
- ☐ mental collapse
- ☐ illness
- ☐ financial hardship

What I want is...
- ☐ total control
- ☐ respect
- ☐ success
- ☐ perfection
- ☐ comfort
- ☐ fairness
- ☐ tranquility
- ☐ all the answers
- ☐ for life to go smoothly
- ☐ to be all things to all people

Self-destructive Behaviour

Active
- ☐ get violent
- ☐ swear
- ☐ slam doors
- ☐ run away
- ☐ overeat
- ☐ harm myself
- ☐ criticise

Passive
- ☐ take it too seriously
- ☐ give up
- ☐ wallow in self pity
- ☐ sulk
- ☐ space out
- ☐ procrastinate
- ☐ give in
- ☐ be controlled

Intense Feelings

Angry feelings
- ☐ hateful
- ☐ aggravated
- ☐ annoyed
- ☐ hostile
- ☐ outraged
- ☐ punitive
- ☐ resentful
- ☐ vengeful

Fearful feelings
- ☐ helpless
- ☐ hopeless
- ☐ disappointed
- ☐ sad
- ☐ attacked
- ☐ worn out
- ☐ rejected
- ☐ jealous
- ☐ afraid
- ☐ exploited
- ☐ lonely
- ☐ abandoned
- ☐ guilty
- ☐ insulted
- ☐ confused
- ☐ disillusioned
- ☐ misunderstood
- ☐ trapped

Bodily Reactions (limbic system)

I am uncomfortable because I am experiencing...
- ☐ tremors
- ☐ nausea
- ☐ sweaty palms
- ☐ stomach-ache
- ☐ pounding heart
- ☐ general tension
- ☐ fatigue
- ☐ imagination on fire
- ☐ headache
- ☐ dry mouth
- ☐ jaw clenching
- ☐ shortness of breath

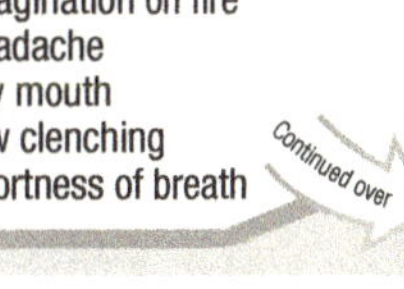

Continued over

B   **F**   **L**

Step Three: The Working-Down Process

Begin with, "Suddenly I realised that I was anxious and that I had choices..." This is the step of self-leadership and trust in one's ability to handle the situation.

Choose helpful thoughts:

I choose to depersonalise
There is no intention to hurt me. He is doing the best he can with the tools he has at the moment.

I choose realism over romanticism
Life presents many obstacles. I lower or raise standards as needed.

There is no right or wrong
Unless it is a moral issue, I will see it simply as a difference of opinion and/or taste.

I choose the total view of positivity
Even though this event is negative, the total view of his behaviour is positive.

I surrender control
Since I cannot change this situation, I choose to let go of it.

I choose to put this event in perspective
This event is not a catastrophe because it is not life threatening. It can be viewed as a trivial life event, a normal life problem that needs to be solved not dramatised.

I choose to view this event as average, falling within the normal range
This event is not exceptional; many people have gone through this.

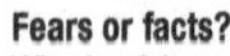

It's temporary - "this too shall pass"
Life is constantly changing and moving through phases and this situation will also change.

Fears or facts?
Why fear? It may not happen!

I choose to focus on this as a learning experience
Every problem that comes my way is an opportunity for me to learn about my strengths and weaknesses, others and life.

Feel soothing emotions:

I choose to feel warm, loving emotions. I do this by focusing on my heart and letting love, trust forgiveness, compassion, hope or gratitude fill my heart space.

Behave constructively:

I choose to work in part acts:
I will break the overwhelming job into manageable parts.

Do the difficult:
I will face what I fear and act with self-discipline.

I choose to solutionise:
I will find a solution by taking advice or doing research.

Prioritise myself:
I will keep my life balanced by meeting friends, doing exercise or laughing.

Compartmentalise:
I will not let this event cloud my whole day; I will focus on something else now.

Utilise calming strategies:

When I:
- relax,
- breathe deeply,
- go for a run,
- shower,
- lie down,
- read,
- watch TV,
- climb into a mental helicopter,
- practice mindfulness/meditation,

my mind and body calm down.

Step Four: The Self Motivation Process

Endorse yourself for any growth no matter how small.

In the past I would have...

____

____

But this time I...

____

____

Tick off the traits that you strengthened when you worked down your anxiety:

☐ generosity	☐ peacefulness
☐ kindness	☐ self-discipline
☐ compassion	☐ forgiveness
☐ consideration	☐ courage
☐ helpfulness	☐ responsibility
☐ respectfulness	☐ reliability
☐ honesty	☐ loyalty
☐ fairness	☐ love
☐ patience	☐ humility

Rate your anxiety on a scale of 0 to 100%:

[   ]%

O

W

Date: _____________

Anxiety Management Worksheet

The purpose of this worksheet is to help you to see every stressful event as an opportunity for
1. greater understanding of yourself, your anxiety and the people around you, and
2. practicing tools to manage your anxiety.

Step One: An Event

Briefly describe an event when you became anxious. Give such details as time, place and people involved, and end with "That's when I began to work myself up…"

____

____

____

____ Rate your anxiety on a scale of 0 to 100%: [   ] %

E

Step Two: The Working-Up Process

Learn about your working up process by identifying your thoughts, feelings, behaviours and bodily reactions during the event. Tick the ones that most resonate with you.

Undermining Beliefs

B

I fear that I have lost…
- ☐ approval
- ☐ control
- ☐ co-operation
- ☐ face
- ☐ respect
- ☐ success
- ☐ trust
- ☐ validation
- ☐ love

This event proves that I am…
- ☐ stupid
- ☐ abnormal
- ☐ incompetent
- ☐ lazy
- ☐ irresponsible
- ☐ a total failure
- ☐ undisciplined
- ☐ untogether
- ☐ useless

I worry that I will suffer…
- ☐ mental collapse
- ☐ illness
- ☐ financial hardship

What I want is…
- ☐ total control
- ☐ respect
- ☐ success
- ☐ perfection
- ☐ comfort
- ☐ fairness
- ☐ tranquility
- ☐ all the answers
- ☐ for life to go smoothly
- ☐ to be all things to all people

Self-destructive Behaviour

Active
- ☐ get violent
- ☐ swear
- ☐ slam doors
- ☐ run away
- ☐ overeat
- ☐ harm myself
- ☐ criticise

Passive
- ☐ take it too seriously
- ☐ give up
- ☐ wallow in self pity
- ☐ sulk
- ☐ space out
- ☐ procrastinate
- ☐ give in
- ☐ be controlled

Intense Feelings

Angry feelings
- ☐ hateful
- ☐ aggravated
- ☐ annoyed
- ☐ hostile
- ☐ outraged
- ☐ punitive
- ☐ resentful
- ☐ vengeful

Fearful feelings
- ☐ helpless
- ☐ hopeless
- ☐ disappointed
- ☐ sad
- ☐ attacked
- ☐ worn out
- ☐ rejected
- ☐ jealous
- ☐ afraid
- ☐ exploited
- ☐ lonely
- ☐ abandoned
- ☐ guilty
- ☐ insulted
- ☐ confused
- ☐ disillusioned
- ☐ misunderstood
- ☐ trapped

Bodily Reactions (limbic system)

I am uncomfortable because I am experiencing…
- ☐ tremors
- ☐ nausea
- ☐ sweaty palms
- ☐ stomach-ache
- ☐ pounding heart
- ☐ general tension
- ☐ fatigue
- ☐ imagination on fire
- ☐ headache
- ☐ dry mouth
- ☐ jaw clenching
- ☐ shortness of breath

B   **F**   **L**

Step Three: The Working-Down Process

Begin with, "Suddenly I realised that I was anxious and that I had choices..." This is the step of self-leadership and trust in one's ability to handle the situation.

Choose helpful thoughts:

I choose to depersonalise
There is no intention to hurt me. He is doing the best he can with the tools he has at the moment.

I choose realism over romanticism
Life presents many obstacles. I lower or raise standards as needed.

There is no right or wrong
Unless it is a moral issue, I will see it simply as a difference of opinion and/or taste.

I choose the total view of positivity
Even though this event is negative, the total view of his behaviour is positive.

I surrender control
Since I cannot change this situation, I choose to let go of it.

I choose to put this event in perspective This event is not a catastrophe because it is not life threatening. It can be viewed as a trivial life event, a normal life problem that needs to be solved not dramatised.

I choose to view this event as average, falling within the normal range
This event is not exceptional; many people have gone through this.

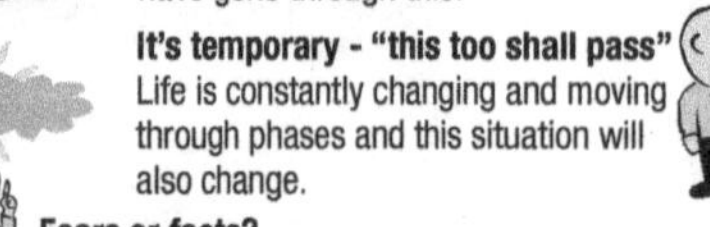

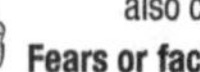

It's temporary - "this too shall pass"
Life is constantly changing and moving through phases and this situation will also change.

Fears or facts?
Why fear? It may not happen!

I choose to focus on this as a learning experience
Every problem that comes my way is an opportunity for me to learn about my strengths and weaknesses, others and life.

Feel soothing emotions:

I choose to feel warm, loving emotions. I do this by focusing on my heart and letting love, trust forgiveness, compassion, hope or gratitude fill my heart space.

Behave constructively:

I choose to work in part acts:
I will break the overwhelming job into manageable parts.

Do the difficult:
I will face what I fear and act with self-discipline.

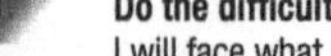

I choose to solutionise:
I will find a solution by taking advice or doing research.

Prioritise myself:
I will keep my life balanced by meeting friends, doing exercise or laughing.

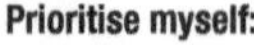

Compartmentalise:
I will not let this event cloud my whole day; I will focus on something else now.

Utilise calming strategies:

When I:
- relax,
- breathe deeply,
- go for a run,
- shower,
- lie down,
- read,
- watch TV,
- climb into a mental helicopter,
- practice mindfulness/meditation,

my mind and body calm down.

Step Four: The Self Motivation Process

Endorse yourself for any growth no matter how small.

In the past I would have...

____

____

But this time I...

____

____

Tick off the traits that you strengthened when you worked down your anxiety:

☐ generosity	☐ peacefulness	
☐ kindness	☐ self-discipline	
☐ compassion	☐ forgiveness	
☐ consideration	☐ courage	
☐ helpfulness	☐ responsibility	
☐ respectfulness	☐ reliability	
☐ honesty	☐ loyalty	
☐ fairness	☐ love	
☐ patience	☐ humility	

Rate your anxiety on a scale of 0 to 100%:

______ %

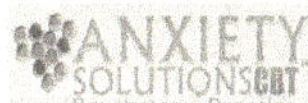

Anxiety Management Worksheet

The purpose of this worksheet is to help you to see every stressful event as an opportunity for
1. greater understanding of yourself, your anxiety and the people around you, and
2. practicing tools to manage your anxiety.

Step One: An Event

Briefly describe an event when you became anxious. Give such details as time, place and people involved, and end with "That's when I began to work myself up…"

____

____

____

_______________________________________ Rate your anxiety on a scale of 0 to 100%: [   ] %

E

Step Two: The Working-Up Process

Learn about your working up process by identifying your thoughts, feelings, behaviours and bodily reactions during the event. Tick the ones that most resonate with you.

Undermining Beliefs

B

I fear that I have lost...

- ☐ approval
- ☐ control
- ☐ co-operation
- ☐ face
- ☐ respect
- ☐ success
- ☐ trust
- ☐ validation
- ☐ love

This event proves that I am...

- ☐ stupid
- ☐ abnormal
- ☐ incompetent
- ☐ lazy
- ☐ irresponsible
- ☐ a total failure
- ☐ undisciplined
- ☐ untogether
- ☐ useless

I worry that I will suffer...

- ☐ mental collapse
- ☐ illness
- ☐ financial hardship

What I want is...

- ☐ total control
- ☐ respect
- ☐ success
- ☐ perfection
- ☐ comfort
- ☐ fairness
- ☐ tranquility
- ☐ all the answers
- ☐ for life to go smoothly
- ☐ to be all things to all people

Self-destructive Behaviour

Active
- ☐ get violent
- ☐ swear
- ☐ slam doors
- ☐ run away
- ☐ overeat
- ☐ harm myself
- ☐ criticise

Passive
- ☐ take it too seriously
- ☐ give up
- ☐ wallow in self pity
- ☐ sulk
- ☐ space out
- ☐ procrastinate
- ☐ give in
- ☐ be controlled

Intense Feelings

Angry feelings
- ☐ hateful
- ☐ aggravated
- ☐ annoyed
- ☐ hostile
- ☐ outraged
- ☐ punitive
- ☐ resentful
- ☐ vengeful

Fearful feelings
- ☐ helpless
- ☐ hopeless
- ☐ disappointed
- ☐ sad

- ☐ attacked
- ☐ worn out
- ☐ rejected
- ☐ jealous
- ☐ afraid
- ☐ exploited
- ☐ lonely
- ☐ abandoned
- ☐ guilty
- ☐ insulted
- ☐ confused
- ☐ disillusioned
- ☐ misunderstood
- ☐ trapped

Bodily Reactions (limbic system)

I am uncomfortable because I am experiencing...

- ☐ tremors
- ☐ nausea
- ☐ sweaty palms
- ☐ stomach-ache
- ☐ pounding heart
- ☐ general tension
- ☐ fatigue
- ☐ imagination on fire
- ☐ headache
- ☐ dry mouth
- ☐ jaw clenching
- ☐ shortness of breath

Continued over

B   **F**   **L**

Step Three: The Working-Down Process

Begin with, "Suddenly I realised that I was anxious and that I had choices..." This is the step of self-leadership and trust in one's ability to handle the situation.

Choose helpful thoughts:

I choose to depersonalise
There is no intention to hurt me. He is doing the best he can with the tools he has at the moment.

I choose realism over romanticism
Life presents many obstacles. I lower or raise standards as needed.

There is no right or wrong
Unless it is a moral issue, I will see it simply as a difference of opinion and/or taste.

I choose the total view of positivity
Even though this event is negative, the total view of his behaviour is positive.

I surrender control
Since I cannot change this situation, I choose to let go of it.

I choose to put this event in perspective This event is not a catastrophe because it is not life threatening. It can be viewed as a trivial life event, a normal life problem that needs to be solved not dramatised.

I choose to view this event as average, falling within the normal range
This event is not exceptional; many people have gone through this.

It's temporary - "this too shall pass"
Life is constantly changing and moving through phases and this situation will also change.

Fears or facts?
Why fear? It may not happen!

I choose to focus on this as a learning experience
Every problem that comes my way is an opportunity for me to learn about my strengths and weaknesses, others and life.

Feel soothing emotions:

I choose to feel warm, loving emotions. I do this by focusing on my heart and letting love, trust forgiveness, compassion, hope or gratitude fill my heart space.

Behave constructively:

I choose to work in part acts:
I will break the overwhelming job into manageable parts.

Do the difficult:
I will face what I fear and act with self-discipline.

I choose to solutionise:
I will find a solution by taking advice or doing research.

Prioritise myself:
I will keep my life balanced by meeting friends, doing exercise or laughing.

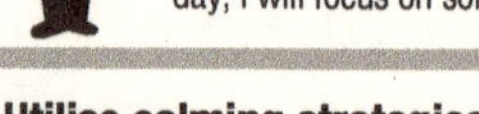

Compartmentalise:
I will not let this event cloud my whole day; I will focus on something else now.

Utilise calming strategies:

When I:
* relax,
* breathe deeply,
* go for a run,
* shower,
* lie down,
* read,
* watch TV,
* climb into a mental helicopter,
* practice mindfulness/meditation,

my mind and body calm down.

Step Four: The Self Motivation Process

Endorse yourself for any growth no matter how small.

In the past I would have...

____

____

But this time I...

____

____

Tick off the traits that you strengthened when you worked down your anxiety:

☐ generosity	☐ peacefulness
☐ kindness	☐ self-discipline
☐ compassion	☐ forgiveness
☐ consideration	☐ courage
☐ helpfulness	☐ responsibility
☐ respectfulness	☐ reliability
☐ honesty	☐ loyalty
☐ fairness	☐ love
☐ patience	☐ humility

Rate your anxiety on a scale of 0 to 100%:

[ ] %

O

W

Anxiety Management Worksheet

The purpose of this worksheet is to help you to see every stressful event as an opportunity for
1. greater understanding of yourself, your anxiety and the people around you, and
2. practicing tools to manage your anxiety.

Step One: An Event

Briefly describe an event when you became anxious. Give such details as time, place and people involved, and end with "That's when I began to work myself up…"

____

____

____   Rate your anxiety on a scale of 0 to 100%: [   ] %

E

Step Two: The Working-Up Process

Learn about your working up process by identifying your thoughts, feelings, behaviours and bodily reactions during the event. Tick the ones that most resonate with you.

Undermining Beliefs

B

I fear that I have lost…
- ☐ approval
- ☐ control
- ☐ co-operation
- ☐ face
- ☐ respect
- ☐ success
- ☐ trust
- ☐ validation
- ☐ love

This event proves that I am…
- ☐ stupid
- ☐ abnormal
- ☐ incompetent
- ☐ lazy
- ☐ irresponsible
- ☐ a total failure
- ☐ undisciplined
- ☐ untogether
- ☐ useless

I worry that I will suffer…
- ☐ mental collapse
- ☐ illness
- ☐ financial hardship

What I want is…
- ☐ total control
- ☐ respect
- ☐ success
- ☐ perfection
- ☐ comfort
- ☐ fairness
- ☐ tranquility
- ☐ all the answers
- ☐ for life to go smoothly
- ☐ to be all things to all people

Self-destructive Behaviour

Active
- ☐ get violent
- ☐ swear
- ☐ slam doors
- ☐ run away
- ☐ overeat
- ☐ harm myself
- ☐ criticise

Passive
- ☐ take it too seriously
- ☐ give up
- ☐ wallow in self pity
- ☐ sulk
- ☐ space out
- ☐ procrastinate
- ☐ give in
- ☐ be controlled

Intense Feelings

Angry feelings
- ☐ hateful
- ☐ aggravated
- ☐ annoyed
- ☐ hostile
- ☐ outraged
- ☐ punitive
- ☐ resentful
- ☐ vengeful

Fearful feelings
- ☐ helpless
- ☐ hopeless
- ☐ disappointed
- ☐ sad
- ☐ attacked
- ☐ worn out
- ☐ rejected
- ☐ jealous
- ☐ afraid
- ☐ exploited
- ☐ lonely
- ☐ abandoned
- ☐ guilty
- ☐ insulted
- ☐ confused
- ☐ disillusioned
- ☐ misunderstood
- ☐ trapped

Bodily Reactions (limbic system)

I am uncomfortable because I am experiencing…
- ☐ tremors
- ☐ nausea
- ☐ sweaty palms
- ☐ stomach-ache
- ☐ pounding heart
- ☐ general tension
- ☐ fatigue
- ☐ imagination on fire
- ☐ headache
- ☐ dry mouth
- ☐ jaw clenching
- ☐ shortness of breath

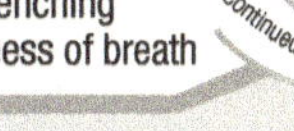

Continued over

B   **F**   **L**

Step Three: The Working-Down Process

Begin with, "Suddenly I realised that I was anxious and that I had choices..." This is the step of self-leadership and trust in one's ability to handle the situation.

Choose helpful thoughts:

I choose to depersonalise
There is no intention to hurt me. He is doing the best he can with the tools he has at the moment.

I choose realism over romanticism
Life presents many obstacles. I lower or raise standards as needed.

There is no right or wrong
Unless it is a moral issue, I will see it simply as a difference of opinion and/or taste.

I choose the total view of positivity
Even though this event is negative, the total view of his behaviour is positive.

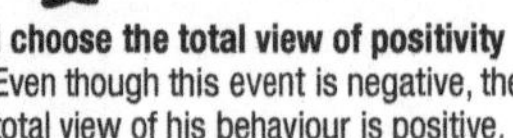

I surrender control
Since I cannot change this situation, I choose to let go of it.

I choose to put this event in perspective This event is not a catastrophe because it is not life threatening. It can be viewed as a trivial life event, a normal life problem that needs to be solved not dramatised.

I choose to view this event as average, falling within the normal range
This event is not exceptional; many people have gone through this.

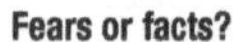

It's temporary - "this too shall pass"
Life is constantly changing and moving through phases and this situation will also change.

Fears or facts?
Why fear? It may not happen!

I choose to focus on this as a learning experience
Every problem that comes my way is an opportunity for me to learn about my strengths and weaknesses, others and life.

Feel soothing emotions:

I choose to feel warm, loving emotions. I do this by focusing on my heart and letting love, trust forgiveness, compassion, hope or gratitude fill my heart space.

Behave constructively:

I choose to work in part acts:
I will break the overwhelming job into manageable parts.

Do the difficult:
I will face what I fear and act with self-discipline.

I choose to solutionise:
I will find a solution by taking advice or doing research.

Prioritise myself:
I will keep my life balanced by meeting friends, doing exercise or laughing.

Compartmentalise:
I will not let this event cloud my whole day; I will focus on something else now.

Utilise calming strategies:

When I:
- relax,
- breathe deeply,
- go for a run,
- shower,
- lie down,
- read,
- watch TV,
- climb into a mental helicopter,
- practice mindfulness/meditation,

my mind and body calm down.

Step Four: The Self Motivation Process

Endorse yourself for any growth no matter how small.

In the past I would have...

____

____

But this time I...

____

____

Tick off the traits that you strengthened when you worked down your anxiety:

☐ generosity	☐ peacefulness
☐ kindness	☐ self-discipline
☐ compassion	☐ forgiveness
☐ consideration	☐ courage
☐ helpfulness	☐ responsibility
☐ respectfulness	☐ reliability
☐ honesty	☐ loyalty
☐ fairness	☐ love
☐ patience	☐ humility

Rate your anxiety on a scale of 0 to 100%:

________%

O

W

Date: ___________

Anxiety Management Worksheet

The purpose of this worksheet is to help you to see every stressful event as an opportunity for
1. greater understanding of yourself, your anxiety and the people around you, and
2. practicing tools to manage your anxiety.

Step One: An Event

Briefly describe an event when you became anxious. Give such details as time, place and people involved, and end with "That's when I began to work myself up..."

____

____

____

____ Rate your anxiety on a scale of 0 to 100%: [   ] %

E

Step Two: The Working-Up Process

Learn about your working up process by identifying your thoughts, feelings, behaviours and bodily reactions during the event. Tick the ones that most resonate with you.

Undermining Beliefs

B

I fear that I have lost...

- ☐ approval
- ☐ control
- ☐ co-operation
- ☐ face
- ☐ respect
- ☐ success
- ☐ trust
- ☐ validation
- ☐ love

This event proves that I am...

- ☐ stupid
- ☐ abnormal
- ☐ incompetent
- ☐ lazy
- ☐ irresponsible
- ☐ a total failure
- ☐ undisciplined
- ☐ untogether
- ☐ useless

I worry that I will suffer...

- ☐ mental collapse
- ☐ illness
- ☐ financial hardship

What I want is...

- ☐ total control
- ☐ respect
- ☐ success
- ☐ perfection
- ☐ comfort
- ☐ fairness
- ☐ tranquility
- ☐ all the answers
- ☐ for life to go smoothly
- ☐ to be all things to all people

Self-destructive Behaviour

Active

- ☐ get violent
- ☐ swear
- ☐ slam doors
- ☐ run away
- ☐ overeat
- ☐ harm myself
- ☐ criticise

Passive

- ☐ take it too seriously
- ☐ give up
- ☐ wallow in self pity
- ☐ sulk
- ☐ space out
- ☐ procrastinate
- ☐ give in
- ☐ be controlled

Intense Feelings

Angry feelings

- ☐ hateful
- ☐ aggravated
- ☐ annoyed
- ☐ hostile
- ☐ outraged
- ☐ punitive
- ☐ resentful
- ☐ vengeful
- ☐ attacked
- ☐ worn out
- ☐ rejected
- ☐ jealous
- ☐ afraid
- ☐ exploited
- ☐ lonely
- ☐ abandoned
- ☐ guilty

Fearful feelings

- ☐ helpless
- ☐ hopeless
- ☐ disappointed
- ☐ sad
- ☐ insulted
- ☐ confused
- ☐ disillusioned
- ☐ misunderstood
- ☐ trapped

Bodily Reactions (limbic system)

I am uncomfortable because I am experiencing...

- ☐ tremors
- ☐ nausea
- ☐ sweaty palms
- ☐ stomach-ache
- ☐ pounding heart
- ☐ general tension
- ☐ fatigue
- ☐ imagination on fire
- ☐ headache
- ☐ dry mouth
- ☐ jaw clenching
- ☐ shortness of breath

Continued over

B   **F**   **L**

Step Three: The Working-Down Process

Begin with, "Suddenly I realised that I was anxious and that I had choices..." This is the step of self-leadership and trust in one's ability to handle the situation.

Choose helpful thoughts:

I choose to depersonalise
There is no intention to hurt me. He is doing the best he can with the tools he has at the moment.

I choose realism over romanticism
Life presents many obstacles. I lower or raise standards as needed.

There is no right or wrong
Unless it is a moral issue, I will see it simply as a difference of opinion and/or taste.

I choose the total view of positivity
Even though this event is negative, the total view of his behaviour is positive.

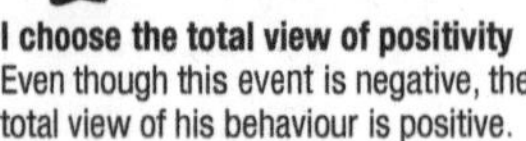

I surrender control
Since I cannot change this situation, I choose to let go of it.

I choose to put this event in perspective This event is not a catastrophe because it is not life threatening. It can be viewed as a trivial life event, a normal life problem that needs to be solved not dramatised.

I choose to view this event as average, falling within the normal range
This event is not exceptional; many people have gone through this.

It's temporary - "this too shall pass"
Life is constantly changing and moving through phases and this situation will also change.

Fears or facts?
Why fear? It may not happen!

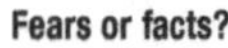

I choose to focus on this as a learning experience
Every problem that comes my way is an opportunity for me to learn about my strengths and weaknesses, others and life.

Feel soothing emotions:

I choose to feel warm, loving emotions. I do this by focusing on my heart and letting love, trust forgiveness, compassion, hope or gratitude fill my heart space.

Behave constructively:

I choose to work in part acts:
I will break the overwhelming job into manageable parts.

Do the difficult:
I will face what I fear and act with self-discipline.

I choose to solutionise:
I will find a solution by taking advice or doing research.

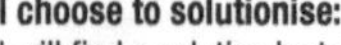

Prioritise myself:
I will keep my life balanced by meeting friends, doing exercise or laughing.

Compartmentalise:
I will not let this event cloud my whole day; I will focus on something else now.

Utilise calming strategies:

When I:
- relax,
- breathe deeply,
- go for a run,
- shower,
- lie down,
- read,
- watch TV,
- climb into a mental helicopter,
- practice mindfulness/meditation,

my mind and body calm down.

Step Four: The Self Motivation Process

Endorse yourself for any growth no matter how small.

In the past I would have...

____

____

But this time I...

____

____

Tick off the traits that you strengthened when you worked down your anxiety:

☐ generosity	☐ peacefulness
☐ kindness	☐ self-discipline
☐ compassion	☐ forgiveness
☐ consideration	☐ courage
☐ helpfulness	☐ responsibility
☐ respectfulness	☐ reliability
☐ honesty	☐ loyalty
☐ fairness	☐ love
☐ patience	☐ humility

Rate your anxiety on a scale of 0 to 100%:

________%

O

W

Week 6

In week six, the tools we will cover are:

1. Realism: thinking tool
2. Laugh: behavioural tool
3. Formal mindfulness: calming tool

Realism: thinking tool

"I choose realism over romanticism. Life presents many obstacles. I lower or raise standards as needed."

Much of our stress is caused by wanting things a certain way although they turn out differently. We all have "romantic" ideals of how life should be. I call this "the house with the picket fence" vision. When we do not get the house/partner/riches/ job of our dreams, we become upset, anxious and maybe even depressed. Hollywood enchants us with fairytales, while our real life experiences are very different. We are often faced with not finding a life partner, no house, illness, divorce, job loss and so on.

By approaching life with a realistic view we can alleviate a lot of the internal stress. A realistic view, by the way, is not a pessimistic view ("nothing ever works out"). It is a balanced view and could be stated philosophically as follows:

*Life is an obstacle course. Sometimes we soar over the
obstacle, other times we struggle over it, and on rare
occasions we do not get over it.
Life can never be constantly smooth.
No matter who we
are, where we come from or what we do.*

The positive outcome of thinking in this realistic way is that when an obstacle comes along, we do not get stressed or shocked. Nor do we start a negative commentary in our heads believing that what is happening is unfair, should not be happening, does not happen to others, or is caused by our stupidity, and so on.

When you indulge in negative self-talk, you double the number of problems that you have. For example, let's imagine that you have lost your purse. This is a problem. You have to deal with it. It certainly is inconvenient and a loss, especially if you have lost money. However, when you start to blame yourself for losing your purse, calling yourself stupid, irresponsible and a loser, you now have two problems. Besides sorting out the purse, you now have to cope with your low self-esteem and other negative emotions.

It is preferable and very calming to think that what happened (a lost purse) is a normal life event, and merely an obstacle that needs to be overcome.

EXERCISE 15

Some commonly held romantic beliefs are itemised below. Please tick those that pertain to you, and add others that are not mentioned. Then compare your romantic views with the realistic views. Notice how you calm down when you see things realistically.

Romantic views	Realistic views
☐ Life can be smooth sailing at all times.	☐ Life is an obstacle course with smooth times and difficult times.
☐ Ultimately, there are always happy endings.	☐ Often, things work out well but sometimes they do not.
☐ As long as I please my boss, I will have a secure job.	☐ While pleasing a boss is important, other factors may result in my losing my job.
☐ If I try hard enough, I will be a millionaire overnight.	☐ While there are a few instant successes, most people become millionaires over a long period of time. I will work toward that goal in the long-term.
☐ If I am kind all the time, everyone will like me.	☐ Some people respond to kindness with friendship. Others do not care either way.
☐ Life is fair and society just.	☐ While these are values I aspire to, I have seen situations that do not seem fair or just.
☐ If I work hard, I will get the reward I deserve.	☐ Sometimes hard work does not pay off.

Are there any romantic views that you have that may be causing you stress? Write down a realistic view that can help you feel less deprived and stressed.

Daily monitoring diary

From this week onwards, there is the opportunity to record how often and how intensely you utilise romantic thinking. Rate your anxiety when you have these thoughts, challenge them with the tool "**realism**," and re-rate your anxiety.

Laugh: behavioural tool

"A good joke is the best medicine."

Laughing is therapeutic. (14) When you laugh, certain hormones and neurotransmitters are released which lead to positive feelings and increased immunity. When you laugh regularly, your mood lifts and you feel calmer. Norman Cousins (20) proved that laughter can literally improve your health. He cured himself of an auto immune disease. As a result, there is now a university department at UCLA dedicated to teaching people about the health benefits of laughter. (21)

Moreover, when you can see the humour in difficult situations, this signifies mental resilience. (14) For example, let's say your shoe breaks and you are forced to walk in a public place with one shoe off. You feel ridiculous. But if you can see the humour in it, and realise how funny you must look, this indicates your resilience. Resilience can be defined as bouncing up in the face of a difficult situation.

Some people laugh more easily than others it is true. But like any skill, you can train yourself to see humour in situations. You can also train yourself to laugh long and hard — what is called a belly laugh.

As a tool to lower your anxiety, ensure that you laugh regularly, long and hard. Read joke books, watch sitcoms and full-length comedy movies. Find the style of humour that appeals to you and indulge. Build having a good laugh into your daily schedule.

EXERCISE 16

What types of humour do you enjoy?

Where do you source it?

Have you ever thought about consciously seeking out laughter?
YES/NO. Describe.

Write a plan of how you can incorporate laughter into your daily life.

Formal mindfulness: calming tool

One type of mindfulness is called formal mindfulness and is similar to meditating. Just as when you meditate, it is important to sit in a quiet space and to focus on something that is ongoing, such as your breathing.

Find a quiet spot and commit 15 or 20 minutes to this practice. Observe your breath entering your lungs and then emptying out. Sooner or later you will lose focus. You will start to think of other things or feel different sensations in your body. Make no judgments. Just gently bring your attention back to your breath.

The more you practise this process, the better you will be at sustaining attention and being non-judgmental.

EXERCISE 17

Are you able to commit to regular sessions of formal mindfulness?

YES/NO

If no, why not? ____

____

____

____

If yes, commit to it now.

I ___________________________ commit to practicing formal mindfulness ______________ times a day/week/month, starting from ____ .

DAILY MONITORING DIARY WEEK ENDING ⎯⎯⎯⎯⎯⎯⎯⎯⎯⎯⎯⎯⎯⎯

Day	M	T	W	T	F	S	S
Overall Anxiety Rating for the day (0-10)							
1. EXERCISE							
How long?							
Anxiety level before (0-10)							
Anxiety level after (0-10)							
2. BREATHING							
How long?							
Anxiety level before (0-10)							
Anxiety level after (0-10)							
3. RELAXATION							
How long?							
Anxiety level before (0-10)							
Anxiety level after (0-10)							
4. PERVASIVE PESSIMISTIC THINKING							
How often this type of thought occurred							
Belief in thoughts before challenging (0-10)							
Belief in thoughts after challenging (0-10)							
5. CATASTROPHIC THINKING							
How often this type of thought occurred							
Belief in thoughts before challenging (0-10)							
Belief in thoughts after challenging (0-10)							

Day	M	T	W	T	F	S	S
6. PERMANENT PESSIMISTIC THINKING							
How often this type of thought occurred							
Belief in thoughts before challenging (0-10)							
Belief in thoughts after challenging (0-10)							
7. MINDFULNESS (FORMAL, GROUNDING, INFORMAL MINDFULNESS)							
How long?							
Anxiety level before (0-10)							
Anxiety level after (0-10)							
8. ROMANTIC THINKING							
How often this type of thought occurred							
Belief in thoughts before challenging (0-10)							
Belief in thoughts after challenging (0-10)							

Date: _______________

Anxiety Management Worksheet

The purpose of this worksheet is to help you to see every stressful event as an opportunity for
1. greater understanding of yourself, your anxiety and the people around you, and
2. practicing tools to manage your anxiety.

Step One: An Event

Briefly describe an event when you became anxious. Give such details as time, place and people involved, and end with "That's when I began to work myself up…"

____

____

____

_______________________________ Rate your anxiety on a scale of 0 to 100%: [   ] %

E

Step Two: The Working-Up Process

Learn about your working up process by identifying your thoughts, feelings, behaviours and bodily reactions during the event. Tick the ones that most resonate with you.

B

Undermining Beliefs

I fear that I have lost...

- ☐ approval
- ☐ control
- ☐ co-operation
- ☐ face
- ☐ respect
- ☐ success
- ☐ trust
- ☐ validation
- ☐ love

This event proves that I am...

- ☐ stupid
- ☐ abnormal
- ☐ incompetent
- ☐ lazy
- ☐ irresponsible
- ☐ a total failure
- ☐ undisciplined
- ☐ untogether
- ☐ useless

I worry that I will suffer...

- ☐ mental collapse
- ☐ illness
- ☐ financial hardship

What I want is...

- ☐ total control
- ☐ respect
- ☐ success
- ☐ perfection
- ☐ comfort
- ☐ fairness
- ☐ tranquility
- ☐ all the answers
- ☐ for life to go smoothly
- ☐ to be all things to all people

Self-destructive Behaviour

Active

- ☐ get violent
- ☐ swear
- ☐ slam doors
- ☐ run away
- ☐ overeat
- ☐ harm myself
- ☐ criticise

Passive

- ☐ take it too seriously
- ☐ give up
- ☐ wallow in self pity
- ☐ sulk
- ☐ space out
- ☐ procrastinate
- ☐ give in
- ☐ be controlled

Intense Feelings

Angry feelings

- ☐ hateful
- ☐ aggravated
- ☐ annoyed
- ☐ hostile
- ☐ outraged
- ☐ punitive
- ☐ resentful
- ☐ vengeful

Fearful feelings

- ☐ helpless
- ☐ hopeless
- ☐ disappointed
- ☐ sad
- ☐ attacked
- ☐ worn out
- ☐ rejected
- ☐ jealous
- ☐ afraid
- ☐ exploited
- ☐ lonely
- ☐ abandoned
- ☐ guilty
- ☐ insulted
- ☐ confused
- ☐ disillusioned
- ☐ misunderstood
- ☐ trapped

Bodily Reactions (limbic system)

I am uncomfortable because I am experiencing...

- ☐ tremors
- ☐ nausea
- ☐ sweaty palms
- ☐ stomach-ache
- ☐ pounding heart
- ☐ general tension
- ☐ fatigue
- ☐ imagination on fire
- ☐ headache
- ☐ dry mouth
- ☐ jaw clenching
- ☐ shortness of breath

Continued over

B   **F**   **L**

Step Three: The Working-Down Process

Begin with, "Suddenly I realised that I was anxious and that I had choices..." This is the step of self-leadership and trust in one's ability to handle the situation.

Choose helpful thoughts:

I choose to depersonalise
There is no intention to hurt me. He is doing the best he can with the tools he has at the moment.

I choose realism over romanticism
Life presents many obstacles. I lower or raise standards as needed.

There is no right or wrong
Unless it is a moral issue, I will see it simply as a difference of opinion and/or taste.

I choose the total view of positivity
Even though this event is negative, the total view of his behaviour is positive.

I surrender control
Since I cannot change this situation, I choose to let go of it.

I choose to put this event in perspective This event is not a catastrophe because it is not life threatening. It can be viewed as a trivial life event, a normal life problem that needs to be solved not dramatised.

I choose to view this event as average, falling within the normal range
This event is not exceptional; many people have gone through this.

It's temporary - "this too shall pass"
Life is constantly changing and moving through phases and this situation will also change.

Fears or facts?
Why fear? It may not happen!

I choose to focus on this as a learning experience
Every problem that comes my way is an opportunity for me to learn about my strengths and weaknesses, others and life.

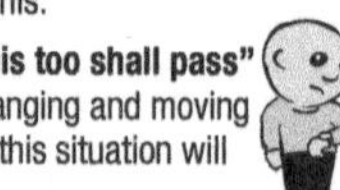

Feel soothing emotions:

I choose to feel warm, loving emotions. I do this by focusing on my heart and letting love, trust forgiveness, compassion, hope or gratitude fill my heart space.

Behave constructively:

I choose to work in part acts:
I will break the overwhelming job into manageable parts.

Do the difficult:
I will face what I fear and act with self-discipline.

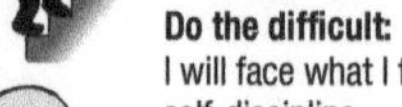

I choose to solutionise:
I will find a solution by taking advice or doing research.

Prioritise myself:
I will keep my life balanced by meeting friends, doing exercise or laughing.

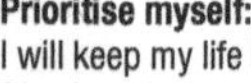

Compartmentalise:
I will not let this event cloud my whole day; I will focus on something else now.

Utilise calming strategies:

When I:
- relax,
- breathe deeply,
- go for a run,
- shower,
- lie down,
- read,
- watch TV,
- climb into a mental helicopter,
- practice mindfulness/meditation,

my mind and body calm down.

Step Four: The Self Motivation Process

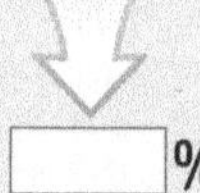

Endorse yourself for any growth no matter how small.

In the past I would have...

____

But this time I...

____

Tick off the traits that you strengthened when you worked down your anxiety:

☐ generosity	☐ peacefulness	
☐ kindness	☐ self-discipline	
☐ compassion	☐ forgiveness	
☐ consideration	☐ courage	
☐ helpfulness	☐ responsibility	
☐ respectfulness	☐ reliability	
☐ honesty	☐ loyalty	
☐ fairness	☐ love	
☐ patience	☐ humility	

Rate your anxiety on a scale of 0 to 100%:

⬇

_____ %

o

w

Date: _______________

Anxiety Management Worksheet

The purpose of this worksheet is to help you to see every stressful event as an opportunity for
1. greater understanding of yourself, your anxiety and the people around you, and
2. practicing tools to manage your anxiety.

Step One: An Event

Briefly describe an event when you became anxious. Give such details as time, place and people involved, and end with "That's when I began to work myself up…"

____

____   **E**

____

____ Rate your anxiety on a scale of 0 to 100%: [   ] %

Step Two: The Working-Up Process

Learn about your working up process by identifying your thoughts, feelings, behaviours and bodily reactions during the event.

Tick the ones that most resonate with you.

Undermining Beliefs   **B**

I fear that I have lost…
- ☐ approval
- ☐ control
- ☐ co-operation
- ☐ face
- ☐ respect
- ☐ success
- ☐ trust
- ☐ validation
- ☐ love

This event proves that I am…
- ☐ stupid
- ☐ abnormal
- ☐ incompetent
- ☐ lazy
- ☐ irresponsible
- ☐ a total failure
- ☐ undisciplined
- ☐ untogether
- ☐ useless

I worry that I will suffer…
- ☐ mental collapse
- ☐ illness
- ☐ financial hardship

What I want is…
- ☐ total control
- ☐ respect
- ☐ success
- ☐ perfection
- ☐ comfort
- ☐ fairness
- ☐ tranquility
- ☐ all the answers
- ☐ for life to go smoothly
- ☐ to be all things to all people

Self-destructive Behaviour

Active
- ☐ get violent
- ☐ swear
- ☐ slam doors
- ☐ run away
- ☐ overeat
- ☐ harm myself
- ☐ criticise

Passive
- ☐ take it too seriously
- ☐ give up
- ☐ wallow in self pity
- ☐ sulk
- ☐ space out
- ☐ procrastinate
- ☐ give in
- ☐ be controlled

B

Intense Feelings

Angry feelings
- ☐ hateful
- ☐ aggravated
- ☐ annoyed
- ☐ hostile
- ☐ outraged
- ☐ punitive
- ☐ resentful
- ☐ vengeful

Fearful feelings
- ☐ helpless
- ☐ hopeless
- ☐ disappointed
- ☐ sad
- ☐ attacked
- ☐ worn out
- ☐ rejected
- ☐ jealous
- ☐ afraid
- ☐ exploited
- ☐ lonely
- ☐ abandoned
- ☐ guilty
- ☐ insulted
- ☐ confused
- ☐ disillusioned
- ☐ misunderstood
- ☐ trapped

F

Bodily Reactions (limbic system)

I am uncomfortable because I am experiencing…
- ☐ tremors
- ☐ nausea
- ☐ sweaty palms
- ☐ stomach-ache
- ☐ pounding heart
- ☐ general tension
- ☐ fatigue
- ☐ imagination on fire
- ☐ headache
- ☐ dry mouth
- ☐ jaw clenching
- ☐ shortness of breath

Continued over

L

Step Three: The Working-Down Process

Begin with, "Suddenly I realised that I was anxious and that I had choices..." This is the step of self-leadership and trust in one's ability to handle the situation.

Choose helpful thoughts:

I choose to depersonalise
There is no intention to hurt me. He is doing the best he can with the tools he has at the moment.

I choose realism over romanticism
Life presents many obstacles. I lower or raise standards as needed.

There is no right or wrong
Unless it is a moral issue, I will see it simply as a difference of opinion and/or taste.

I choose the total view of positivity
Even though this event is negative, the total view of his behaviour is positive.

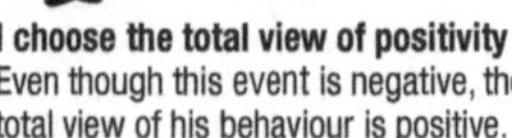

I surrender control
Since I cannot change this situation, I choose to let go of it.

I choose to put this event in perspective This event is not a catastrophe because it is not life threatening. It can be viewed as a trivial life event, a normal life problem that needs to be solved not dramatised.

I choose to view this event as average, falling within the normal range
This event is not exceptional; many people have gone through this.

It's temporary - "this too shall pass"
Life is constantly changing and moving through phases and this situation will also change.

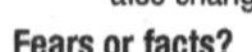

Fears or facts?
Why fear? It may not happen!

I choose to focus on this as a learning experience
Every problem that comes my way is an opportunity for me to learn about my strengths and weaknesses, others and life.

Feel soothing emotions:

I choose to feel warm, loving emotions. I do this by focusing on my heart and letting love, trust forgiveness, compassion, hope or gratitude fill my heart space.

Behave constructively:

I choose to work in part acts:
I will break the overwhelming job into manageable parts.

Do the difficult:
I will face what I fear and act with self-discipline.

I choose to solutionise:
I will find a solution by taking advice or doing research.

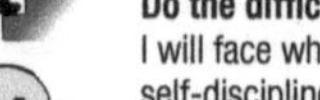

Prioritise myself:
I will keep my life balanced by meeting friends, doing exercise or laughing.

Compartmentalise:
I will not let this event cloud my whole day; I will focus on something else now.

Utilise calming strategies:

When I:
- relax,
- breathe deeply,
- go for a run,
- shower,
- lie down,
- read,
- watch TV,
- climb into a mental helicopter,
- practice mindfulness/meditation,

my mind and body calm down.

Step Four: The Self Motivation Process

Endorse yourself for any growth no matter how small.

In the past I would have...

____

____

But this time I...

____

____

Tick off the traits that you strengthened when you worked down your anxiety:

☐ generosity ☐ peacefulness
☐ kindness ☐ self-discipline
☐ compassion ☐ forgiveness
☐ consideration ☐ courage
☐ helpfulness ☐ responsibility
☐ respectfulness ☐ reliability
☐ honesty ☐ loyalty
☐ fairness ☐ love
☐ patience ☐ humility

Rate your anxiety on a scale of 0 to 100%:

[____]%

O

W

Date: _____________

Anxiety Management Worksheet

The purpose of this worksheet is to help you to see every stressful event as an opportunity for
1. greater understanding of yourself, your anxiety and the people around you, and
2. practicing tools to manage your anxiety.

Step One: An Event

Briefly describe an event when you became anxious. Give such details as time, place and people involved, and end with "That's when I began to work myself up…"

____

____

____

____ Rate your anxiety on a scale of 0 to 100%: ⬚ %

E

Step Two: The Working-Up Process

Learn about your working up process by identifying your thoughts, feelings, behaviours and bodily reactions during the event. Tick the ones that most resonate with you.

B

Undermining Beliefs

I fear that I have lost…
- ☐ approval
- ☐ control
- ☐ co-operation
- ☐ face
- ☐ respect
- ☐ success
- ☐ trust
- ☐ validation
- ☐ love

This event proves that I am…
- ☐ stupid
- ☐ abnormal
- ☐ incompetent
- ☐ lazy
- ☐ irresponsible
- ☐ a total failure
- ☐ undisciplined
- ☐ untogether
- ☐ useless

I worry that I will suffer…
- ☐ mental collapse
- ☐ illness
- ☐ financial hardship

What I want is…
- ☐ total control
- ☐ respect
- ☐ success
- ☐ perfection
- ☐ comfort
- ☐ fairness
- ☐ tranquility
- ☐ all the answers
- ☐ for life to go smoothly
- ☐ to be all things to all people

Self-destructive Behaviour

Active
- ☐ get violent
- ☐ swear
- ☐ slam doors
- ☐ run away
- ☐ overeat
- ☐ harm myself
- ☐ criticise

Passive
- ☐ take it too seriously
- ☐ give up
- ☐ wallow in self pity
- ☐ sulk
- ☐ space out
- ☐ procrastinate
- ☐ give in
- ☐ be controlled

Intense Feelings

Angry feelings
- ☐ hateful
- ☐ aggravated
- ☐ annoyed
- ☐ hostile
- ☐ outraged
- ☐ punitive
- ☐ resentful
- ☐ vengeful
- ☐ attacked
- ☐ worn out
- ☐ rejected
- ☐ jealous
- ☐ afraid
- ☐ exploited
- ☐ lonely
- ☐ abandoned
- ☐ guilty

Fearful feelings
- ☐ helpless
- ☐ hopeless
- ☐ disappointed
- ☐ sad
- ☐ insulted
- ☐ confused
- ☐ disillusioned
- ☐ misunderstood
- ☐ trapped

Bodily Reactions (limbic system)

I am uncomfortable because I am experiencing…
- ☐ tremors
- ☐ nausea
- ☐ sweaty palms
- ☐ stomach-ache
- ☐ pounding heart
- ☐ general tension
- ☐ fatigue
- ☐ imagination on fire
- ☐ headache
- ☐ dry mouth
- ☐ jaw clenching
- ☐ shortness of breath

Continued over

B   **F**   **L**

Step Three: The Working-Down Process

Begin with, "Suddenly I realised that I was anxious and that I had choices..." This is the step of self-leadership and trust in one's ability to handle the situation.

Choose helpful thoughts:

I choose to depersonalise
There is no intention to hurt me. He is doing the best he can with the tools he has at the moment.

I choose realism over romanticism
Life presents many obstacles. I lower or raise standards as needed.

There is no right or wrong
Unless it is a moral issue, I will see it simply as a difference of opinion and/or taste.

I choose the total view of positivity
Even though this event is negative, the total view of his behaviour is positive.

I surrender control
Since I cannot change this situation, I choose to let go of it.

I choose to put this event in perspective This event is not a catastrophe because it is not life threatening. It can be viewed as a trivial life event, a normal life problem that needs to be solved not dramatised.

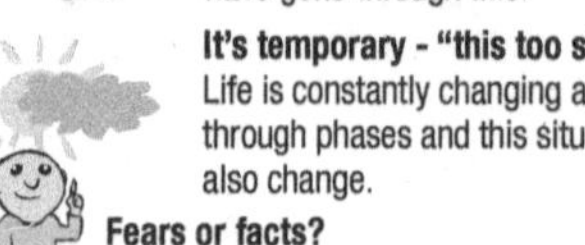

I choose to view this event as average, falling within the normal range
This event is not exceptional; many people have gone through this.

It's temporary - "this too shall pass"
Life is constantly changing and moving through phases and this situation will also change.

Fears or facts?
Why fear? It may not happen!

I choose to focus on this as a learning experience
Every problem that comes my way is an opportunity for me to learn about my strengths and weaknesses, others and life.

Feel soothing emotions:

I choose to feel warm, loving emotions. I do this by focusing on my heart and letting love, trust forgiveness, compassion, hope or gratitude fill my heart space.

Behave constructively:

I choose to work in part acts:
I will break the overwhelming job into manageable parts.

Do the difficult:
I will face what I fear and act with self-discipline.

I choose to solutionise:
I will find a solution by taking advice or doing research.

Prioritise myself:
I will keep my life balanced by meeting friends, doing exercise or laughing.

Compartmentalise:
I will not let this event cloud my whole day; I will focus on something else now.

Utilise calming strategies:

When I:
- relax,
- breathe deeply,
- go for a run,
- shower,
- lie down,
- read,
- watch TV,
- climb into a mental helicopter,
- practice mindfulness/meditation,

my mind and body calm down.

Step Four: The Self Motivation Process

Endorse yourself for any growth no matter how small.

In the past I would have...

____

____

But this time I...

____

____

Tick off the traits that you strengthened when you worked down your anxiety:

- ☐ generosity
- ☐ kindness
- ☐ compassion
- ☐ consideration
- ☐ helpfulness
- ☐ respectfulness
- ☐ honesty
- ☐ fairness
- ☐ patience
- ☐ peacefulness
- ☐ self-discipline
- ☐ forgiveness
- ☐ courage
- ☐ responsibility
- ☐ reliability
- ☐ loyalty
- ☐ love
- ☐ humility

Rate your anxiety on a scale of 0 to 100%:

________ %

O

W

Date: ___________

Anxiety Management Worksheet

The purpose of this worksheet is to help you to see every stressful event as an opportunity for
1. greater understanding of yourself, your anxiety and the people around you, and
2. practicing tools to manage your anxiety.

Step One: An Event

Briefly describe an event when you became anxious. Give such details as time, place and people involved, and end with "That's when I began to work myself up..."

____

____   **E**

____

____ Rate your anxiety on a scale of 0 to 100%: [   ] %

Step Two: The Working-Up Process

Learn about your working up process by identifying your thoughts, feelings, behaviours and bodily reactions during the event. Tick the ones that most resonate with you.

Undermining Beliefs   **B**

I fear that I have lost...

- ☐ approval
- ☐ control
- ☐ co-operation
- ☐ face
- ☐ respect
- ☐ success
- ☐ trust
- ☐ validation
- ☐ love

This event proves that I am...

- ☐ stupid
- ☐ abnormal
- ☐ incompetent
- ☐ lazy
- ☐ irresponsible
- ☐ a total failure
- ☐ undisciplined
- ☐ untogether
- ☐ useless

I worry that I will suffer...

- ☐ mental collapse
- ☐ illness
- ☐ financial hardship

What I want is...

- ☐ total control
- ☐ respect
- ☐ success
- ☐ perfection
- ☐ comfort
- ☐ fairness
- ☐ tranquility
- ☐ all the answers
- ☐ for life to go smoothly
- ☐ to be all things to all people

Self-destructive Behaviour   **B**

Active

- ☐ get violent
- ☐ swear
- ☐ slam doors
- ☐ run away
- ☐ overeat
- ☐ harm myself
- ☐ criticise

Passive

- ☐ take it too seriously
- ☐ give up
- ☐ wallow in self pity
- ☐ sulk
- ☐ space out
- ☐ procrastinate
- ☐ give in
- ☐ be controlled

Intense Feelings   **F**

Angry feelings

- ☐ hateful
- ☐ aggravated
- ☐ annoyed
- ☐ hostile
- ☐ outraged
- ☐ punitive
- ☐ resentful
- ☐ vengeful
- ☐ attacked
- ☐ worn out
- ☐ rejected
- ☐ jealous
- ☐ afraid
- ☐ exploited
- ☐ lonely
- ☐ abandoned
- ☐ guilty
- ☐ insulted

Fearful feelings

- ☐ helpless
- ☐ hopeless
- ☐ disappointed
- ☐ sad
- ☐ confused
- ☐ disillusioned
- ☐ misunderstood
- ☐ trapped

Bodily Reactions (limbic system)   **L**

I am uncomfortable because I am experiencing...

- ☐ tremors
- ☐ nausea
- ☐ sweaty palms
- ☐ stomach-ache
- ☐ pounding heart
- ☐ general tension
- ☐ fatigue
- ☐ imagination on fire
- ☐ headache
- ☐ dry mouth
- ☐ jaw clenching
- ☐ shortness of breath

Continued over

Step Three: The Working-Down Process

Begin with, "Suddenly I realised that I was anxious and that I had choices..." This is the step of self-leadership and trust in one's ability to handle the situation.

Choose helpful thoughts:

I choose to depersonalise
There is no intention to hurt me. He is doing the best he can with the tools he has at the moment.

I choose realism over romanticism
Life presents many obstacles. I lower or raise standards as needed.

There is no right or wrong
Unless it is a moral issue, I will see it simply as a difference of opinion and/or taste.

I choose the total view of positivity
Even though this event is negative, the total view of his behaviour is positive.

I surrender control
Since I cannot change this situation, I choose to let go of it.

I choose to put this event in perspective This event is not a catastrophe because it is not life threatening. It can be viewed as a trivial life event, a normal life problem that needs to be solved not dramatised.

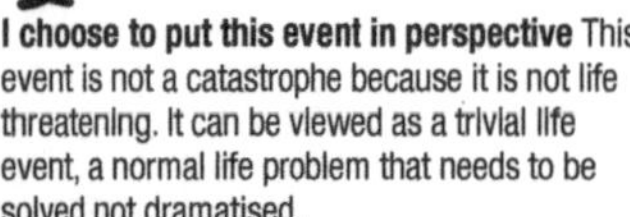

I choose to view this event as average, falling within the normal range
This event is not exceptional; many people have gone through this.

It's temporary - "this too shall pass"
Life is constantly changing and moving through phases and this situation will also change.

Fears or facts?
Why fear? It may not happen!

I choose to focus on this as a learning experience
Every problem that comes my way is an opportunity for me to learn about my strengths and weaknesses, others and life.

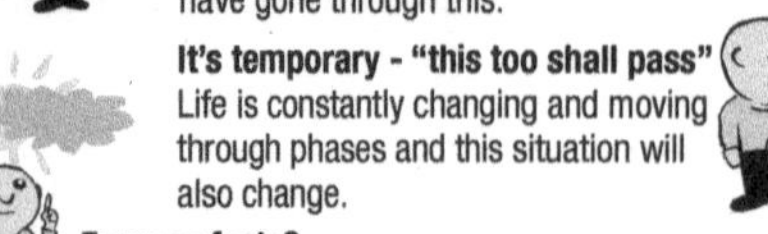

Feel soothing emotions:

I choose to feel warm, loving emotions. I do this by focusing on my heart and letting love, trust forgiveness, compassion, hope or gratitude fill my heart space.

Behave constructively:

I choose to work in part acts:
I will break the overwhelming job into manageable parts.

Do the difficult:
I will face what I fear and act with self-discipline.

I choose to solutionise:
I will find a solution by taking advice or doing research.

Prioritise myself:
I will keep my life balanced by meeting friends, doing exercise or laughing.

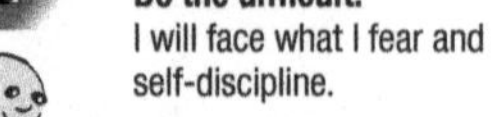

Compartmentalise:
I will not let this event cloud my whole day; I will focus on something else now.

Utilise calming strategies:

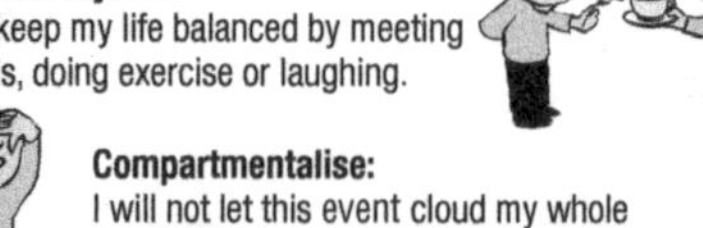

When I:
- relax,
- breathe deeply,
- go for a run,
- shower,
- lie down,
- read,
- watch TV,
- climb into a mental helicopter,
- practice mindfulness/meditation,

my mind and body calm down.

Step Four: The Self Motivation Process

Endorse yourself for any growth no matter how small.

In the past I would have...

____

____

But this time I...

____

____

Tick off the traits that you strengthened when you worked down your anxiety:

☐ generosity	☐ peacefulness	Rate your anxiety on a scale of 0 to 100%:
☐ kindness	☐ self-discipline	
☐ compassion	☐ forgiveness	
☐ consideration	☐ courage	
☐ helpfulness	☐ responsibility	
☐ respectfulness	☐ reliability	
☐ honesty	☐ loyalty	
☐ fairness	☐ love	
☐ patience	☐ humility	________ %

O

W

Date: ___________

Anxiety Management Worksheet

The purpose of this worksheet is to help you to see every stressful event as an opportunity for
1. greater understanding of yourself, your anxiety and the people around you, and
2. practicing tools to manage your anxiety.

Step One: An Event

Briefly describe an event when you became anxious. Give such details as time, place and people involved, and end with "That's when I began to work myself up..."

____

____

____

____ Rate your anxiety on a scale of 0 to 100%: [   ] %

E

Step Two: The Working-Up Process

Learn about your working up process by identifying your thoughts, feelings, behaviours and bodily reactions during the event.
Tick the ones that most resonate with you.

B

Undermining Beliefs

I fear that I have lost...

- ☐ approval
- ☐ control
- ☐ co-operation
- ☐ face
- ☐ respect
- ☐ success
- ☐ trust
- ☐ validation
- ☐ love

This event proves that I am...

- ☐ stupid
- ☐ abnormal
- ☐ incompetent
- ☐ lazy
- ☐ irresponsible
- ☐ a total failure
- ☐ undisciplined
- ☐ untogether
- ☐ useless

I worry that I will suffer...

- ☐ mental collapse
- ☐ illness
- ☐ financial hardship

What I want is...

- ☐ total control
- ☐ respect
- ☐ success
- ☐ perfection
- ☐ comfort
- ☐ fairness
- ☐ tranquility
- ☐ all the answers
- ☐ for life to go smoothly
- ☐ to be all things to all people

Self-destructive Behaviour

Active

- ☐ get violent
- ☐ swear
- ☐ slam doors
- ☐ run away
- ☐ overeat
- ☐ harm myself
- ☐ criticise

Passive

- ☐ take it too seriously
- ☐ give up
- ☐ wallow in self pity
- ☐ sulk
- ☐ space out
- ☐ procrastinate
- ☐ give in
- ☐ be controlled

Intense Feelings

Angry feelings

- ☐ hateful
- ☐ aggravated
- ☐ annoyed
- ☐ hostile
- ☐ outraged
- ☐ punitive
- ☐ resentful
- ☐ vengeful
- ☐ attacked
- ☐ worn out
- ☐ rejected
- ☐ jealous
- ☐ afraid
- ☐ exploited
- ☐ lonely
- ☐ abandoned
- ☐ guilty

Fearful feelings

- ☐ helpless
- ☐ hopeless
- ☐ disappointed
- ☐ sad
- ☐ insulted
- ☐ confused
- ☐ disillusioned
- ☐ misunderstood
- ☐ trapped

Bodily Reactions (limbic system)

I am uncomfortable because I am experiencing...

- ☐ tremors
- ☐ nausea
- ☐ sweaty palms
- ☐ stomach-ache
- ☐ pounding heart
- ☐ general tension
- ☐ fatigue
- ☐ imagination on fire
- ☐ headache
- ☐ dry mouth
- ☐ jaw clenching
- ☐ shortness of breath

Continued over

B   **F**   **L**

Step Three: The Working-Down Process

Begin with, "Suddenly I realised that I was anxious and that I had choices..." This is the step of self-leadership and trust in one's ability to handle the situation.

Choose helpful thoughts:

I choose to depersonalise
There is no intention to hurt me. He is doing the best he can with the tools he has at the moment.

I choose realism over romanticism
Life presents many obstacles. I lower or raise standards as needed.

There is no right or wrong
Unless it is a moral issue, I will see it simply as a difference of opinion and/or taste.

I choose the total view of positivity
Even though this event is negative, the total view of his behaviour is positive.

I surrender control
Since I cannot change this situation, I choose to let go of it.

I choose to put this event in perspective This event is not a catastrophe because it is not life threatening. It can be viewed as a trivial life event, a normal life problem that needs to be solved not dramatised.

I choose to view this event as average, falling within the normal range
This event is not exceptional; many people have gone through this.

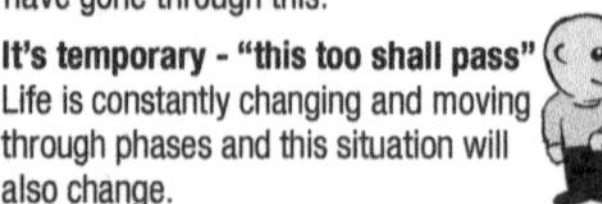

It's temporary - "this too shall pass"
Life is constantly changing and moving through phases and this situation will also change.

Fears or facts?
Why fear? It may not happen!

I choose to focus on this as a learning experience
Every problem that comes my way is an opportunity for me to learn about my strengths and weaknesses, others and life.

Feel soothing emotions:

I choose to feel warm, loving emotions. I do this by focusing on my heart and letting love, trust forgiveness, compassion, hope or gratitude fill my heart space.

Behave constructively:

I choose to work in part acts:
I will break the overwhelming job into manageable parts.

Do the difficult:
I will face what I fear and act with self-discipline.

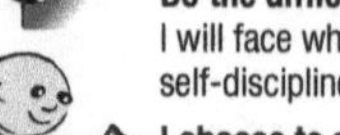

I choose to solutionise:
I will find a solution by taking advice or doing research.

Prioritise myself:
I will keep my life balanced by meeting friends, doing exercise or laughing.

Compartmentalise:
I will not let this event cloud my whole day; I will focus on something else now.

Utilise calming strategies:

When I:
- relax,
- breathe deeply,
- go for a run,
- shower,
- lie down,
- read,
- watch TV,
- climb into a mental helicopter,
- practice mindfulness/meditation,

my mind and body calm down.

Step Four: The Self Motivation Process

Endorse yourself for any growth no matter how small.

In the past I would have...

____

____

But this time I...

____

____

Tick off the traits that you strengthened when you worked down your anxiety:

☐ generosity	☐ peacefulness	
☐ kindness	☐ self-discipline	
☐ compassion	☐ forgiveness	
☐ consideration	☐ courage	
☐ helpfulness	☐ responsibility	
☐ respectfulness	☐ reliability	
☐ honesty	☐ loyalty	
☐ fairness	☐ love	
☐ patience	☐ humility	

Rate your anxiety on a scale of 0 to 100%:

☐ %

O

W

Date: _______________

Anxiety Management Worksheet

The purpose of this worksheet is to help you to see every stressful event as an opportunity for
1. greater understanding of yourself, your anxiety and the people around you, and
2. practicing tools to manage your anxiety.

Step One: An Event

Briefly describe an event when you became anxious. Give such details as time, place and people involved, and end with "That's when I began to work myself up..."

____

____

____ **E**

Rate your anxiety on a scale of 0 to 100%: ________ %

Step Two: The Working-Up Process

Learn about your working up process by identifying your thoughts, feelings, behaviours and bodily reactions during the event.

Tick the ones that most resonate with you. **B**

Undermining Beliefs

I fear that I have lost...
- ☐ approval
- ☐ control
- ☐ co-operation
- ☐ face
- ☐ respect
- ☐ success
- ☐ trust
- ☐ validation
- ☐ love

This event proves that I am...
- ☐ stupid
- ☐ abnormal
- ☐ incompetent
- ☐ lazy
- ☐ irresponsible
- ☐ a total failure
- ☐ undisciplined
- ☐ untogether
- ☐ useless

I worry that I will suffer...
- ☐ mental collapse
- ☐ illness
- ☐ financial hardship

What I want is...
- ☐ total control
- ☐ respect
- ☐ success
- ☐ perfection
- ☐ comfort
- ☐ fairness
- ☐ tranquility
- ☐ all the answers
- ☐ for life to go smoothly
- ☐ to be all things to all people

Self-destructive Behaviour

Active
- ☐ get violent
- ☐ swear
- ☐ slam doors
- ☐ run away
- ☐ overeat
- ☐ harm myself
- ☐ criticise

Passive
- ☐ take it too seriously
- ☐ give up
- ☐ wallow in self pity
- ☐ sulk
- ☐ space out
- ☐ procrastinate
- ☐ give in
- ☐ be controlled

Intense Feelings

Angry feelings
- ☐ hateful
- ☐ aggravated
- ☐ annoyed
- ☐ hostile
- ☐ outraged
- ☐ punitive
- ☐ resentful
- ☐ vengeful
- ☐ attacked
- ☐ worn out
- ☐ rejected
- ☐ jealous
- ☐ afraid
- ☐ exploited
- ☐ lonely
- ☐ abandoned
- ☐ guilty

Fearful feelings
- ☐ helpless
- ☐ hopeless
- ☐ disappointed
- ☐ sad
- ☐ insulted
- ☐ confused
- ☐ disillusioned
- ☐ misunderstood
- ☐ trapped

Bodily Reactions (limbic system)

I am uncomfortable because I am experiencing...
- ☐ tremors
- ☐ nausea
- ☐ sweaty palms
- ☐ stomach-ache
- ☐ pounding heart
- ☐ general tension
- ☐ fatigue
- ☐ imagination on fire
- ☐ headache
- ☐ dry mouth
- ☐ jaw clenching
- ☐ shortness of breath

Continued over

B   **F**   **L**

Step Three: The Working-Down Process

Begin with, "Suddenly I realised that I was anxious and that I had choices…" This is the step of self-leadership and trust in one's ability to handle the situation.

Choose helpful thoughts:

I choose to depersonalise
There is no intention to hurt me. He is doing the best he can with the tools he has at the moment.

I choose realism over romanticism
Life presents many obstacles. I lower or raise standards as needed.

There is no right or wrong
Unless it is a moral issue, I will see it simply as a difference of opinion and/or taste.

I choose the total view of positivity
Even though this event is negative, the total view of his behaviour is positive.

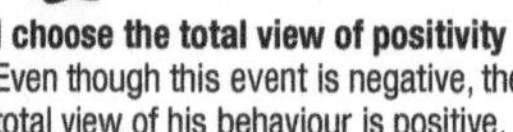

I surrender control
Since I cannot change this situation, I choose to let go of it.

I choose to put this event in perspective This event is not a catastrophe because it is not life threatening. It can be viewed as a trivial life event, a normal life problem that needs to be solved not dramatised.

I choose to view this event as average, falling within the normal range
This event is not exceptional; many people have gone through this.

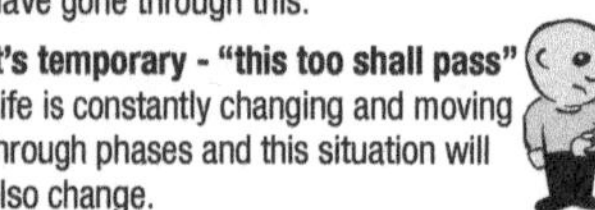

It's temporary - "this too shall pass"
Life is constantly changing and moving through phases and this situation will also change.

Fears or facts?
Why fear? It may not happen!

I choose to focus on this as a learning experience
Every problem that comes my way is an opportunity for me to learn about my strengths and weaknesses, others and life.

Feel soothing emotions:

I choose to feel warm, loving emotions. I do this by focusing on my heart and letting love, trust forgiveness, compassion, hope or gratitude fill my heart space.

Behave constructively:

I choose to work in part acts:
I will break the overwhelming job into manageable parts.

Do the difficult:
I will face what I fear and act with self-discipline.

I choose to solutionise:
I will find a solution by taking advice or doing research.

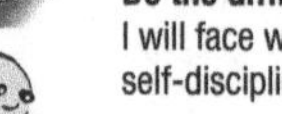

Prioritise myself:
I will keep my life balanced by meeting friends, doing exercise or laughing.

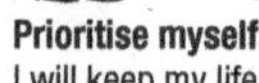

Compartmentalise:
I will not let this event cloud my whole day; I will focus on something else now.

Utilise calming strategies:

When I:
- relax,
- breathe deeply,
- go for a run,
- shower,
- lie down,
- read,
- watch TV,
- climb into a mental helicopter,
- practice mindfulness/meditation,

my mind and body calm down.

Step Four: The Self Motivation Process

Endorse yourself for any growth no matter how small.

In the past I would have…

____

____

But this time I…

____

____

Tick off the traits that you strengthened when you worked down your anxiety:

- ☐ generosity
- ☐ kindness
- ☐ compassion
- ☐ consideration
- ☐ helpfulness
- ☐ respectfulness
- ☐ honesty
- ☐ fairness
- ☐ patience
- ☐ peacefulness
- ☐ self-discipline
- ☐ forgiveness
- ☐ courage
- ☐ responsibility
- ☐ reliability
- ☐ loyalty
- ☐ love
- ☐ humility

Rate your anxiety on a scale of 0 to 100%:

________ %

O

W

Date: _______________

Anxiety Management Worksheet

The purpose of this worksheet is to help you to see every stressful event as an opportunity for
1. greater understanding of yourself, your anxiety and the people around you, and
2. practicing tools to manage your anxiety.

Step One: An Event

Briefly describe an event when you became anxious. Give such details as time, place and people involved, and end with "That's when I began to work myself up…"

____

____

____

____ Rate your anxiety on a scale of 0 to 100%: [   ] %

E

Step Two: The Working-Up Process

Learn about your working up process by identifying your thoughts, feelings, behaviours and bodily reactions during the event.
Tick the ones that most resonate with you.

Undermining Beliefs

B

I fear that I have lost...
- ☐ approval
- ☐ control
- ☐ co-operation
- ☐ face
- ☐ respect
- ☐ success
- ☐ trust
- ☐ validation
- ☐ love

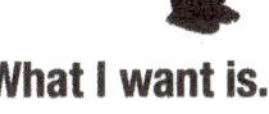

This event proves that I am...
- ☐ stupid
- ☐ abnormal
- ☐ incompetent
- ☐ lazy
- ☐ irresponsible
- ☐ a total failure
- ☐ undisciplined
- ☐ untogether
- ☐ useless

I worry that I will suffer...
- ☐ mental collapse
- ☐ illness
- ☐ financial hardship

What I want is...
- ☐ total control
- ☐ respect
- ☐ success
- ☐ perfection
- ☐ comfort
- ☐ fairness
- ☐ tranquility
- ☐ all the answers
- ☐ for life to go smoothly
- ☐ to be all things to all people

Self-destructive Behaviour

Active
- ☐ get violent
- ☐ swear
- ☐ slam doors
- ☐ run away
- ☐ overeat
- ☐ harm myself
- ☐ criticise

Passive
- ☐ take it too seriously
- ☐ give up
- ☐ wallow in self pity
- ☐ sulk
- ☐ space out
- ☐ procrastinate
- ☐ give in
- ☐ be controlled

Intense Feelings

Angry feelings
- ☐ hateful
- ☐ aggravated
- ☐ annoyed
- ☐ hostile
- ☐ outraged
- ☐ punitive
- ☐ resentful
- ☐ vengeful
- ☐ attacked
- ☐ worn out
- ☐ rejected
- ☐ jealous
- ☐ afraid
- ☐ exploited
- ☐ lonely
- ☐ abandoned
- ☐ guilty
- ☐ insulted

Fearful feelings
- ☐ helpless
- ☐ hopeless
- ☐ disappointed
- ☐ sad
- ☐ confused
- ☐ disillusioned
- ☐ misunderstood
- ☐ trapped

Bodily Reactions (limbic system)

I am uncomfortable because I am experiencing...
- ☐ tremors
- ☐ nausea
- ☐ sweaty palms
- ☐ stomach-ache
- ☐ pounding heart
- ☐ general tension
- ☐ fatigue
- ☐ imagination on fire
- ☐ headache
- ☐ dry mouth
- ☐ jaw clenching
- ☐ shortness of breath

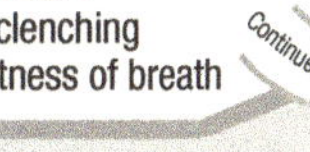
Continued over

B   **F**   **L**

Step Three: The Working-Down Process

Begin with, "Suddenly I realised that I was anxious and that I had choices…" This is the step of self-leadership and trust in one's ability to handle the situation.

Choose helpful thoughts:

I choose to depersonalise
There is no intention to hurt me. He is doing the best he can with the tools he has at the moment.

I choose realism over romanticism
Life presents many obstacles. I lower or raise standards as needed.

There is no right or wrong
Unless it is a moral issue, I will see it simply as a difference of opinion and/or taste.

I choose the total view of positivity
Even though this event is negative, the total view of his behaviour is positive.

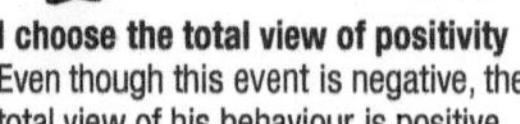

I surrender control
Since I cannot change this situation, I choose to let go of it.

I choose to put this event in perspective This event is not a catastrophe because it is not life threatening. It can be viewed as a trivial life event, a normal life problem that needs to be solved not dramatised.

I choose to view this event as average, falling within the normal range
This event is not exceptional; many people have gone through this.

It's temporary - "this too shall pass"
Life is constantly changing and moving through phases and this situation will also change.

Fears or facts?
Why fear? It may not happen!

I choose to focus on this as a learning experience
Every problem that comes my way is an opportunity for me to learn about my strengths and weaknesses, others and life.

Feel soothing emotions:

I choose to feel warm, loving emotions. I do this by focusing on my heart and letting love, trust forgiveness, compassion, hope or gratitude fill my heart space.

Behave constructively:

I choose to work in part acts:
I will break the overwhelming job into manageable parts.

Do the difficult:
I will face what I fear and act with self-discipline.

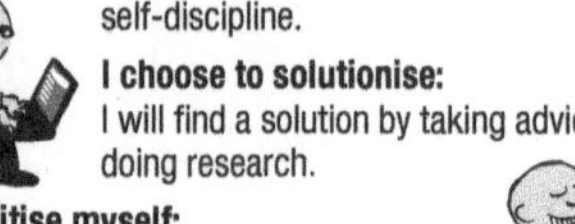

I choose to solutionise:
I will find a solution by taking advice or doing research.

Prioritise myself:
I will keep my life balanced by meeting friends, doing exercise or laughing.

Compartmentalise:
I will not let this event cloud my whole day; I will focus on something else now.

Utilise calming strategies:

When I:
- relax,
- breathe deeply,
- go for a run,
- shower,
- lie down,
- read,
- watch TV,
- climb into a mental helicopter,
- practice mindfulness/meditation,

my mind and body calm down.

Step Four: The Self Motivation Process

Endorse yourself for any growth no matter how small.

In the past I would have...

____

____

But this time I...

____

____

Tick off the traits that you strengthened when you worked down your anxiety:

☐ generosity	☐ peacefulness	
☐ kindness	☐ self-discipline	
☐ compassion	☐ forgiveness	
☐ consideration	☐ courage	
☐ helpfulness	☐ responsibility	
☐ respectfulness	☐ reliability	
☐ honesty	☐ loyalty	
☐ fairness	☐ love	
☐ patience	☐ humility	

Rate your anxiety on a scale of 0 to 100%:

______%

O   W

Week 7

The week seven segment comprises the following three tools:

1. No right or wrong: thinking tool
2. Do the difficult: behavioural tool
3. Defuse: calming tool

No right or wrong: thinking tool

"There is no right or wrong. Unless it is a moral issue, I will see the situation simply as a difference of opinion and/or taste."

Every person has an inner voice that tells them when something is right or wrong, good or bad. That inner voice is the awful feeling you have when you tell a lie or yell at another person excessively.

Stephen Covey (17) describes the inner voice as a moral compass that tells us when we have done something wrong. He explains that just like a compass will always point towards north, so too our moral compass is there to guide us to do what is right. I agree with this view. Simply put, we all instinctively know the difference between right and wrong.

This tool will help you to discern if somebody has actually committed an "offence" or merely acted in a way that differs from the way you would act. Utilising this tool will set you free — free from the unnecessary stress which arises from incorrectly judging others.

So much of our daily stress and anger comes from believing a person has done something wrong to us. However, when we dig deep into our moral compass, we frequently find that the behaviour was not wrong but based on a difference of taste or opinion.

> Jane was brought up in a town where the men always let ladies go first. When she moved to a big city, she found that men would not wait for her to get in a lift nor hold the door open for her. Moreover, at times they would even push in front of her.
>
> *Jane became enraged to the point that she lectured her boss, colleague, and any stranger who listened on how bad this behaviour was. Jane discussed it with a close friend who explained that the culture of the city is different from Jane's hometown. In the city, people are rushed and act on the premise of "first come first served" regardless of gender or age.*
>
> *The explanation eased Jane's mind. She understood that it was her opinion, and preference, that women should go first but not necessarily everybody else's opinion or preference. Once she relaxed about it, she became happier and her work environment improved too.*

> Fred likes to wear formal clothing, in particular expensive suits. Once he invited friends over for a drink for his birthday and was horrified that one friend (Jack) arrived in a tracksuit. He felt it was unacceptable and yelled at Jack about it.
>
> *Jack was confused. For the life of him he could not work out what he had done that merited such an attack.*

Over time, Fred realised that few people actually wear suits anymore and that fashion has changed. Once he accepted that fashion varies and that different people follow fashion in different ways, he felt calm.

> Trish spends a good deal of her time observing others, judging them and stewing about their behaviour. She believes that Sonya is a bad mother because she feeds on schedule and Trish believes in demand feeding. She criticises Peter for taking his son to footy matches because in her opinion footy is violent. She views Margaret as the worst hostess ever because she uses plastic, disposable cutlery. According to Trish, any decent hostess knows that only silverware will do.

The truth is that there is ongoing debate about how to nurse babies. There is no consensus about footy or the style of cutlery; these things are personal choices made by individuals and families based on their own views and tastes. Trish would be so much more relaxed and content if she learned this tool.

By working through parts A, B and C of Exercise 18, you will illuminate your inner moral compass. You will establish a range of behaviours for reference in the future. Your reference list will assist you to clarify if a behaviour that is bothering you is "wrong" and merits judgment, or not.

EXERCISE 18

PART A

Here is a list of behaviours that are seen as immoral or bad by most cultures and societies. Feel free to add any others in the space provided.

> Murder
> Stealing
> Adultery
> Rape

> Paedophilia
> Kidnapping
> Perjury

Do you disagree with any of these? If so, why?

PART B

Here is a list of behaviours often seen as unethical in the Western world. Feel free to add any others in the space provided.

> Opening someone else's mail
> Breaking a promise/ commitment
> Breaking a confidence

> Invading a person's privacy
> Gossiping
> Telling lies

Do you disagree with any of these? If so, why?

PART C

The list of unacceptable behaviours below was compiled by a team I worked with in a large corporation. If you work in a team, add your own additional unacceptable behaviours at the bottom of the list.

> Taking time out to smoke when a job needs to be done
> Coming late to work
> Dressing inappropriately
> Leaving without checking if it is ok with others
> Not being punctual
> Answering somebody else's telephone calls without permission
> Swearing
> Not helping others

....

....

....

Here is a list of expectations commonly held by families:

> Taking one's plate to the sink
> Making one's bed
> Taking laundry to the laundry bin
> Contributing to the telephone bill
> Discussing family conflicts with others

Please make your own list of expectations you hold for your family here.

....

....

....

What expectations do your family hold for you?

....

....

....

In summary, the list in Part A would be agreed upon by nearly everybody. The list in Part B would be agreed upon by most people in Western society. The list in Part C is specific to each unique company, team or family.

It is important that you clarify your expectations with your family or team before you can judge them. Only once you have all articulated and agreed to abide by your shared expectations, would it be appropriate for you to judge people negatively if the expectations are broken.

You may be wondering why we should judge at all. After all, is it not an ideal to accept everyone and everything? I think not. I believe that there are behaviours that are unacceptable. Our moral compass warns us that something is amiss so that we can protect ourselves.

> Freda's second husband did not have children of his own and embraced her daughter Emily (aged 10) as his own. However, when he began to spend large chunks of time with Emily, Freda did not feel comfortable. Freda became vigilant and, sure enough, she caught him walking into the bathroom when Emily was in the shower.
>
> *She had to protect Emily no matter the cost. She could not use this tool. On the contrary, she judged the behaviour as inappropriate and took strong action. She ended her second marriage.*

In other words, if a moral code has been infringed upon, this tool would not be appropriate. Nor would it be useful if unethical behaviour or broken expectations were noted.

The comprehensive list of behaviours that you completed above is now your reference point. Tell yourself that all other behaviours that annoy, frustrate or infuriate you are merely a difference of opinion or taste and let them go. You will find that you are more relaxed overall when you "live and let live".

EXERCISE 19

Think of a person around whom you feel stressed. Name him/her.

List the behaviours he/she is doing that may be causing you stress.

Can any of the behaviours on this list be found on lists you compiled in parts A, B or C?   YES/NO

If you answered "yes," then you cannot utilise this tool. Think of another person and try again.

If you answered "no," tell yourself, "Unless it is a moral issue, I will see it simply as a difference of opinion and/or taste."

Daily monitoring diary

How often do you judge others critically causing yourself to be worked up? Filling in the daily monitoring diary from this week may surprise you when you begin to jot down how often you have these judgmental thoughts and how they escalate your anxiety. As soon as you become aware of these thoughts, challenge them with the tool "**no right or wrong**," and notice how your anxiety decreases.

Do the difficult: behavioural tool

"I choose to do the difficult. I will face what I fear and act with self-discipline."

"Facing what you fear" is described in several well-known idioms such as "taking the bull by the horns" and "getting right back on the horse after he has thrown you." However, despite knowing this intellectually, we often do not achieve our goals because we cannot face our fears.

Facing your fears is the best way to overcome specific fears like the fear of flying, open spaces, confined spaces, crowds, spiders, dogs, snakes or lifts. Behavioural psychology teaches that being in the feared situation long enough lowers fears. Avoiding feared situations heightens fears.

Sometimes we are encouraged to tackle our biggest fear first: to "jump in the deep end" and get it over with. However, if you try to tackle your biggest fear straight away, you may become overwhelmed and more anxious than when you started. Therefore, the preferred approach is taking it step-by-step which is less confronting and more effective. Behavioural psychologists call this "graded exposure".

Graded exposure consists of structured and repeated exposure to anxiety-provoking situations. These are presented in levels of difficulty, starting with the situation that provokes the least amount of anxiety and moving towards more challenging situations step-by-step. Graded exposure can be done in relation to the real object of the fear or with visualisation. For example, if you are afraid of going in a lift, you will gradually work your way towards getting into a lift. However, if your fear concerns snakes, your therapist may help you become deeply relaxed and then expose you to a snake in your imagination. Either way you will be exposed gradually, allowed to get used to one level, then taken on to the next level of closeness to the feared object.

This tool encourages you to face your fears in a systematic, structured way. At first, your anxiety will be high. However, when you stay in the feared situation long enough, your primitive brain realises that there is no real danger after all and your anxiety disappears.

It is important to stress that you need to stay in the situation long enough so that your body adjusts your anxiety downwards. After a while, these situations lose their power to evoke anxiety and you will slowly build up your confidence.

Panic surfing

Did you know that anxiety is self-limiting? What this means is that if you do not fight your anxiety and instead "surf" it, as you would a large wave, it will subside of its own accord. Anxiety is literally like a wave that starts big then devolves into smaller and smaller waves until it reaches the beach. This takes no more than 3–4 minutes.

When you surf the wave of fear and do not fight it, your anxiety will limit itself in a short space of time. However, if you fight the fear, it will increase the panic and may cause it to last for hours.

EXERCISE 20

Let's look at the situations that you fear.

What is one of your biggest anxieties or fears?

Example: Being in the presence of a dog.

What are you afraid might happen?

Example: The dog will jump on me.

What is the worst case scenario — what is the worst that could happen?

Example: The dog will bite me.

What other possible, more positive outcomes can you think of?

Example: The dog and I could become friends.

Graded exposure

Develop your own program of graded exposure in relation to one of your major fears.

The principles to bear in mind:

> Set SMART goals — goals that are specific, measureable, achievable, realistic and timely. If you set goals that are unrealistic, you will not achieve them which will demotivate you.

> Obtain support from a friend, family member or professional.

Your support person will give you confidence and ensure that you follow through with your goals.

An exposure ladder

You avoid going out to shopping centres.

GOAL: You want to be able to visit a shopping centre alone.

Goal: specific, measurable, achievable, realistic, timely (SMART)	Anxiety rating: (Use any number between 0 and 10 to represent how much distress you would feel in the situation)

	Step	Anxiety rating at start	Anxiety rating at end
1.	Go to the local shopping centre on a week day afternoon (with a friend who knows about the problem), stay for 10 minutes	10	5 (after 10 minutes with breathing)
2.	Go to the local shopping centre on a weekday afternoon (with a friend who knows about the problem), walk around, stay for 30 minutes	8	4 (after 30 minutes with breathing & mindfulness)
3.	Go to the local shopping centre on a busy Thursday evening, stay for 10 minutes (with a friend who knows about the problem)	10	4 (after 10 minutes with breathing)

Step	Anxiety rating at start	Anxiety rating at end
4. Go to the local shopping centre on a weekend, stay at least 30 minutes (with a friend who knows about the problem)	7	3 (after 30 minutes with breathing and mindfulness)
5. Go to the local shopping centre on a weekend staying for two hours (with a friend who knows about the problem), and walk into one shop for five minutes	7	1 (after 30 minutes with breathing, mindfulness and laughter)
6. Go to the local shopping centre on a weekend staying for two hours, going into a shop for 15 minutes	5	1

EXERCISE 21

Build an exposure ladder in relation to your biggest fear.

Name your fear:

Goal: ________________ ________________ specific, measurable, achievable, realistic, timely (SMART)	Anxiety rating: (Use any number between 0 and 10 to represent how much distress you would feel in the situation)

Fill in the steps you aim to achieve. Fill in your anxiety levels before and after you achieve your goal.

Step	Anxiety rating at start	Anxiety rating at end
1.		
2.		
3.		
4.		
5.		
6.		

EXERCISE 22

Have you ever tackled a situation that you were really afraid to tackle?   YES/NO

If you answered "yes," please describe.

How did you feel afterwards?

Were your good feelings related to the success of your endeavour or to your feeling of self-accomplishment?

If you answered "no," what do you think you lost by not tackling the situation?

Now that you have tapped into the good feelings that are brought about by being bold and tackling a challenge, the next exercise will inspire you to tackle a problem you have been putting off, or avoiding, because of anxiety.

EXERCISE 23

Are there any situations in your life that need to be addressed but that you have been too afraid or anxious to address?   YES/NO

If you answered "yes," what are they?

Choose one of them and write down how you could tackle it (safely and effectively) in the very near future.

If there are others that can be done concurrently, please explain how you will go about addressing them.

Defuse: calming tool

Acceptance and commitment therapy (ACT)(22) describes two types of thoughts: one type of thought is conscious and rational and the other type comprises random thoughts that pop into your head from nowhere.

Conscious thoughts, which have intention, result in planning and appropriate behaviour. For example, "I must lock the door when I leave home." Random thoughts are frequently irrational, negative and self-defeating.

Common random thoughts include:

> "Those people are mocking me."
> "Someone may be watching the house — I am terrified."
> "I think I left the door open — I am pathetic."
> "I am a failure."
> "Nobody likes me."
> "I forgot my book. I am such an idiot."
> "Who will bury me? "

These pessimistic, critical thoughts destroy your self-esteem. Therefore, it is best that you ignore them. Focusing on these random thoughts, and giving them mental time, means that you internalise or "fuse" with them. It is vital that you do the opposite which is to "*defuse*".

One way of not fusing with the non-deliberate thought is to distract yourself. Simply think about something else. One popular distraction thought is to imagine that you just won the lottery. Spend time working out what you would do with the money, who you would donate to and how it will change your life.

Another way to defuse is to observe a thought, not judge it and simply bring your focus back to your conscious plan.

Let us say you are walking to a railway station to catch a train to work. You walk purposefully because you need to get there in time to catch the ten o'clock train. As you walk up the block, there are people walking in the opposite direction, some standing still and a few overtaking you. You hardly give these people your attention. You may notice some colours or movement but you keep your focus on getting to the station on time. Even if one individual tried to get you to stop for a chat, you would quickly move on.

This is exactly what you must do in order to defuse. Keep your focus on your conscious intention. All other distracting thoughts are passed by just like you passed by the people on the way to the station in the analogy.

There is an expression that says *"Stray thoughts are like stray dogs. The more you feed them the more they keep coming back."* When you defuse, you are making sure that you are not feeding unwanted thoughts, self-criticism and judgments.

EXERCISE 24

Are you aware of ongoing, negative judgments you have about yourself? What are they?

Practise defusing.

In summary, not all thoughts need to be given energy or time. They can be ignored while you focus on your goals.

DAILY MONITORING DIARY WEEK ENDING _______________

Day	M	T	W	T	F	S	S
Overall Anxiety Rating for the day (0-10)							
1. EXERCISE							
How long?							
Anxiety level before (0-10)							
Anxiety level after (0-10)							
2. BREATHING							
How long?							
Anxiety level before (0-10)							
Anxiety level after (0-10)							
3. RELAXATION							
How long?							
Anxiety level before (0-10)							
Anxiety level after (0-10)							
4. PERVASIVE PESSIMISTIC THINKING							
How often this type of thought occurred							
Belief in thoughts before challenging (0-10)							
Belief in thoughts after challenging (0-10)							
5. CATASTROPHIC THINKING							
How often this type of thought occurred							
Belief in thoughts before challenging (0-10)							
Belief in thoughts after challenging (0-10)							

Day	M	T	W	T	F	S	S
6. PERMANENT PESSIMISTIC THINKING							
How often this type of thought occurred							
Belief in thoughts before challenging (0-10)							
Belief in thoughts after challenging (0-10)							
7. MINDFULNESS (FORMAL, GROUNDING, INFORMAL MINDFULNESS)							
How long?							
Anxiety level before (0-10)							
Anxiety level after (0-10)							
8. ROMANTIC THINKING							
How often this type of thought occurred							
Belief in thoughts before challenging (0-10)							
Belief in thoughts after challenging (0-10)							
9. NEGATIVE JUDGMENTAL THINKING							
How often this type of thought occurred							
Belief in thoughts before challenging (0-10)							
Belief in thoughts after challenging (0-10)							

Anxiety Management Worksheet

The purpose of this worksheet is to help you to see every stressful event as an opportunity for
1. greater understanding of yourself, your anxiety and the people around you, and
2. practicing tools to manage your anxiety.

Step One: An Event

Briefly describe an event when you became anxious. Give such details as time, place and people involved, and end with "That's when I began to work myself up..."

____

____

____

__________________________________   Rate your anxiety on a scale of 0 to 100%: [   ] %

E

Step Two: The Working-Up Process

Learn about your working up process by identifying your thoughts, feelings, behaviours and bodily reactions during the event. Tick the ones that most resonate with you.

Undermining Beliefs

B

I fear that I have lost...
- ☐ approval
- ☐ control
- ☐ co-operation
- ☐ face
- ☐ respect
- ☐ success
- ☐ trust
- ☐ validation
- ☐ love

This event proves that I am...
- ☐ stupid
- ☐ abnormal
- ☐ incompetent
- ☐ lazy
- ☐ irresponsible
- ☐ a total failure
- ☐ undisciplined
- ☐ untogether
- ☐ useless

I worry that I will suffer...
- ☐ mental collapse
- ☐ illness
- ☐ financial hardship

What I want is...
- ☐ total control
- ☐ respect
- ☐ success
- ☐ perfection
- ☐ comfort
- ☐ fairness
- ☐ tranquility
- ☐ all the answers
- ☐ for life to go smoothly
- ☐ to be all things to all people

Self-destructive Behaviour

Active
- ☐ get violent
- ☐ swear
- ☐ slam doors
- ☐ run away
- ☐ overeat
- ☐ harm myself
- ☐ criticise

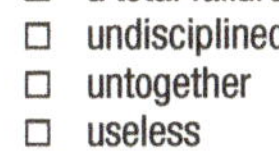

Passive
- ☐ take it too seriously
- ☐ give up
- ☐ wallow in self pity
- ☐ sulk
- ☐ space out
- ☐ procrastinate
- ☐ give in
- ☐ be controlled

Intense Feelings

Angry feelings
- ☐ hateful
- ☐ aggravated
- ☐ annoyed
- ☐ hostile
- ☐ outraged
- ☐ punitive
- ☐ resentful
- ☐ vengeful

Fearful feelings
- ☐ helpless
- ☐ hopeless
- ☐ disappointed
- ☐ sad

- ☐ attacked
- ☐ worn out
- ☐ rejected
- ☐ jealous
- ☐ afraid
- ☐ exploited
- ☐ lonely
- ☐ abandoned
- ☐ guilty
- ☐ insulted
- ☐ confused
- ☐ disillusioned
- ☐ misunderstood
- ☐ trapped

Bodily Reactions (limbic system)

I am uncomfortable because I am experiencing...
- ☐ tremors
- ☐ nausea
- ☐ sweaty palms
- ☐ stomach-ache
- ☐ pounding heart
- ☐ general tension
- ☐ fatigue
- ☐ imagination on fire
- ☐ headache
- ☐ dry mouth
- ☐ jaw clenching
- ☐ shortness of breath

Continued over

B   **F**   **L**

Step Three: The Working-Down Process

Begin with, "Suddenly I realised that I was anxious and that I had choices..." This is the step of self-leadership and trust in one's ability to handle the situation.

Choose helpful thoughts:

I choose to depersonalise
There is no intention to hurt me. He is doing the best he can with the tools he has at the moment.

I choose realism over romanticism
Life presents many obstacles. I lower or raise standards as needed.

There is no right or wrong
Unless it is a moral issue, I will see it simply as a difference of opinion and/or taste.

I choose the total view of positivity
Even though this event is negative, the total view of his behaviour is positive.

I surrender control
Since I cannot change this situation, I choose to let go of it.

I choose to put this event in perspective This event is not a catastrophe because it is not life threatening. It can be viewed as a trivial life event, a normal life problem that needs to be solved not dramatised.

I choose to view this event as average, falling within the normal range
This event is not exceptional; many people have gone through this.

It's temporary - "this too shall pass"
Life is constantly changing and moving through phases and this situation will also change.

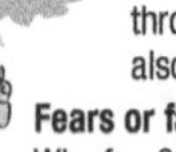

Fears or facts?
Why fear? It may not happen!

I choose to focus on this as a learning experience
Every problem that comes my way is an opportunity for me to learn about my strengths and weaknesses, others and life.

Feel soothing emotions:

I choose to feel warm, loving emotions. I do this by focusing on my heart and letting love, trust forgiveness, compassion, hope or gratitude fill my heart space.

Behave constructively:

I choose to work in part acts:
I will break the overwhelming job into manageable parts.

Do the difficult:
I will face what I fear and act with self-discipline.

I choose to solutionise:
I will find a solution by taking advice or doing research.

Prioritise myself:
I will keep my life balanced by meeting friends, doing exercise or laughing.

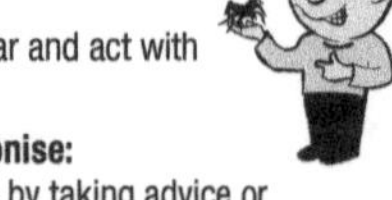

Compartmentalise:
I will not let this event cloud my whole day; I will focus on something else now.

Utilise calming strategies:

When I:
- relax,
- breathe deeply,
- go for a run,
- shower,
- lie down,
- read,
- watch TV,
- climb into a mental helicopter,
- practice mindfulness/meditation,

my mind and body calm down.

Step Four: The Self Motivation Process

Endorse yourself for any growth no matter how small.

In the past I would have...

____

____

But this time I...

____

____

Tick off the traits that you strengthened when you worked down your anxiety:

☐ generosity   ☐ peacefulness
☐ kindness   ☐ self-discipline
☐ compassion   ☐ forgiveness
☐ consideration   ☐ courage
☐ helpfulness   ☐ responsibility
☐ respectfulness   ☐ reliability
☐ honesty   ☐ loyalty
☐ fairness   ☐ love
☐ patience   ☐ humility

Rate your anxiety on a scale of 0 to 100%:

______ %

O

W

Date: _____________

Anxiety Management Worksheet

The purpose of this worksheet is to help you to see every stressful event as an opportunity for
1. greater understanding of yourself, your anxiety and the people around you, and
2. practicing tools to manage your anxiety.

Step One: An Event

Briefly describe an event when you became anxious. Give such details as time, place and people involved, and end with "That's when I began to work myself up..."

____

____

____

__________________________________ Rate your anxiety on a scale of 0 to 100%: [   ] %

E

Step Two: The Working-Up Process

Learn about your working up process by identifying your thoughts, feelings, behaviours and bodily reactions during the event. Tick the ones that most resonate with you.

Undermining Beliefs

B

I fear that I have lost...
- [ ] approval
- [ ] success
- [ ] control
- [ ] trust
- [ ] co-operation
- [ ] validation
- [ ] face
- [ ] love
- [ ] respect

This event proves that I am...
- [ ] stupid
- [ ] a total failure
- [ ] abnormal
- [ ] undisciplined
- [ ] incompetent
- [ ] untogether
- [ ] lazy
- [ ] useless
- [ ] irresponsible

I worry that I will suffer...
- [ ] mental collapse
- [ ] illness
- [ ] financial hardship

What I want is...
- [ ] total control
- [ ] tranquility
- [ ] respect
- [ ] all the answers
- [ ] success
- [ ] for life to go smoothly
- [ ] perfection
- [ ] comfort
- [ ] to be all things to all people
- [ ] fairness

Self-destructive Behaviour

Active
- [ ] get violent
- [ ] swear
- [ ] slam doors
- [ ] run away
- [ ] overeat
- [ ] harm myself
- [ ] criticise

Passive
- [ ] take it too seriously
- [ ] give up
- [ ] wallow in self pity
- [ ] sulk
- [ ] space out
- [ ] procrastinate
- [ ] give in
- [ ] be controlled

Intense Feelings

Angry feelings
- [ ] hateful
- [ ] attacked
- [ ] aggravated
- [ ] worn out
- [ ] annoyed
- [ ] rejected
- [ ] hostile
- [ ] jealous
- [ ] outraged
- [ ] afraid
- [ ] punitive
- [ ] exploited
- [ ] resentful
- [ ] lonely
- [ ] vengeful
- [ ] abandoned

Fearful feelings
- [ ] guilty
- [ ] helpless
- [ ] insulted
- [ ] hopeless
- [ ] confused
- [ ] disappointed
- [ ] disillusioned
- [ ] sad
- [ ] misunderstood
- [ ] trapped

Bodily Reactions (limbic system)

I am uncomfortable because I am experiencing...
- [ ] tremors
- [ ] nausea
- [ ] sweaty palms
- [ ] stomach-ache
- [ ] pounding heart
- [ ] general tension
- [ ] fatigue
- [ ] imagination on fire
- [ ] headache
- [ ] dry mouth
- [ ] jaw clenching
- [ ] shortness of breath

Continued over

B   **F**   **L**

Step Three: The Working-Down Process

Begin with, "Suddenly I realised that I was anxious and that I had choices..." This is the step of self-leadership and trust in one's ability to handle the situation.

Choose helpful thoughts:

I choose to depersonalise
There is no intention to hurt me. He is doing the best he can with the tools he has at the moment.

I choose realism over romanticism
Life presents many obstacles. I lower or raise standards as needed.

There is no right or wrong
Unless it is a moral issue, I will see it simply as a difference of opinion and/or taste.

I choose the total view of positivity
Even though this event is negative, the total view of his behaviour is positive.

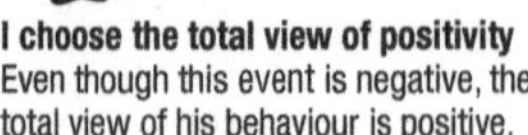

I surrender control
Since I cannot change this situation, I choose to let go of it.

I choose to put this event in perspective This event is not a catastrophe because it is not life threatening. It can be viewed as a trivial life event, a normal life problem that needs to be solved not dramatised.

I choose to view this event as average, falling within the normal range
This event is not exceptional; many people have gone through this.

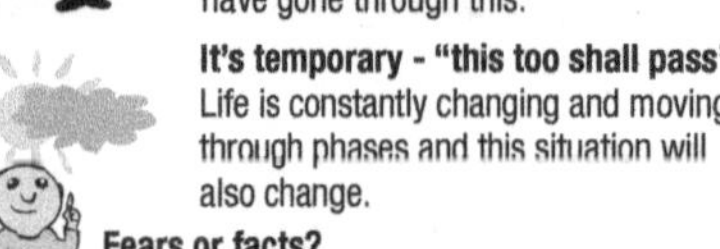

It's temporary - "this too shall pass"
Life is constantly changing and moving through phases and this situation will also change.

Fears or facts?
Why fear? It may not happen!

I choose to focus on this as a learning experience
Every problem that comes my way is an opportunity for me to learn about my strengths and weaknesses, others and life.

Feel soothing emotions:

I choose to feel warm, loving emotions. I do this by focusing on my heart and letting love, trust forgiveness, compassion, hope or gratitude fill my heart space.

Behave constructively:

I choose to work in part acts:
I will break the overwhelming job into manageable parts.

Do the difficult:
I will face what I fear and act with self-discipline.

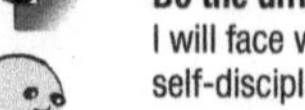
I choose to solutionise:
I will find a solution by taking advice or doing research.

Prioritise myself:
I will keep my life balanced by meeting friends, doing exercise or laughing.

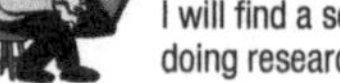

Compartmentalise:
I will not let this event cloud my whole day; I will focus on something else now.

Utilise calming strategies:

When I:
- relax,
- breathe deeply,
- go for a run,
- shower,
- lie down,
- read,
- watch TV,
- climb into a mental helicopter,
- practice mindfulness/meditation,

my mind and body calm down.

Step Four: The Self Motivation Process

Endorse yourself for any growth no matter how small.

In the past I would have...

____

____

But this time I...

____

____

Tick off the traits that you strengthened when you worked down your anxiety:

☐ generosity	☐ peacefulness	
☐ kindness	☐ self-discipline	
☐ compassion	☐ forgiveness	
☐ consideration	☐ courage	
☐ helpfulness	☐ responsibility	
☐ respectfulness	☐ reliability	
☐ honesty	☐ loyalty	
☐ fairness	☐ love	
☐ patience	☐ humility	

Rate your anxiety on a scale of 0 to 100%:

_______ %

Date: _______________

Anxiety Management Worksheet

The purpose of this worksheet is to help you to see every stressful event as an opportunity for
1. greater understanding of yourself, your anxiety and the people around you, and
2. practicing tools to manage your anxiety.

Step One: An Event

Briefly describe an event when you became anxious. Give such details as time, place and people involved, and end with "That's when I began to work myself up…"

____

____   **E**

____

____ Rate your anxiety on a scale of 0 to 100%: [   ] **%**

Step Two: The Working-Up Process

Learn about your working up process by identifying your thoughts, feelings, behaviours and bodily reactions during the event.
Tick the ones that most resonate with you.

Undermining Beliefs

B

I fear that I have lost...

- ☐ approval
- ☐ control
- ☐ co-operation
- ☐ face
- ☐ respect
- ☐ success
- ☐ trust
- ☐ validation
- ☐ love

This event proves that I am...

- ☐ stupid
- ☐ abnormal
- ☐ incompetent
- ☐ lazy
- ☐ irresponsible
- ☐ a total failure
- ☐ undisciplined
- ☐ untogether
- ☐ useless

I worry that I will suffer...

- ☐ mental collapse
- ☐ illness
- ☐ financial hardship

What I want is...

- ☐ total control
- ☐ respect
- ☐ success
- ☐ perfection
- ☐ comfort
- ☐ fairness
- ☐ tranquility
- ☐ all the answers
- ☐ for life to go smoothly
- ☐ to be all things to all people

Self-destructive Behaviour

Active

- ☐ get violent
- ☐ swear
- ☐ slam doors
- ☐ run away
- ☐ overeat
- ☐ harm myself
- ☐ criticise

Passive

- ☐ take it too seriously
- ☐ give up
- ☐ wallow in self pity
- ☐ sulk
- ☐ space out
- ☐ procrastinate
- ☐ give in
- ☐ be controlled

Intense Feelings

Angry feelings

- ☐ hateful
- ☐ aggravated
- ☐ annoyed
- ☐ hostile
- ☐ outraged
- ☐ punitive
- ☐ resentful
- ☐ vengeful

Fearful feelings

- ☐ helpless
- ☐ hopeless
- ☐ disappointed
- ☐ sad
- ☐ attacked
- ☐ worn out
- ☐ rejected
- ☐ jealous
- ☐ afraid
- ☐ exploited
- ☐ lonely
- ☐ abandoned
- ☐ guilty
- ☐ insulted
- ☐ confused
- ☐ disillusioned
- ☐ misunderstood
- ☐ trapped

Bodily Reactions (limbic system)

I am uncomfortable because I am experiencing...

- ☐ tremors
- ☐ nausea
- ☐ sweaty palms
- ☐ stomach-ache
- ☐ pounding heart
- ☐ general tension
- ☐ fatigue
- ☐ imagination on fire
- ☐ headache
- ☐ dry mouth
- ☐ jaw clenching
- ☐ shortness of breath

B   **F**   **L**

Step Three: The Working-Down Process

Begin with, "Suddenly I realised that I was anxious and that I had choices..." This is the step of self-leadership and trust in one's ability to handle the situation.

Choose helpful thoughts:

I choose to depersonalise
There is no intention to hurt me. He is doing the best he can with the tools he has at the moment.

I choose realism over romanticism
Life presents many obstacles. I lower or raise standards as needed.

There is no right or wrong
Unless it is a moral issue, I will see it simply as a difference of opinion and/or taste.

I choose the total view of positivity
Even though this event is negative, the total view of his behaviour is positive.

I surrender control
Since I cannot change this situation, I choose to let go of it.

I choose to put this event in perspective This event is not a catastrophe because it is not life threatening. It can be viewed as a trivial life event, a normal life problem that needs to be solved not dramatised.

I choose to view this event as average, falling within the normal range
This event is not exceptional; many people have gone through this.

It's temporary - "this too shall pass"
Life is constantly changing and moving through phases and this situation will also change.

Fears or facts?
Why fear? It may not happen!

I choose to focus on this as a learning experience
Every problem that comes my way is an opportunity for me to learn about my strengths and weaknesses, others and life.

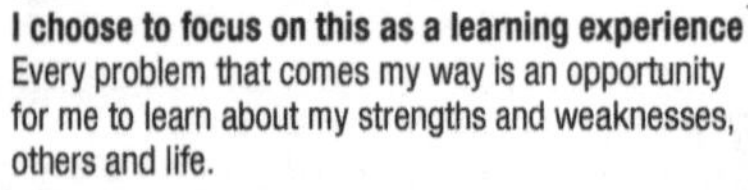

Feel soothing emotions:

I choose to feel warm, loving emotions. I do this by focusing on my heart and letting love, trust forgiveness, compassion, hope or gratitude fill my heart space.

Behave constructively:

I choose to work in part acts:
I will break the overwhelming job into manageable parts.

Do the difficult:
I will face what I fear and act with self-discipline.

I choose to solutionise:
I will find a solution by taking advice or doing research.

Prioritise myself:
I will keep my life balanced by meeting friends, doing exercise or laughing.

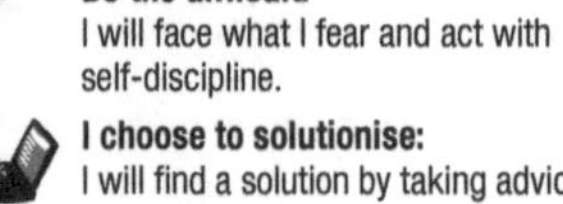

Compartmentalise:
I will not let this event cloud my whole day; I will focus on something else now.

Utilise calming strategies:

When I:
- relax,
- breathe deeply,
- go for a run,
- shower,
- lie down,
- read,
- watch TV,
- climb into a mental helicopter,
- practice mindfulness/meditation,

my mind and body calm down.

Step Four: The Self Motivation Process

Endorse yourself for any growth no matter how small.

In the past I would have...

____

____

But this time I...

____

____

Tick off the traits that you strengthened when you worked down your anxiety:

- ☐ generosity
- ☐ kindness
- ☐ compassion
- ☐ consideration
- ☐ helpfulness
- ☐ respectfulness
- ☐ honesty
- ☐ fairness
- ☐ patience
- ☐ peacefulness
- ☐ self-discipline
- ☐ forgiveness
- ☐ courage
- ☐ responsibility
- ☐ reliability
- ☐ loyalty
- ☐ love
- ☐ humility

Rate your anxiety on a scale of 0 to 100%:

[______] %

O

W

Date: _______________

Anxiety Management Worksheet

The purpose of this worksheet is to help you to see every stressful event as an opportunity for
1. greater understanding of yourself, your anxiety and the people around you, and
2. practicing tools to manage your anxiety.

Step One: An Event

Briefly describe an event when you became anxious. Give such details as time, place and people involved, and end with "That's when I began to work myself up..."

____

____

____

____ Rate your anxiety on a scale of 0 to 100%: [   ] %

E

Step Two: The Working-Up Process

Learn about your working up process by identifying your thoughts, feelings, behaviours and bodily reactions during the event.
Tick the ones that most resonate with you.

B

Undermining Beliefs

I fear that I have lost...
- ☐ approval
- ☐ control
- ☐ co-operation
- ☐ face
- ☐ respect
- ☐ success
- ☐ trust
- ☐ validation
- ☐ love

This event proves that I am...
- ☐ stupid
- ☐ abnormal
- ☐ incompetent
- ☐ lazy
- ☐ irresponsible
- ☐ a total failure
- ☐ undisciplined
- ☐ untogether
- ☐ useless

I worry that I will suffer...
- ☐ mental collapse
- ☐ illness
- ☐ financial hardship

What I want is...
- ☐ total control
- ☐ respect
- ☐ success
- ☐ perfection
- ☐ comfort
- ☐ fairness
- ☐ tranquility
- ☐ all the answers
- ☐ for life to go smoothly
- ☐ to be all things to all people

Self-destructive Behaviour

Active
- ☐ get violent
- ☐ swear
- ☐ slam doors
- ☐ run away
- ☐ overeat
- ☐ harm myself
- ☐ criticise

Passive
- ☐ take it too seriously
- ☐ give up
- ☐ wallow in self pity
- ☐ sulk
- ☐ space out
- ☐ procrastinate
- ☐ give in
- ☐ be controlled

Intense Feelings

Angry feelings
- ☐ hateful
- ☐ aggravated
- ☐ annoyed
- ☐ hostile
- ☐ outraged
- ☐ punitive
- ☐ resentful
- ☐ vengeful

Fearful feelings
- ☐ helpless
- ☐ hopeless
- ☐ disappointed
- ☐ sad
- ☐ attacked
- ☐ worn out
- ☐ rejected
- ☐ jealous
- ☐ afraid
- ☐ exploited
- ☐ lonely
- ☐ abandoned
- ☐ guilty
- ☐ insulted
- ☐ confused
- ☐ disillusioned
- ☐ misunderstood
- ☐ trapped

Bodily Reactions (limbic system)

I am uncomfortable because I am experiencing...
- ☐ tremors
- ☐ nausea
- ☐ sweaty palms
- ☐ stomach-ache
- ☐ pounding heart
- ☐ general tension
- ☐ fatigue
- ☐ imagination on fire
- ☐ headache
- ☐ dry mouth
- ☐ jaw clenching
- ☐ shortness of breath

Continued over

B   **F**   **L**

Step Three: The Working-Down Process

Begin with, "Suddenly I realised that I was anxious and that I had choices…" This is the step of self-leadership and trust in one's ability to handle the situation.

Choose helpful thoughts:

I choose to depersonalise
There is no intention to hurt me. He is doing the best he can with the tools he has at the moment.

I choose realism over romanticism
Life presents many obstacles. I lower or raise standards as needed.

There is no right or wrong
Unless it is a moral issue, I will see it simply as a difference of opinion and/or taste.

I choose the total view of positivity
Even though this event is negative, the total view of his behaviour is positive.

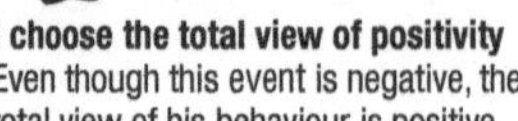

I surrender control
Since I cannot change this situation, I choose to let go of it.

I choose to put this event in perspective This event is not a catastrophe because it is not life threatening. It can be viewed as a trivial life event, a normal life problem that needs to be solved not dramatised.

I choose to view this event as average, falling within the normal range
This event is not exceptional; many people have gone through this.

It's temporary - "this too shall pass"
Life is constantly changing and moving through phases and this situation will also change.

Fears or facts?
Why fear? It may not happen!

I choose to focus on this as a learning experience
Every problem that comes my way is an opportunity for me to learn about my strengths and weaknesses, others and life.

Feel soothing emotions:

I choose to feel warm, loving emotions. I do this by focusing on my heart and letting love, trust forgiveness, compassion, hope or gratitude fill my heart space.

Behave constructively:

I choose to work in part acts:
I will break the overwhelming job into manageable parts.

Do the difficult:
I will face what I fear and act with self-discipline.

I choose to solutionise:
I will find a solution by taking advice or doing research.

Prioritise myself:
I will keep my life balanced by meeting friends, doing exercise or laughing.

Compartmentalise:
I will not let this event cloud my whole day; I will focus on something else now.

Utilise calming strategies:

When I:
- relax,
- breathe deeply,
- go for a run,
- shower,
- lie down,
- read,
- watch TV,
- climb into a mental helicopter,
- practice mindfulness/meditation,

my mind and body calm down.

Step Four: The Self Motivation Process

Endorse yourself for any growth no matter how small.

In the past I would have…

____

____

But this time I…

____

____

Tick off the traits that you strengthened when you worked down your anxiety:

- ☐ generosity
- ☐ kindness
- ☐ compassion
- ☐ consideration
- ☐ helpfulness
- ☐ respectfulness
- ☐ honesty
- ☐ fairness
- ☐ patience
- ☐ peacefulness
- ☐ self-discipline
- ☐ forgiveness
- ☐ courage
- ☐ responsibility
- ☐ reliability
- ☐ loyalty
- ☐ love
- ☐ humility

Rate your anxiety on a scale of 0 to 100%:

________ %

O

W

Date: ____________

Anxiety Management Worksheet

The purpose of this worksheet is to help you to see every stressful event as an opportunity for
1. greater understanding of yourself, your anxiety and the people around you, and
2. practicing tools to manage your anxiety.

Step One: An Event

Briefly describe an event when you became anxious. Give such details as time, place and people involved, and end with "That's when I began to work myself up…"

____

____

____

______________________________________   Rate your anxiety on a scale of 0 to 100%: ☐ %

E

Step Two: The Working-Up Process

Learn about your working up process by identifying your thoughts, feelings, behaviours and bodily reactions during the event.
Tick the ones that most resonate with you.

Undermining Beliefs

B

I fear that I have lost...
- ☐ approval
- ☐ success
- ☐ control
- ☐ trust
- ☐ co-operation
- ☐ validation
- ☐ face
- ☐ love
- ☐ respect

This event proves that I am...
- ☐ stupid
- ☐ a total failure
- ☐ abnormal
- ☐ undisciplined
- ☐ incompetent
- ☐ untogether
- ☐ lazy
- ☐ useless
- ☐ irresponsible

I worry that I will suffer...
- ☐ mental collapse
- ☐ illness
- ☐ financial hardship

What I want is...
- ☐ total control
- ☐ tranquility
- ☐ respect
- ☐ all the answers
- ☐ success
- ☐ for life to go smoothly
- ☐ perfection
- ☐ comfort
- ☐ to be all things to all people
- ☐ fairness

Self-destructive Behaviour

Active
- ☐ get violent
- ☐ swear
- ☐ slam doors
- ☐ run away
- ☐ overeat
- ☐ harm myself
- ☐ criticise

Passive
- ☐ take it too seriously
- ☐ give up
- ☐ wallow in self pity
- ☐ sulk
- ☐ space out
- ☐ procrastinate
- ☐ give in
- ☐ be controlled

B

Intense Feelings

Angry feelings
- ☐ hateful
- ☐ attacked
- ☐ aggravated
- ☐ worn out
- ☐ annoyed
- ☐ rejected
- ☐ hostile
- ☐ jealous
- ☐ outraged
- ☐ afraid
- ☐ punitive
- ☐ exploited
- ☐ resentful
- ☐ lonely
- ☐ vengeful
- ☐ abandoned

Fearful feelings
- ☐ guilty
- ☐ helpless
- ☐ insulted
- ☐ hopeless
- ☐ confused
- ☐ disappointed
- ☐ disillusioned
- ☐ sad
- ☐ misunderstood
- ☐ trapped

F

Bodily Reactions (limbic system)

I am uncomfortable because I am experiencing...
- ☐ tremors
- ☐ nausea
- ☐ sweaty palms
- ☐ stomach-ache
- ☐ pounding heart
- ☐ general tension
- ☐ fatigue
- ☐ imagination on fire
- ☐ headache
- ☐ dry mouth
- ☐ jaw clenching
- ☐ shortness of breath

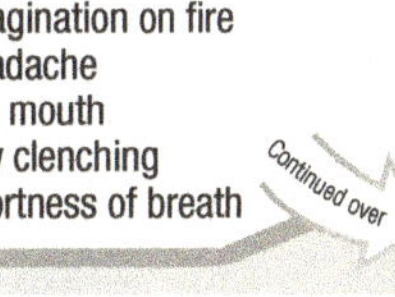

Continued over

L

Step Three: The Working-Down Process

Begin with, "Suddenly I realised that I was anxious and that I had choices..." This is the step of self-leadership and trust in one's ability to handle the situation.

Choose helpful thoughts:

I choose to depersonalise
There is no intention to hurt me. He is doing the best he can with the tools he has at the moment.

I choose realism over romanticism
Life presents many obstacles. I lower or raise standards as needed.

There is no right or wrong
Unless it is a moral issue, I will see it simply as a difference of opinion and/or taste.

I choose the total view of positivity
Even though this event is negative, the total view of his behaviour is positive.

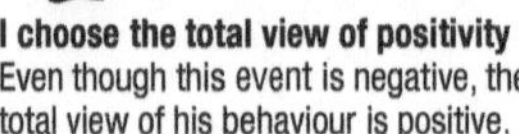

I surrender control
Since I cannot change this situation, I choose to let go of it.

I choose to put this event in perspective
This event is not a catastrophe because it is not life threatening. It can be viewed as a trivial life event, a normal life problem that needs to be solved not dramatised.

I choose to view this event as average, falling within the normal range
This event is not exceptional; many people have gone through this.

It's temporary - "this too shall pass"
Life is constantly changing and moving through phases and this situation will also change.

Fears or facts?
Why fear? It may not happen!

I choose to focus on this as a learning experience
Every problem that comes my way is an opportunity for me to learn about my strengths and weaknesses, others and life.

Feel soothing emotions:

I choose to feel warm, loving emotions. I do this by focusing on my heart and letting love, trust, forgiveness, compassion, hope or gratitude fill my heart space.

Behave constructively:

I choose to work in part acts:
I will break the overwhelming job into manageable parts.

Do the difficult:
I will face what I fear and act with self-discipline.

I choose to solutionise:
I will find a solution by taking advice or doing research.

Prioritise myself:
I will keep my life balanced by meeting friends, doing exercise or laughing.

Compartmentalise:
I will not let this event cloud my whole day; I will focus on something else now.

Utilise calming strategies:

When I:
- relax,
- breathe deeply,
- go for a run,
- shower,
- lie down,
- read,
- watch TV,
- climb into a mental helicopter,
- practice mindfulness/meditation,

my mind and body calm down.

Step Four: The Self Motivation Process

Endorse yourself for any growth no matter how small.

In the past I would have...

____

____

But this time I...

____

____

Tick off the traits that you strengthened when you worked down your anxiety:

☐ generosity	☐ peacefulness
☐ kindness	☐ self-discipline
☐ compassion	☐ forgiveness
☐ consideration	☐ courage
☐ helpfulness	☐ responsibility
☐ respectfulness	☐ reliability
☐ honesty	☐ loyalty
☐ fairness	☐ love
☐ patience	☐ humility

Rate your anxiety on a scale of 0 to 100%:

[____]%

Date: ______________

Anxiety Management Worksheet

The purpose of this worksheet is to help you to see every stressful event as an opportunity for
1. greater understanding of yourself, your anxiety and the people around you, and
2. practicing tools to manage your anxiety.

Step One: An Event

Briefly describe an event when you became anxious. Give such details as time, place and people involved, and end with "That's when I began to work myself up..."

____

____

____

__________________________________ Rate your anxiety on a scale of 0 to 100%: [＿＿] %

E

Step Two: The Working-Up Process

Learn about your working up process by identifying your thoughts, feelings, behaviours and bodily reactions during the event. Tick the ones that most resonate with you.

Undermining Beliefs

B

I fear that I have lost...
- ☐ approval
- ☐ control
- ☐ co-operation
- ☐ face
- ☐ respect
- ☐ success
- ☐ trust
- ☐ validation
- ☐ love

This event proves that I am...
- ☐ stupid
- ☐ abnormal
- ☐ incompetent
- ☐ lazy
- ☐ irresponsible
- ☐ a total failure
- ☐ undisciplined
- ☐ untogether
- ☐ useless

I worry that I will suffer...
- ☐ mental collapse
- ☐ illness
- ☐ financial hardship

What I want is...
- ☐ total control
- ☐ respect
- ☐ success
- ☐ perfection
- ☐ comfort
- ☐ fairness
- ☐ tranquility
- ☐ all the answers
- ☐ for life to go smoothly
- ☐ to be all things to all people

Self-destructive Behaviour

Active
- ☐ get violent
- ☐ swear
- ☐ slam doors
- ☐ run away
- ☐ overeat
- ☐ harm myself
- ☐ criticise

Passive
- ☐ take it too seriously
- ☐ give up
- ☐ wallow in self pity
- ☐ sulk
- ☐ space out
- ☐ procrastinate
- ☐ give in
- ☐ be controlled

Intense Feelings

Angry feelings
- ☐ hateful
- ☐ aggravated
- ☐ annoyed
- ☐ hostile
- ☐ outraged
- ☐ punitive
- ☐ resentful
- ☐ vengeful

Fearful feelings
- ☐ helpless
- ☐ hopeless
- ☐ disappointed
- ☐ sad
- ☐ attacked
- ☐ worn out
- ☐ rejected
- ☐ jealous
- ☐ afraid
- ☐ exploited
- ☐ lonely
- ☐ abandoned
- ☐ guilty
- ☐ insulted
- ☐ confused
- ☐ disillusioned
- ☐ misunderstood
- ☐ trapped

Bodily Reactions (limbic system)

I am uncomfortable because I am experiencing...
- ☐ tremors
- ☐ nausea
- ☐ sweaty palms
- ☐ stomach-ache
- ☐ pounding heart
- ☐ general tension
- ☐ fatigue
- ☐ imagination on fire
- ☐ headache
- ☐ dry mouth
- ☐ jaw clenching
- ☐ shortness of breath

Continued over

B **F** **L**

Step Three: The Working-Down Process

Begin with, "Suddenly I realised that I was anxious and that I had choices..." This is the step of self-leadership and trust in one's ability to handle the situation.

Choose helpful thoughts:

I choose to depersonalise
There is no intention to hurt me. He is doing the best he can with the tools he has at the moment.

I choose realism over romanticism
Life presents many obstacles. I lower or raise standards as needed.

There is no right or wrong
Unless it is a moral issue, I will see it simply as a difference of opinion and/or taste.

I choose the total view of positivity
Even though this event is negative, the total view of his behaviour is positive.

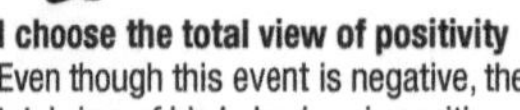

I surrender control
Since I cannot change this situation, I choose to let go of it.

I choose to put this event in perspective This event is not a catastrophe because it is not life threatening. It can be viewed as a trivial life event, a normal life problem that needs to be solved not dramatised.

I choose to view this event as average, falling within the normal range
This event is not exceptional; many people have gone through this.

It's temporary - "this too shall pass"
Life is constantly changing and moving through phases and this situation will also change.

Fears or facts?
Why fear? It may not happen!

I choose to focus on this as a learning experience
Every problem that comes my way is an opportunity for me to learn about my strengths and weaknesses, others and life.

Feel soothing emotions:

I choose to feel warm, loving emotions. I do this by focusing on my heart and letting love, trust forgiveness, compassion, hope or gratitude fill my heart space.

Behave constructively:

I choose to work in part acts:
I will break the overwhelming job into manageable parts.

Do the difficult:
I will face what I fear and act with self-discipline.

I choose to solutionise:
I will find a solution by taking advice or doing research.

Prioritise myself:
I will keep my life balanced by meeting friends, doing exercise or laughing.

Compartmentalise:
I will not let this event cloud my whole day; I will focus on something else now.

Utilise calming strategies:

When I:
- relax,
- breathe deeply,
- go for a run,
- shower,
- lie down,
- read,
- watch TV,
- climb into a mental helicopter,
- practice mindfulness/meditation,

my mind and body calm down.

Step Four: The Self Motivation Process

Endorse yourself for any growth no matter how small.

In the past I would have...

____

____

But this time I...

____

____

Tick off the traits that you strengthened when you worked down your anxiety:

☐ generosity	☐ peacefulness
☐ kindness	☐ self-discipline
☐ compassion	☐ forgiveness
☐ consideration	☐ courage
☐ helpfulness	☐ responsibility
☐ respectfulness	☐ reliability
☐ honesty	☐ loyalty
☐ fairness	☐ love
☐ patience	☐ humility

Rate your anxiety on a scale of 0 to 100%:

☐ %

Date: ___________

Anxiety Management Worksheet

The purpose of this worksheet is to help you to see every stressful event as an opportunity for
1. greater understanding of yourself, your anxiety and the people around you, and
2. practicing tools to manage your anxiety.

Step One: An Event

Briefly describe an event when you became anxious. Give such details as time, place and people involved, and end with "That's when I began to work myself up…"

E

____

____

____

_______________________________________ Rate your anxiety on a scale of 0 to 100%: [＿＿] %

Step Two: The Working-Up Process

Learn about your working up process by identifying your thoughts, feelings, behaviours and bodily reactions during the event.
Tick the ones that most resonate with you.

Undermining Beliefs

B

I fear that I have lost...

- ☐ approval
- ☐ control
- ☐ co-operation
- ☐ face
- ☐ respect
- ☐ success
- ☐ trust
- ☐ validation
- ☐ love

This event proves that I am...

- ☐ stupid
- ☐ abnormal
- ☐ incompetent
- ☐ lazy
- ☐ irresponsible
- ☐ a total failure
- ☐ undisciplined
- ☐ untogether
- ☐ useless

I worry that I will suffer...

- ☐ mental collapse
- ☐ illness
- ☐ financial hardship

What I want is...

- ☐ total control
- ☐ respect
- ☐ success
- ☐ perfection
- ☐ comfort
- ☐ fairness
- ☐ tranquility
- ☐ all the answers
- ☐ for life to go smoothly
- ☐ to be all things to all people

Self-destructive Behaviour

Active

- ☐ get violent
- ☐ swear
- ☐ slam doors
- ☐ run away
- ☐ overeat
- ☐ harm myself
- ☐ criticise

Passive

- ☐ take it too seriously
- ☐ give up
- ☐ wallow in self pity
- ☐ sulk
- ☐ space out
- ☐ procrastinate
- ☐ give in
- ☐ be controlled

Intense Feelings

Angry feelings

- ☐ hateful
- ☐ aggravated
- ☐ annoyed
- ☐ hostile
- ☐ outraged
- ☐ punitive
- ☐ resentful
- ☐ vengeful
- ☐ attacked
- ☐ worn out
- ☐ rejected
- ☐ jealous
- ☐ afraid
- ☐ exploited
- ☐ lonely
- ☐ abandoned
- ☐ guilty

Fearful feelings

- ☐ helpless
- ☐ hopeless
- ☐ disappointed
- ☐ sad
- ☐ insulted
- ☐ confused
- ☐ disillusioned
- ☐ misunderstood
- ☐ trapped

Bodily Reactions (limbic system)

I am uncomfortable because I am experiencing...

- ☐ tremors
- ☐ nausea
- ☐ sweaty palms
- ☐ stomach-ache
- ☐ pounding heart
- ☐ general tension
- ☐ fatigue
- ☐ imagination on fire
- ☐ headache
- ☐ dry mouth
- ☐ jaw clenching
- ☐ shortness of breath

Continued over

B   F   L

Step Three: The Working-Down Process

Begin with, "Suddenly I realised that I was anxious and that I had choices..." This is the step of self-leadership and trust in one's ability to handle the situation.

Choose helpful thoughts:

I choose to depersonalise
There is no intention to hurt me. He is doing the best he can with the tools he has at the moment.

I choose realism over romanticism
Life presents many obstacles. I lower or raise standards as needed.

There is no right or wrong
Unless it is a moral issue, I will see it simply as a difference of opinion and/or taste.

I choose the total view of positivity
Even though this event is negative, the total view of his behaviour is positive.

I surrender control
Since I cannot change this situation, I choose to let go of it.

I choose to put this event in perspective This event is not a catastrophe because it is not life threatening. It can be viewed as a trivial life event, a normal life problem that needs to be solved not dramatised.

I choose to view this event as average, falling within the normal range
This event is not exceptional; many people have gone through this.

It's temporary - "this too shall pass"
Life is constantly changing and moving through phases and this situation will also change.

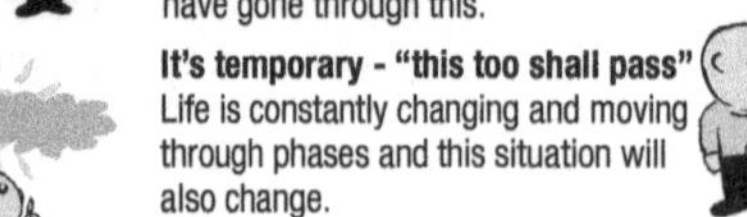

Fears or facts?
Why fear? It may not happen!

I choose to focus on this as a learning experience
Every problem that comes my way is an opportunity for me to learn about my strengths and weaknesses, others and life.

Feel soothing emotions:

I choose to feel warm, loving emotions. I do this by focusing on my heart and letting love, trust forgiveness, compassion, hope or gratitude fill my heart space.

Behave constructively:

I choose to work in part acts:
I will break the overwhelming job into manageable parts.

Do the difficult:
I will face what I fear and act with self-discipline.

I choose to solutionise:
I will find a solution by taking advice or doing research.

Prioritise myself:
I will keep my life balanced by meeting friends, doing exercise or laughing.

Compartmentalise:
I will not let this event cloud my whole day; I will focus on something else now.

Utilise calming strategies:

When I:
- relax,
- breathe deeply,
- go for a run,
- shower,
- lie down,
- read,
- watch TV,
- climb into a mental helicopter,
- practice mindfulness/meditation,

my mind and body calm down.

Step Four: The Self Motivation Process

Endorse yourself for any growth no matter how small.

In the past I would have...

____

____

But this time I...

____

____

Tick off the traits that you strengthened when you worked down your anxiety:

- ☐ generosity
- ☐ kindness
- ☐ compassion
- ☐ consideration
- ☐ helpfulness
- ☐ respectfulness
- ☐ honesty
- ☐ fairness
- ☐ patience
- ☐ peacefulness
- ☐ self-discipline
- ☐ forgiveness
- ☐ courage
- ☐ responsibility
- ☐ reliability
- ☐ loyalty
- ☐ love
- ☐ humility

Rate your anxiety on a scale of 0 to 100%:

☐ %

O   W

Week 8

You have reached week eight which means you are three quarters through the course. By now you will be feeling calmer, happier and more focused. Do not stop now because you feel good. Continue to learn new tools and keep practising the four-step process to ensure long-term change.

The tools we cover in week eight are:

1. Surrender control: thinking tool
2. Compartmentalise: behavioural tool
3. Meditation: calming tool

Surrender control: thinking tool

"I surrender control. Since I cannot change this situation, I choose to let go of it."

Perseverance frequently leads to success. However, when hammering away does not bring you your desired results, it is best to surrender control and to let go.

The wisdom of the serenity prayer (23) is well-known.

"God grant me the serenity
to accept the things I cannot change,
the courage to change the things I can,
and the wisdom to know the difference."

While many people agree with this wisdom, most of the people I have worked with find it nearly impossible to "let go" even if they desperately want to.

Choosing to surrender control and to let go of a problem means not worrying constantly about it. It means being able to focus on other things in the here and now. It means realising that it is futile to pour endless energy, time and worry into a problem that you cannot change.

Here are a few practical suggestions of how to let go. Choose the ones that resonate with you.

1. Hand your problem over to a higher power. This concept is central in Alcohol Anonymous (AA) and all the twelve step programs. These programs teach the importance of acknowledging that an addict is powerless and can only recover by "letting go and letting God".

According to the twelve step programs, God is not necessarily defined by a religion, instead God is defined as "the God of your understanding". (23) For some people, God is defined by their religion, while for others the higher power is defined as the universe, nature, or even the group itself. If you relate to handing your problem over to a higher power, the way you conceptualise your higher power is totally personal and subjective.

There is a story told of a poor man, who is offered a ride in a wagon. He climbs into the wagon, sits down and holds his luggage on his lap. The driver tells him to put the luggage on the floor of the wagon but the poor man replies "No thank you. I feel so grateful already that you are giving me a lift that I do not want to burden you further by putting my luggage on the wagon." The driver replies, "You silly man. Don't you realise that the wagon is carrying the weight anyway whether it is on your lap or on the floor? You might as well put it down and have a comfortable ride."

If you believe in a higher power, this image can help you. Put your baggage down and enjoy the ride because your higher power is carrying you and your problem.

2. Utilise visualisation to help you to let go. For instance, you can imagine putting your problem in a rocket and sending it, at lightning speed, out of your orbit of consciousness.

3. Write down the things that are bothering you.
    For instance, if you are in a difficult situation (like a messy divorce). Write down your issues on some toilet paper and flush them down the toilet. This will give you huge relief.

    Or, if you cannot sleep at night, keep a piece of paper next to your bed and write down your thoughts and worries. This will reassure you that you can afford to switch off now and go to sleep, because you will not forget your problems. You have recorded them which will ensure that you will be able to work on them in the morning.

4. Mindfulness is a popular way of letting go (see page 146).

5. Relaxation and meditation can assist you to focus on stilling your mind and letting go of worrying thoughts.

EXERCISE 25

Even though you now have strategies, it may be difficult for you to surrender control because you still need to feel in control. The following exercise will get you to examine your need for control. There are no right or wrong answers.

Are you a person who likes to be in control?   YES/NO

If yes, do you find that you need to be in control:

a) in every aspect of your life *OR*   YES/NO

b) only in certain aspects of your life?   YES/NO

If you answered that you need to be in control in all circumstances, please elaborate further.

If you answered that you only need to be in control in certain circumstances, please fill in below those areas that apply to you:

> Home
> Food
> Work
> Relationships
> Other

Please elaborate on your choices:

Does your need for control prevent you from relaxing?   YES/NO

Do you believe that your need for control helps you to reach your goals or hampers you?

Please explain your answer:

Has your need for control ever damaged a relationship?   YES/NO

If you answered "yes," when and how?

Do you wish to change the manner in which you take control and if so, in which areas and how?

Are there any other ways of relinquishing control when appropriate that have helped you in the past?

Remember: Relinquishing control does not indicate weakness because you are not being intimidated to let go, you are CHOOSING to surrender control.

Daily monitoring diary

Whenever you find that you are unable to surrender control, note it down in the daily monitoring diary. Then practise one of the methods suggested to relinquish control and rate your anxiety before and after. Note how surrendering control lowers your anxiety.

Compartmentalise: behavioural tool

"I will not let this incident cloud my whole day: I will focus on something else now."

Separating yourself from a problem is an active choice that you can make to help you become more rational and self-disciplined. You re-focus your attention away from anxious thinking, and rumination, to something neutral.

Anxious thinking, and ruminating, can ruin your whole day and serve no real purpose. It is best to "fix it or ignore it". How to ignore it? By distracting yourself with something else.

Finding a distraction is not the same as spacing out or disassociating. The latter are self-destructive behaviours because they are escape mechanisms. They prevent you from being in the moment or getting on with things. Distraction is not about trying to avoid reality. You are simply making a choice to intentionally focus on something else. You are fully in the moment, and being productive, but with an activity that is affirming rather than debilitating. When you distract yourself, your anxiety will subside.

There are hundreds of ways that you can distract yourself from your anxious feelings or persistent worry. Here is a sample:

> doodling on a piece of paper
> flipping through a magazine
> playing a game, including electronic games
> spending time connecting on Facebook
> going to a movie, watching TV or a video, listening to a lecture
> focusing on anything that interests you such as playing the

> piano, reading a gripping novel, painting, gardening, sewing or scrapbooking
> putting all your energies into a new project
> doing any activity that you enjoy will work to calm you down and soothe your anxiety levels

Crafts and creative pursuits soothe the soul. However, crafts and hobbies seem to have lost their appeal with the advent of technology. I would like to encourage you to bring a hobby into your life as an effective tool to manage anxiety. A hobby can be used in a curative manner. For instance, when you feel anxious and go outside to garden, you will calm down.

Being engaged in a hobby can also be preventative. For instance, people who garden regularly, derive immense satisfaction, well-being and purpose from gardening which goes a long way towards reducing anxiety long-term.

EXERCISE 26

Complete this exercise to help you think about your hobbies and interests. Hobbies include crafts, creative endeavours or collections. They do not include sport or exercise.

What are your hobbies?

Which ones are constantly accessible? For example, reading

Which ones are only accessible at times?

Do you think you could utilise any of the above listed hobbies to distract yourself from your worries?

Can you think of any other hobbies that could work for you in the future?

How could you go about incorporating these new hobbies into your life?

Meditation: calming tool

Like deep breathing and relaxation, meditation is a well-known form of switching off. Like all of these disciplines, there is a multitude of ways that meditation is taught and practised. Therefore, if you practise meditation already, and enjoy your method, keep going.

While relaxation is all about removing the tension from your body, meditation is all about focusing the mind. If your mind wanders, gently bring yourself back to the point of focus. You do not judge your thoughts.

My preferred method is to focus on a flame. I like this method because a flame moves and has colour. I have found anxious people find it easier to focus on a moving object than meditating on a musical note or golden energy. However, it is an extremely personal and subjective choice and I encourage you to find the one that is right for you.

EXERCISE 27

Light a candle while you take a bath. Set a timer for ten minutes, and then keep looking at the flame for that time. When your mind wanders, or you feel like dozing, gently bring yourself back to focusing on the candle.

Even if your thoughts seem helpful, ignore them and go back to the flame. For example, you may start telling yourself *"I have to focus more"* or *"I know I can do this if I try hard enough"*. Or you may have negative thoughts like *"I am useless at everything I try"* or *"Here I go again, not doing the right thing"*. All thoughts which are not about the flame need to be observed, not judged, and allowed to pass on.

DAILY MONITORING DIARY WEEK ENDING ....

Day	M	T	W	T	F	S	S
Overall Anxiety Rating for the day (0-10)							
1. EXERCISE							
How long?							
Anxiety level before (0-10)							
Anxiety level after (0-10)							
2. BREATHING							
How long?							
Anxiety level before (0-10)							
Anxiety level after (0-10)							
3. RELAXATION							
How long?							
Anxiety level before (0-10)							
Anxiety level after (0-10)							
4. PERVASIVE PESSIMISTIC THINKING							
How often this type of thought occurred							
Belief in thoughts before challenging (0-10)							
Belief in thoughts after challenging (0-10)							

Day	M	T	W	T	F	S	S
5. CATASTROPHIC THINKING							
How often this type of thought occurred							
Belief in thoughts before challenging (0-10)							
Belief in thoughts after challenging (0-10)							
6. PERMANENT PESSIMISTIC THINKING							
How often this type of thought occurred							
Belief in thoughts before challenging (0-10)							
Belief in thoughts after challenging (0-10)							
7. MINDFULNESS (FORMAL, GROUNDING, INFORMAL MINDFULNESS)							
How long?							
Anxiety level before (0-10)							
Anxiety level after (0-10)							
8. ROMANTIC THINKING							
How often this type of thought occurred							
Belief in thoughts before challenging (0-10)							
Belief in thoughts after challenging (0-10)							

Day	M	T	W	T	F	S	S
9. NEGATIVE JUDGMENTAL THINKING							
How often this type of thought occurred							
Belief in thoughts before challenging (0-10)							
Belief in thoughts after challenging (0-10)							
10. CAN'T LET GO THINKING							
How often this type of thought occurred							
Belief in thoughts before challenging (0-10)							
Belief in thoughts after challenging (0-10)							
11. MEDITATION							
How long?							
Anxiety level before (0-10)							
Anxiety level after (0-10)							

Date: _______________

Anxiety Management Worksheet

The purpose of this worksheet is to help you to see every stressful event as an opportunity for
1. greater understanding of yourself, your anxiety and the people around you, and
2. practicing tools to manage your anxiety.

Step One: An Event

Briefly describe an event when you became anxious. Give such details as time, place and people involved, and end with "That's when I began to work myself up..."

____

____

____

_________________________________ Rate your anxiety on a scale of 0 to 100%: [   ] %

E

Step Two: The Working-Up Process

Learn about your working up process by identifying your thoughts, feelings, behaviours and bodily reactions during the event. Tick the ones that most resonate with you.

B

Undermining Beliefs

I fear that I have lost...

- ☐ approval
- ☐ control
- ☐ co-operation
- ☐ face
- ☐ respect
- ☐ success
- ☐ trust
- ☐ validation
- ☐ love

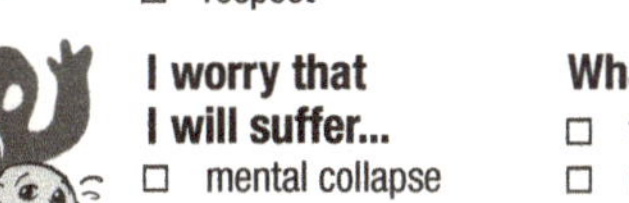

This event proves that I am...

- ☐ stupid
- ☐ abnormal
- ☐ incompetent
- ☐ lazy
- ☐ irresponsible
- ☐ a total failure
- ☐ undisciplined
- ☐ untogether
- ☐ useless

I worry that I will suffer...

- ☐ mental collapse
- ☐ illness
- ☐ financial hardship

What I want is...

- ☐ total control
- ☐ respect
- ☐ success
- ☐ perfection
- ☐ comfort
- ☐ fairness
- ☐ tranquility
- ☐ all the answers
- ☐ for life to go smoothly
- ☐ to be all things to all people

Self-destructive Behaviour

Active
- ☐ get violent
- ☐ swear
- ☐ slam doors
- ☐ run away
- ☐ overeat
- ☐ harm myself
- ☐ criticise

Passive
- ☐ take it too seriously
- ☐ give up
- ☐ wallow in self pity
- ☐ sulk
- ☐ space out
- ☐ procrastinate
- ☐ give in
- ☐ be controlled

Intense Feelings

Angry feelings
- ☐ hateful
- ☐ aggravated
- ☐ annoyed
- ☐ hostile
- ☐ outraged
- ☐ punitive
- ☐ resentful
- ☐ vengeful

Fearful feelings
- ☐ helpless
- ☐ hopeless
- ☐ disappointed
- ☐ sad
- ☐ attacked
- ☐ worn out
- ☐ rejected
- ☐ jealous
- ☐ afraid
- ☐ exploited
- ☐ lonely
- ☐ abandoned
- ☐ guilty
- ☐ insulted
- ☐ confused
- ☐ disillusioned
- ☐ misunderstood
- ☐ trapped

Bodily Reactions (limbic system)

I am uncomfortable because I am experiencing...

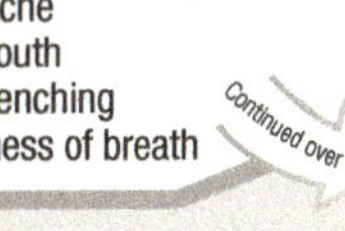

- ☐ tremors
- ☐ nausea
- ☐ sweaty palms
- ☐ stomach-ache
- ☐ pounding heart
- ☐ general tension
- ☐ fatigue
- ☐ imagination on fire
- ☐ headache
- ☐ dry mouth
- ☐ jaw clenching
- ☐ shortness of breath

Continued over

B   **F**   **L**

Step Three: The Working-Down Process

Begin with, "Suddenly I realised that I was anxious and that I had choices..." This is the step of self-leadership and trust in one's ability to handle the situation.

Choose helpful thoughts:

I choose to depersonalise
There is no intention to hurt me. He is doing the best he can with the tools he has at the moment.

I choose realism over romanticism
Life presents many obstacles. I lower or raise standards as needed.

There is no right or wrong
Unless it is a moral issue, I will see it simply as a difference of opinion and/or taste.

I choose the total view of positivity
Even though this event is negative, the total view of his behaviour is positive.

I surrender control
Since I cannot change this situation, I choose to let go of it.

I choose to put this event in perspective This event is not a catastrophe because it is not life threatening. It can be viewed as a trivial life event, a normal life problem that needs to be solved not dramatised.

I choose to view this event as average, falling within the normal range
This event is not exceptional; many people have gone through this.

It's temporary - "this too shall pass"
Life is constantly changing and moving through phases and this situation will also change.

Fears or facts?
Why fear? It may not happen!

I choose to focus on this as a learning experience
Every problem that comes my way is an opportunity for me to learn about my strengths and weaknesses, others and life.

Feel soothing emotions:

I choose to feel warm, loving emotions. I do this by focusing on my heart and letting love, trust forgiveness, compassion, hope or gratitude fill my heart space.

Behave constructively:

I choose to work in part acts:
I will break the overwhelming job into manageable parts.

Do the difficult:
I will face what I fear and act with self-discipline.

I choose to solutionise:
I will find a solution by taking advice or doing research.

Prioritise myself:
I will keep my life balanced by meeting friends, doing exercise or laughing.

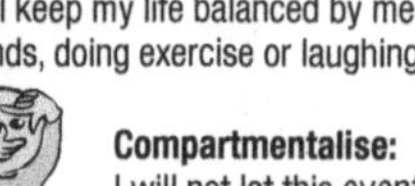

Compartmentalise:
I will not let this event cloud my whole day; I will focus on something else now.

Utilise calming strategies:

When I:
- relax,
- breathe deeply,
- go for a run,
- shower,
- lie down,
- read,
- watch TV,
- climb into a mental helicopter,
- practice mindfulness/meditation,

my mind and body calm down.

Step Four: The Self Motivation Process

Endorse yourself for any growth no matter how small.

In the past I would have...

____

____

But this time I...

____

____

Tick off the traits that you strengthened when you worked down your anxiety:

- ☐ generosity
- ☐ kindness
- ☐ compassion
- ☐ consideration
- ☐ helpfulness
- ☐ respectfulness
- ☐ honesty
- ☐ fairness
- ☐ patience
- ☐ peacefulness
- ☐ self-discipline
- ☐ forgiveness
- ☐ courage
- ☐ responsibility
- ☐ reliability
- ☐ loyalty
- ☐ love
- ☐ humility

Rate your anxiety on a scale of 0 to 100%:

⬇

[ ]%

O   W

Date: ___________

Anxiety Management Worksheet

The purpose of this worksheet is to help you to see every stressful event as an opportunity for
1. greater understanding of yourself, your anxiety and the people around you, and
2. practicing tools to manage your anxiety.

Step One: An Event

Briefly describe an event when you became anxious. Give such details as time, place and people involved, and end with "That's when I began to work myself up..."

____

____

____

_______________________________________ Rate your anxiety on a scale of 0 to 100%: [＿＿＿] %

E

Step Two: The Working-Up Process

Learn about your working up process by identifying your thoughts, feelings, behaviours and bodily reactions during the event.
Tick the ones that most resonate with you.

Undermining Beliefs

B

I fear that I have lost...
- ☐ approval
- ☐ control
- ☐ co-operation
- ☐ face
- ☐ respect
- ☐ success
- ☐ trust
- ☐ validation
- ☐ love

This event proves that I am...
- ☐ stupid
- ☐ abnormal
- ☐ incompetent
- ☐ lazy
- ☐ irresponsible
- ☐ a total failure
- ☐ undisciplined
- ☐ untogether
- ☐ useless

I worry that I will suffer...
- ☐ mental collapse
- ☐ illness
- ☐ financial hardship

What I want is...
- ☐ total control
- ☐ respect
- ☐ success
- ☐ perfection
- ☐ comfort
- ☐ fairness
- ☐ tranquility
- ☐ all the answers
- ☐ for life to go smoothly
- ☐ to be all things to all people

Self-destructive Behaviour

Active
- ☐ get violent
- ☐ swear
- ☐ slam doors
- ☐ run away
- ☐ overeat
- ☐ harm myself
- ☐ criticise

Passive
- ☐ take it too seriously
- ☐ give up
- ☐ wallow in self pity
- ☐ sulk
- ☐ space out
- ☐ procrastinate
- ☐ give in
- ☐ be controlled

Intense Feelings

Angry feelings
- ☐ hateful
- ☐ aggravated
- ☐ annoyed
- ☐ hostile
- ☐ outraged
- ☐ punitive
- ☐ resentful
- ☐ vengeful

Fearful feelings
- ☐ helpless
- ☐ hopeless
- ☐ disappointed
- ☐ sad
- ☐ attacked
- ☐ worn out
- ☐ rejected
- ☐ jealous
- ☐ afraid
- ☐ exploited
- ☐ lonely
- ☐ abandoned
- ☐ guilty
- ☐ insulted
- ☐ confused
- ☐ disillusioned
- ☐ misunderstood
- ☐ trapped

Bodily Reactions (limbic system)

I am uncomfortable because I am experiencing...
- ☐ tremors
- ☐ nausea
- ☐ sweaty palms
- ☐ stomach-ache
- ☐ pounding heart
- ☐ general tension
- ☐ fatigue
- ☐ imagination on fire
- ☐ headache
- ☐ dry mouth
- ☐ jaw clenching
- ☐ shortness of breath

Continued over

B   **F**   **L**

Step Three: The Working-Down Process

Begin with, "Suddenly I realised that I was anxious and that I had choices..." This is the step of self-leadership and trust in one's ability to handle the situation.

Choose helpful thoughts:

I choose to depersonalise
There is no intention to hurt me. He is doing the best he can with the tools he has at the moment.

I choose realism over romanticism
Life presents many obstacles. I lower or raise standards as needed.

There is no right or wrong
Unless it is a moral issue, I will see it simply as a difference of opinion and/or taste.

I choose the total view of positivity
Even though this event is negative, the total view of his behaviour is positive.

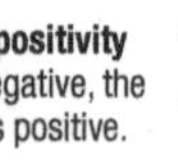

I surrender control
Since I cannot change this situation, I choose to let go of it.

I choose to put this event in perspective This event is not a catastrophe because it is not life threatening. It can be viewed as a trivial life event, a normal life problem that needs to be solved not dramatised.

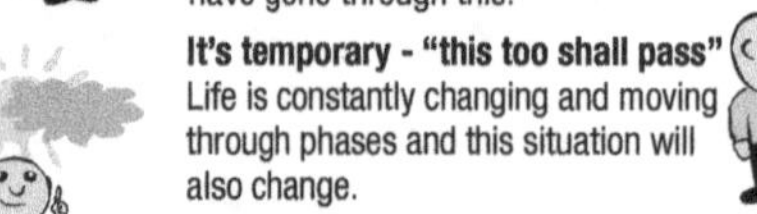

I choose to view this event as average, falling within the normal range
This event is not exceptional; many people have gone through this.

It's temporary - "this too shall pass"
Life is constantly changing and moving through phases and this situation will also change.

Fears or facts?
Why fear? It may not happen!

I choose to focus on this as a learning experience
Every problem that comes my way is an opportunity for me to learn about my strengths and weaknesses, others and life.

Feel soothing emotions:

I choose to feel warm, loving emotions. I do this by focusing on my heart and letting love, trust forgiveness, compassion, hope or gratitude fill my heart space.

Behave constructively:

I choose to work in part acts:
I will break the overwhelming job into manageable parts.

Do the difficult:
I will face what I fear and act with self-discipline.

I choose to solutionise:
I will find a solution by taking advice or doing research.

Prioritise myself:
I will keep my life balanced by meeting friends, doing exercise or laughing.

Compartmentalise:
I will not let this event cloud my whole day; I will focus on something else now.

Utilise calming strategies:

When I:
- relax,
- breathe deeply,
- go for a run,
- shower,
- lie down,
- read,
- watch TV,
- climb into a mental helicopter,
- practice mindfulness/meditation,

my mind and body calm down.

Step Four: The Self Motivation Process

Endorse yourself for any growth no matter how small.

In the past I would have...

____

____

But this time I...

____

____

Tick off the traits that you strengthened when you worked down your anxiety:

☐ generosity	☐ peacefulness
☐ kindness	☐ self-discipline
☐ compassion	☐ forgiveness
☐ consideration	☐ courage
☐ helpfulness	☐ responsibility
☐ respectfulness	☐ reliability
☐ honesty	☐ loyalty
☐ fairness	☐ love
☐ patience	☐ humility

Rate your anxiety on a scale of 0 to 100%:

[____]%

O

W

Date: ___________

Anxiety Management Worksheet

The purpose of this worksheet is to help you to see every stressful event as an opportunity for
1. greater understanding of yourself, your anxiety and the people around you, and
2. practicing tools to manage your anxiety.

Step One: An Event

Briefly describe an event when you became anxious. Give such details as time, place and people involved, and end with "That's when I began to work myself up…"

____

____

____

____ Rate your anxiety on a scale of 0 to 100%: [ ] %

E

Step Two: The Working-Up Process

Learn about your working up process by identifying your thoughts, feelings, behaviours and bodily reactions during the event.
Tick the ones that most resonate with you.

Undermining Beliefs

B

I fear that I have lost...
- ☐ approval
- ☐ control
- ☐ co-operation
- ☐ face
- ☐ respect
- ☐ success
- ☐ trust
- ☐ validation
- ☐ love

This event proves that I am...
- ☐ stupid
- ☐ abnormal
- ☐ incompetent
- ☐ lazy
- ☐ irresponsible
- ☐ a total failure
- ☐ undisciplined
- ☐ untogether
- ☐ useless

I worry that I will suffer...
- ☐ mental collapse
- ☐ illness
- ☐ financial hardship

What I want is...
- ☐ total control
- ☐ respect
- ☐ success
- ☐ perfection
- ☐ comfort
- ☐ fairness
- ☐ tranquility
- ☐ all the answers
- ☐ for life to go smoothly
- ☐ to be all things to all people

Self-destructive Behaviour

Active
- ☐ get violent
- ☐ swear
- ☐ slam doors
- ☐ run away
- ☐ overeat
- ☐ harm myself
- ☐ criticise

Passive
- ☐ take it too seriously
- ☐ give up
- ☐ wallow in self pity
- ☐ sulk
- ☐ space out
- ☐ procrastinate
- ☐ give in
- ☐ be controlled

Intense Feelings

Angry feelings
- ☐ hateful
- ☐ aggravated
- ☐ annoyed
- ☐ hostile
- ☐ outraged
- ☐ punitive
- ☐ resentful
- ☐ vengeful

Fearful feelings
- ☐ helpless
- ☐ hopeless
- ☐ disappointed
- ☐ sad
- ☐ attacked
- ☐ worn out
- ☐ rejected
- ☐ jealous
- ☐ afraid
- ☐ exploited
- ☐ lonely
- ☐ abandoned
- ☐ guilty
- ☐ insulted
- ☐ confused
- ☐ disillusioned
- ☐ misunderstood
- ☐ trapped

Bodily Reactions (limbic system)

I am uncomfortable because I am experiencing...
- ☐ tremors
- ☐ nausea
- ☐ sweaty palms
- ☐ stomach-ache
- ☐ pounding heart
- ☐ general tension
- ☐ fatigue
- ☐ imagination on fire
- ☐ headache
- ☐ dry mouth
- ☐ jaw clenching
- ☐ shortness of breath

Continued over

B　　　　**F**　　　　**L**

Step Three: The Working-Down Process

Begin with, "Suddenly I realised that I was anxious and that I had choices..." This is the step of self-leadership and trust in one's ability to handle the situation.

Choose helpful thoughts:

I choose to depersonalise
There is no intention to hurt me. He is doing the best he can with the tools he has at the moment.

I choose realism over romanticism
Life presents many obstacles. I lower or raise standards as needed.

There is no right or wrong
Unless it is a moral issue, I will see it simply as a difference of opinion and/or taste.

I choose the total view of positivity
Even though this event is negative, the total view of his behaviour is positive.

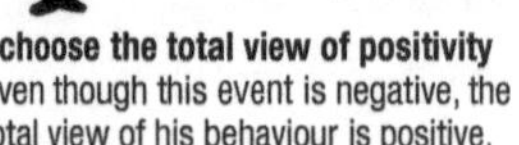

I surrender control
Since I cannot change this situation, I choose to let go of it.

I choose to put this event in perspective
This event is not a catastrophe because it is not life threatening. It can be viewed as a trivial life event, a normal life problem that needs to be solved not dramatised.

I choose to view this **event as average, falling within the normal range**
This event is not exceptional; many people have gone through this.

It's temporary - "this too shall pass"
Life is constantly changing and moving through phases and this situation will also change.

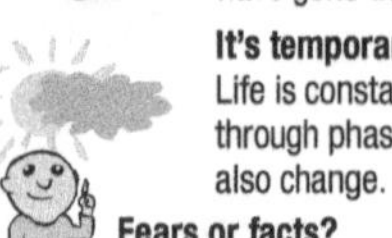

Fears or facts?
Why fear? It may not happen!

I choose to focus on this as a learning experience
Every problem that comes my way is an opportunity for me to learn about my strengths and weaknesses, others and life.

Feel soothing emotions:

I choose to feel warm, loving emotions. I do this by focusing on my heart and letting love, trust forgiveness, compassion, hope or gratitude fill my heart space.

Behave constructively:

I choose to work in part acts:
I will break the overwhelming job into manageable parts.

Do the difficult:
I will face what I fear and act with self-discipline.

I choose to solutionise:
I will find a solution by taking advice or doing research.

Prioritise myself:
I will keep my life balanced by meeting friends, doing exercise or laughing.

Compartmentalise:
I will not let this event cloud my whole day; I will focus on something else now.

Utilise calming strategies:

When I:
- relax,
- breathe deeply,
- go for a run,
- shower,
- lie down,
- read,
- watch TV,
- climb into a mental helicopter,
- practice mindfulness/meditation,

my mind and body calm down.

Step Four: The Self Motivation Process

Endorse yourself for any growth no matter how small.

In the past I would have...

____

____

But this time I...

____

____

Tick off the traits that you strengthened when you worked down your anxiety:

☐ generosity	☐ peacefulness		
☐ kindness	☐ self-discipline		
☐ compassion	☐ forgiveness		
☐ consideration	☐ courage		
☐ helpfulness	☐ responsibility		
☐ respectfulness	☐ reliability		
☐ honesty	☐ loyalty		
☐ fairness	☐ love		
☐ patience	☐ humility		

Rate your anxiety on a scale of 0 to 100%:

⬇

______ %

O   W

Date: ___________

Anxiety Management Worksheet

The purpose of this worksheet is to help you to see every stressful event as an opportunity for
1. greater understanding of yourself, your anxiety and the people around you, and
2. practicing tools to manage your anxiety.

Step One: An Event

Briefly describe an event when you became anxious. Give such details as time, place and people involved, and end with "That's when I began to work myself up..."

____

____

____

_______________________________________ Rate your anxiety on a scale of 0 to 100%: [   ] %

E

Step Two: The Working-Up Process

Learn about your working up process by identifying your thoughts, feelings, behaviours and bodily reactions during the event. Tick the ones that most resonate with you.

Undermining Beliefs

B

I fear that I have lost...
- ☐ approval
- ☐ control
- ☐ co-operation
- ☐ face
- ☐ respect
- ☐ success
- ☐ trust
- ☐ validation
- ☐ love

This event proves that I am...
- ☐ stupid
- ☐ abnormal
- ☐ incompetent
- ☐ lazy
- ☐ irresponsible
- ☐ a total failure
- ☐ undisciplined
- ☐ untogether
- ☐ useless

I worry that I will suffer...
- ☐ mental collapse
- ☐ illness
- ☐ financial hardship

What I want is...
- ☐ total control
- ☐ respect
- ☐ success
- ☐ perfection
- ☐ comfort
- ☐ fairness
- ☐ tranquility
- ☐ all the answers
- ☐ for life to go smoothly
- ☐ to be all things to all people

Self-destructive Behaviour

Active
- ☐ get violent
- ☐ swear
- ☐ slam doors
- ☐ run away
- ☐ overeat
- ☐ harm myself
- ☐ criticise

Passive
- ☐ take it too seriously
- ☐ give up
- ☐ wallow in self pity
- ☐ sulk
- ☐ space out
- ☐ procrastinate
- ☐ give in
- ☐ be controlled

Intense Feelings

Angry feelings
- ☐ hateful
- ☐ aggravated
- ☐ annoyed
- ☐ hostile
- ☐ outraged
- ☐ punitive
- ☐ resentful
- ☐ vengeful
- ☐ attacked
- ☐ worn out
- ☐ rejected
- ☐ jealous
- ☐ afraid
- ☐ exploited
- ☐ lonely
- ☐ abandoned
- ☐ guilty
- ☐ insulted

Fearful feelings
- ☐ helpless
- ☐ hopeless
- ☐ disappointed
- ☐ sad
- ☐ confused
- ☐ disillusioned
- ☐ misunderstood
- ☐ trapped

Bodily Reactions (limbic system)

I am uncomfortable because I am experiencing...
- ☐ tremors
- ☐ nausea
- ☐ sweaty palms
- ☐ stomach-ache
- ☐ pounding heart
- ☐ general tension
- ☐ fatigue
- ☐ imagination on fire
- ☐ headache
- ☐ dry mouth
- ☐ jaw clenching
- ☐ shortness of breath

Continued over

B   **F**   **L**

Step Three: The Working-Down Process

Begin with, "Suddenly I realised that I was anxious and that I had choices..." This is the step of self-leadership and trust in one's ability to handle the situation.

Choose helpful thoughts:

I choose to depersonalise
There is no intention to hurt me. He is doing the best he can with the tools he has at the moment.

I choose realism over romanticism
Life presents many obstacles. I lower or raise standards as needed.

There is no right or wrong
Unless it is a moral issue, I will see it simply as a difference of opinion and/or taste.

I choose the total view of positivity
Even though this event is negative, the total view of his behaviour is positive.

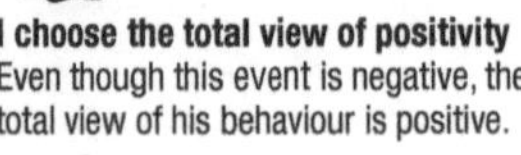

I surrender control
Since I cannot change this situation, I choose to let go of it.

I choose to put this event in perspective This event is not a catastrophe because it is not life threatening. It can be viewed as a trivial life event, a normal life problem that needs to be solved not dramatised.

I choose to view this event as average, falling within the normal range
This event is not exceptional; many people have gone through this.

It's temporary - "this too shall pass"
Life is constantly changing and moving through phases and this situation will also change.

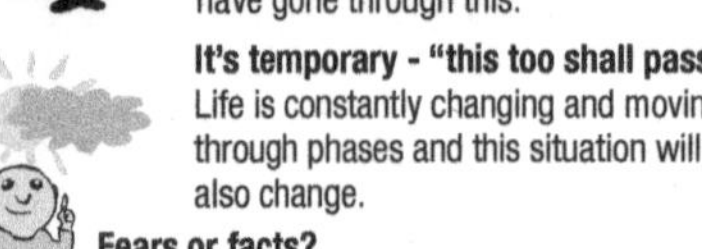

Fears or facts?
Why fear? It may not happen!

I choose to focus on this as a learning experience
Every problem that comes my way is an opportunity for me to learn about my strengths and weaknesses, others and life.

Feel soothing emotions:

I choose to feel warm, loving emotions. I do this by focusing on my heart and letting love, trust forgiveness, compassion, hope or gratitude fill my heart space.

Behave constructively:

I choose to work in part acts:
I will break the overwhelming job into manageable parts.

Do the difficult:
I will face what I fear and act with self-discipline.

I choose to solutionise:
I will find a solution by taking advice or doing research.

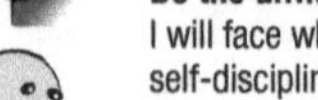

Prioritise myself:
I will keep my life balanced by meeting friends, doing exercise or laughing.

Compartmentalise:
I will not let this event cloud my whole day; I will focus on something else now.

Utilise calming strategies:

When I:
- relax,
- breathe deeply,
- go for a run,
- shower,
- lie down,
- read,
- watch TV,
- climb into a mental helicopter,
- practice mindfulness/meditation,
  my mind and body calm down.

Step Four: The Self Motivation Process

Endorse yourself for any growth no matter how small.

In the past I would have...

____

____

But this time I...

____

____

Tick off the traits that you strengthened when you worked down your anxiety:

☐ generosity	☐ peacefulness
☐ kindness	☐ self-discipline
☐ compassion	☐ forgiveness
☐ consideration	☐ courage
☐ helpfulness	☐ responsibility
☐ respectfulness	☐ reliability
☐ honesty	☐ loyalty
☐ fairness	☐ love
☐ patience	☐ humility

Rate your anxiety on a scale of 0 to 100%:

[____]%

O

W

Anxiety Management Worksheet

The purpose of this worksheet is to help you to see every stressful event as an opportunity for
1. greater understanding of yourself, your anxiety and the people around you, and
2. practicing tools to manage your anxiety.

Step One: An Event

Briefly describe an event when you became anxious. Give such details as time, place and people involved, and end with "That's when I began to work myself up..."

____

____

____

____ Rate your anxiety on a scale of 0 to 100%: [＿＿] %

E

Step Two: The Working-Up Process

Learn about your working up process by identifying your thoughts, feelings, behaviours and bodily reactions during the event.

Tick the ones that most resonate with you.

Undermining Beliefs

B

I fear that I have lost...

- ☐ approval
- ☐ control
- ☐ co-operation
- ☐ face
- ☐ respect
- ☐ success
- ☐ trust
- ☐ validation
- ☐ love

This event proves that I am...

- ☐ stupid
- ☐ abnormal
- ☐ incompetent
- ☐ lazy
- ☐ irresponsible
- ☐ a total failure
- ☐ undisciplined
- ☐ untogether
- ☐ useless

I worry that I will suffer...

- ☐ mental collapse
- ☐ illness
- ☐ financial hardship

What I want is...

- ☐ total control
- ☐ respect
- ☐ success
- ☐ perfection
- ☐ comfort
- ☐ fairness
- ☐ tranquility
- ☐ all the answers
- ☐ for life to go smoothly
- ☐ to be all things to all people

Self-destructive Behaviour

Active
- ☐ get violent
- ☐ swear
- ☐ slam doors
- ☐ run away
- ☐ overeat
- ☐ harm myself
- ☐ criticise

Passive
- ☐ take it too seriously
- ☐ give up
- ☐ wallow in self pity
- ☐ sulk
- ☐ space out
- ☐ procrastinate
- ☐ give in
- ☐ be controlled

B

Intense Feelings

Angry feelings
- ☐ hateful
- ☐ aggravated
- ☐ annoyed
- ☐ hostile
- ☐ outraged
- ☐ punitive
- ☐ resentful
- ☐ vengeful
- ☐ attacked
- ☐ worn out
- ☐ rejected
- ☐ jealous
- ☐ afraid
- ☐ exploited
- ☐ lonely
- ☐ abandoned
- ☐ guilty
- ☐ insulted

Fearful feelings
- ☐ helpless
- ☐ hopeless
- ☐ disappointed
- ☐ sad
- ☐ confused
- ☐ disillusioned
- ☐ misunderstood
- ☐ trapped

F

Bodily Reactions (limbic system)

I am uncomfortable because I am experiencing...
- ☐ tremors
- ☐ nausea
- ☐ sweaty palms
- ☐ stomach-ache
- ☐ pounding heart
- ☐ general tension
- ☐ fatigue
- ☐ imagination on fire
- ☐ headache
- ☐ dry mouth
- ☐ jaw clenching
- ☐ shortness of breath

Continued over

L

Step Three: The Working-Down Process

Begin with, "Suddenly I realised that I was anxious and that I had choices..." This is the step of self-leadership and trust in one's ability to handle the situation.

Choose helpful thoughts:

I choose to depersonalise
There is no intention to hurt me. He is doing the best he can with the tools he has at the moment.

I choose realism over romanticism
Life presents many obstacles. I lower or raise standards as needed.

There is no right or wrong
Unless it is a moral issue, I will see it simply as a difference of opinion and/or taste.

I choose the total view of positivity
Even though this event is negative, the total view of his behaviour is positive.

I surrender control
Since I cannot change this situation, I choose to let go of it.

I choose to put this event in perspective This event is not a catastrophe because it is not life threatening. It can be viewed as a trivial life event, a normal life problem that needs to be solved not dramatised.

I choose to view this event as average, falling within the normal range
This event is not exceptional; many people have gone through this.

It's temporary - "this too shall pass"
Life is constantly changing and moving through phases and this situation will also change.

Fears or facts?
Why fear? It may not happen!

I choose to focus on this as a learning experience
Every problem that comes my way is an opportunity for me to learn about my strengths and weaknesses, others and life.

Feel soothing emotions:

I choose to feel warm, loving emotions. I do this by focusing on my heart and letting love, trust forgiveness, compassion, hope or gratitude fill my heart space.

Behave constructively:

I choose to work in part acts:
I will break the overwhelming job into manageable parts.

Do the difficult:
I will face what I fear and act with self-discipline.

I choose to solutionise:
I will find a solution by taking advice or doing research.

Prioritise myself:
I will keep my life balanced by meeting friends, doing exercise or laughing.

Compartmentalise:
I will not let this event cloud my whole day; I will focus on something else now.

Utilise calming strategies:

When I:
- relax,
- breathe deeply,
- go for a run,
- shower,
- lie down,
- read,
- watch TV,
- climb into a mental helicopter,
- practice mindfulness/meditation,

my mind and body calm down.

Step Four: The Self Motivation Process

Endorse yourself for any growth no matter how small.

In the past I would have...

____

____

But this time I...

____

____

Tick off the traits that you strengthened when you worked down your anxiety:

☐ generosity	☐ peacefulness
☐ kindness	☐ self-discipline
☐ compassion	☐ forgiveness
☐ consideration	☐ courage
☐ helpfulness	☐ responsibility
☐ respectfulness	☐ reliability
☐ honesty	☐ loyalty
☐ fairness	☐ love
☐ patience	☐ humility

Rate your anxiety on a scale of 0 to 100%:

______ %

O

W

Date: ____________

Anxiety Management Worksheet

The purpose of this worksheet is to help you to see every stressful event as an opportunity for
1. greater understanding of yourself, your anxiety and the people around you, and
2. practicing tools to manage your anxiety.

Step One: An Event

Briefly describe an event when you became anxious. Give such details as time, place and people involved, and end with "That's when I began to work myself up..."

____

____

____

____ Rate your anxiety on a scale of 0 to 100%: [ ] %

E

Step Two: The Working-Up Process

Learn about your working up process by identifying your thoughts, feelings, behaviours and bodily reactions during the event.
Tick the ones that most resonate with you.

Undermining Beliefs

B

I fear that I have lost...

- ☐ approval
- ☐ control
- ☐ co-operation
- ☐ face
- ☐ respect
- ☐ success
- ☐ trust
- ☐ validation
- ☐ love

This event proves that I am...

- ☐ stupid
- ☐ abnormal
- ☐ incompetent
- ☐ lazy
- ☐ irresponsible
- ☐ a total failure
- ☐ undisciplined
- ☐ untogether
- ☐ useless

I worry that I will suffer...

- ☐ mental collapse
- ☐ illness
- ☐ financial hardship

What I want is...

- ☐ total control
- ☐ respect
- ☐ success
- ☐ perfection
- ☐ comfort
- ☐ fairness
- ☐ tranquility
- ☐ all the answers
- ☐ for life to go smoothly
- ☐ to be all things to all people

Self-destructive Behaviour

Active

- ☐ get violent
- ☐ swear
- ☐ slam doors
- ☐ run away
- ☐ overeat
- ☐ harm myself
- ☐ criticise

Passive

- ☐ take it too seriously
- ☐ give up
- ☐ wallow in self pity
- ☐ sulk
- ☐ space out
- ☐ procrastinate
- ☐ give in
- ☐ be controlled

Intense Feelings

Angry feelings

- ☐ hateful
- ☐ aggravated
- ☐ annoyed
- ☐ hostile
- ☐ outraged
- ☐ punitive
- ☐ resentful
- ☐ vengeful

Fearful feelings

- ☐ helpless
- ☐ hopeless
- ☐ disappointed
- ☐ sad
- ☐ attacked
- ☐ worn out
- ☐ rejected
- ☐ jealous
- ☐ afraid
- ☐ exploited
- ☐ lonely
- ☐ abandoned
- ☐ guilty
- ☐ insulted
- ☐ confused
- ☐ disillusioned
- ☐ misunderstood
- ☐ trapped

Bodily Reactions (limbic system)

I am uncomfortable because I am experiencing...

- ☐ tremors
- ☐ nausea
- ☐ sweaty palms
- ☐ stomach-ache
- ☐ pounding heart
- ☐ general tension
- ☐ fatigue
- ☐ imagination on fire
- ☐ headache
- ☐ dry mouth
- ☐ jaw clenching
- ☐ shortness of breath

Continued over

B   **F**   **L**

Step Three: The Working-Down Process

Begin with, "Suddenly I realised that I was anxious and that I had choices..." This is the step of self-leadership and trust in one's ability to handle the situation.

Choose helpful thoughts:

I choose to depersonalise
There is no intention to hurt me. He is doing the best he can with the tools he has at the moment.

I choose realism over romanticism
Life presents many obstacles. I lower or raise standards as needed.

There is no right or wrong
Unless it is a moral issue, I will see it simply as a difference of opinion and/or taste.

I choose the total view of positivity
Even though this event is negative, the total view of his behaviour is positive.

I surrender control
Since I cannot change this situation, I choose to let go of it.

I choose to put this event in perspective This event is not a catastrophe because it is not life threatening. It can be viewed as a trivial life event, a normal life problem that needs to be solved not dramatised.

I choose to view this event as average, falling within the normal range
This event is not exceptional; many people have gone through this.

It's temporary - "this too shall pass"
Life is constantly changing and moving through phases and this situation will also change.

Fears or facts?
Why fear? It may not happen!

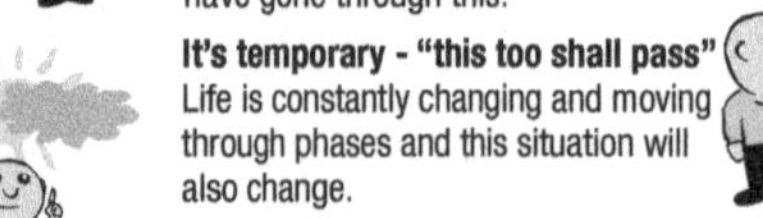

I choose to focus on this as a learning experience
Every problem that comes my way is an opportunity for me to learn about my strengths and weaknesses, others and life.

Feel soothing emotions:

I choose to feel warm, loving emotions. I do this by focusing on my heart and letting love, trust forgiveness, compassion, hope or gratitude fill my heart space.

Behave constructively:

I choose to work in part acts:
I will break the overwhelming job into manageable parts.

Do the difficult:
I will face what I fear and act with self-discipline.

I choose to solutionise:
I will find a solution by taking advice or doing research.

Prioritise myself:
I will keep my life balanced by meeting friends, doing exercise or laughing.

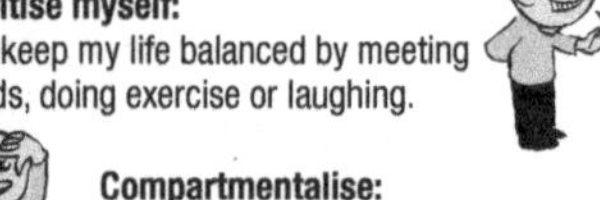

Compartmentalise:
I will not let this event cloud my whole day; I will focus on something else now.

Utilise calming strategies:

When I:
- relax,
- breathe deeply,
- go for a run,
- shower,
- lie down,
- read,
- watch TV,
- climb into a mental helicopter,
- practice mindfulness/meditation,

my mind and body calm down.

Step Four: The Self Motivation Process

Endorse yourself for any growth no matter how small.

In the past I would have...

____

____

But this time I...

____

____

Tick off the traits that you strengthened when you worked down your anxiety:

☐ generosity	☐ peacefulness
☐ kindness	☐ self-discipline
☐ compassion	☐ forgiveness
☐ consideration	☐ courage
☐ helpfulness	☐ responsibility
☐ respectfulness	☐ reliability
☐ honesty	☐ loyalty
☐ fairness	☐ love
☐ patience	☐ humility

Rate your anxiety on a scale of 0 to 100%:

_______ %

Anxiety Management Worksheet

The purpose of this worksheet is to help you to see every stressful event as an opportunity for
1. greater understanding of yourself, your anxiety and the people around you, and
2. practicing tools to manage your anxiety.

Step One: An Event

Briefly describe an event when you became anxious. Give such details as time, place and people involved, and end with "That's when I began to work myself up..."

____

____

____

_______________________________________ Rate your anxiety on a scale of 0 to 100%: ☐ %

E

Step Two: The Working-Up Process

Learn about your working up process by identifying your thoughts, feelings, behaviours and bodily reactions during the event.
Tick the ones that most resonate with you.

Undermining Beliefs

B

I fear that I have lost...
- ☐ approval
- ☐ control
- ☐ co-operation
- ☐ face
- ☐ respect
- ☐ success
- ☐ trust
- ☐ validation
- ☐ love

This event proves that I am...
- ☐ stupid
- ☐ abnormal
- ☐ incompetent
- ☐ lazy
- ☐ irresponsible
- ☐ a total failure
- ☐ undisciplined
- ☐ untogether
- ☐ useless

I worry that I will suffer...
- ☐ mental collapse
- ☐ illness
- ☐ financial hardship

What I want is...
- ☐ total control
- ☐ respect
- ☐ success
- ☐ perfection
- ☐ comfort
- ☐ fairness
- ☐ tranquility
- ☐ all the answers
- ☐ for life to go smoothly
- ☐ to be all things to all people

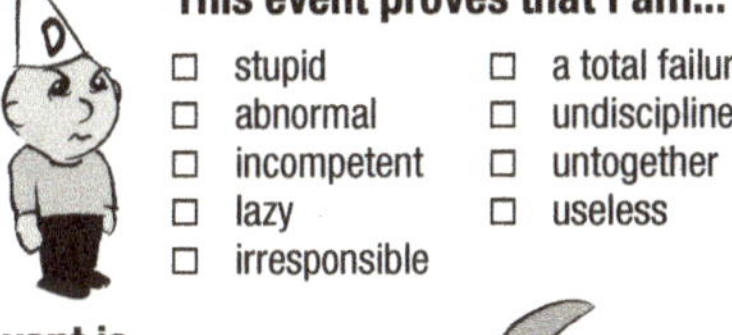

Self-destructive Behaviour

Active
- ☐ get violent
- ☐ swear
- ☐ slam doors
- ☐ run away
- ☐ overeat
- ☐ harm myself
- ☐ criticise

Passive
- ☐ take it too seriously
- ☐ give up
- ☐ wallow in self pity
- ☐ sulk
- ☐ space out
- ☐ procrastinate
- ☐ give in
- ☐ be controlled

Intense Feelings

Angry feelings
- ☐ hateful
- ☐ aggravated
- ☐ annoyed
- ☐ hostile
- ☐ outraged
- ☐ punitive
- ☐ resentful
- ☐ vengeful

Fearful feelings
- ☐ helpless
- ☐ hopeless
- ☐ disappointed
- ☐ sad

- ☐ attacked
- ☐ worn out
- ☐ rejected
- ☐ jealous
- ☐ afraid
- ☐ exploited
- ☐ lonely
- ☐ abandoned
- ☐ guilty
- ☐ insulted
- ☐ confused
- ☐ disillusioned
- ☐ misunderstood
- ☐ trapped

Bodily Reactions (limbic system)

I am uncomfortable because I am experiencing...
- ☐ tremors
- ☐ nausea
- ☐ sweaty palms
- ☐ stomach-ache
- ☐ pounding heart
- ☐ general tension
- ☐ fatigue
- ☐ imagination on fire
- ☐ headache
- ☐ dry mouth
- ☐ jaw clenching
- ☐ shortness of breath

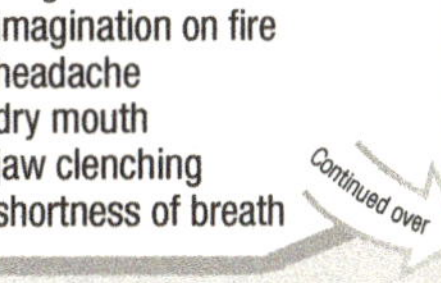

Continued over

B   **F**   **L**

Step Three: The Working-Down Process

Begin with, "Suddenly I realised that I was anxious and that I had choices..." This is the step of self-leadership and trust in one's ability to handle the situation.

Choose helpful thoughts:

I choose to depersonalise
There is no intention to hurt me. He is doing the best he can with the tools he has at the moment.

I choose realism over romanticism
Life presents many obstacles. I lower or raise standards as needed.

There is no right or wrong
Unless it is a moral issue, I will see it simply as a difference of opinion and/or taste.

I choose the total view of positivity
Even though this event is negative, the total view of his behaviour is positive.

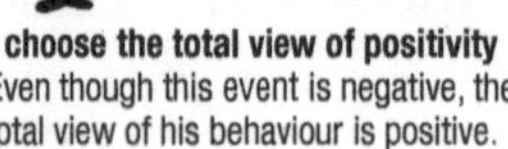

I surrender control
Since I cannot change this situation, I choose to let go of it.

I choose to put this event in perspective This event is not a catastrophe because it is not life threatening. It can be viewed as a trivial life event, a normal life problem that needs to be solved not dramatised.

I choose to view this event as average, falling within the normal range
This event is not exceptional; many people have gone through this.

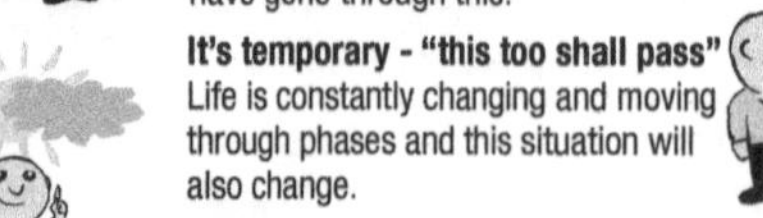
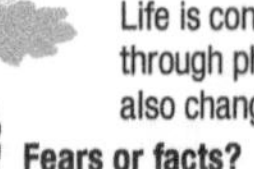

It's temporary - "this too shall pass"
Life is constantly changing and moving through phases and this situation will also change.

Fears or facts?
Why fear? It may not happen!

I choose to focus on this as a learning experience
Every problem that comes my way is an opportunity for me to learn about my strengths and weaknesses, others and life.

Feel soothing emotions:

I choose to feel warm, loving emotions. I do this by focusing on my heart and letting love, trust forgiveness, compassion, hope or gratitude fill my heart space.

Behave constructively:

I choose to work in part acts:
I will break the overwhelming job into manageable parts.

Do the difficult:
I will face what I fear and act with self-discipline.

I choose to solutionise:
I will find a solution by taking advice or doing research.

Prioritise myself:
I will keep my life balanced by meeting friends, doing exercise or laughing.

Compartmentalise:
I will not let this event cloud my whole day; I will focus on something else now.

Utilise calming strategies:

When I:
- relax,
- breathe deeply,
- go for a run,
- shower,
- lie down,
- read,
- watch TV,
- climb into a mental helicopter,
- practice mindfulness/meditation,

my mind and body calm down.

Step Four: The Self Motivation Process

Endorse yourself for any growth no matter how small.

In the past I would have...

____

____

But this time I...

____

____

Tick off the traits that you strengthened when you worked down your anxiety:

☐ generosity	☐ peacefulness	
☐ kindness	☐ self-discipline	
☐ compassion	☐ forgiveness	
☐ consideration	☐ courage	
☐ helpfulness	☐ responsibility	
☐ respectfulness	☐ reliability	
☐ honesty	☐ loyalty	
☐ fairness	☐ love	
☐ patience	☐ humility	

Rate your anxiety on a scale of 0 to 100%:

☐ %

Week 9

The three tools that we will focus on in week nine are:

1. Depersonalise: thinking tool
2. Find a solution: behavioural tool
3. Grounding: calming tool

Depersonalise: thinking tool

"I choose to depersonalise. There is no intention to hurt me. He is doing the best he can with the tools he has at the moment."

We live in a world where we are constantly interacting with others. An enormous source of our "fight or flight" reaction is the belief that other people deliberately set out to hurt/disappoint/neglect/exclude us.

> Your partner does not wash his dinner plate but leaves it in the sink. You think, "He knows how important it is to me that he keeps the sink clean, yet he still left his dirty plate in the sink. He is so unkind."
>
> If you examine the thinking behind the wording, it is: *"My partner thought it through and deliberately left the sink messy. His motive was cruelty."* No wonder you felt hurt and angry.

> Your child leaves dirty laundry lying on her bedroom floor. You think: "She is so disrespectful to me. I have told her a million times to put her dirty laundry in the laundry bin, but she just ignores my wishes."

In this case, you believe your daughter's actions are motivated by disrespect and rebelliousness.

> Your work colleagues go out for a drink one day when you are off sick. You think, "They waited for me to be away so that they did not have to include me. Now I know where I stand and I will avoid being friends with them in the future."

In this illustration, you have fearful thoughts: *"They do not like me. They plotted and planned to wait for the day that I was ill so that they could go out and have fun without me. They obviously do not want to socialise with me. I will retreat."*

Simply put, the implication in all these illustrations is that people, even those nearest and dearest to you, make deliberate decisions to hurt you in some way.

The reality is that:

> Every individual is busy with their own agenda and you are not at the centre of each person's thinking every minute of every day.

> Every human is imperfect, makes mistakes and is limited in various ways. This means that there are times when each one of us forgets, is lazy, careless, infantile, impulsive and pre-occupied. Moreover, when making a decision or taking action, we will be limited at that time by our level of intelligence, level of maturity, time restraints, budget, emotional capacity, needs, stresses and priorities.

Let us now reframe the above illustrations in a new light. Using this tool you could say: *"I choose to depersonalise. My partner left a dirty dish in the sink today. He probably got caught up in a tele-phone call and forgot about it."*

In other words, there was no intention to hurt me. I was not even on his mind. He was doing the best he could with the time and energy at his disposal.

In the second illustration, you could realise that the last thing your child wants to do is upset you. However, like countless other children, she did not remember to put her laundry in the bin. She is young and forgetful and laundry is not at the top of her priority list as it is on yours.

In the third illustration, it is highly unlikely that your work colleagues plotted and planned anything. It is more likely that you were not even on their radar when they decided impulsively to go out and have a drink.

Truthfully, there may be a small percentage of people who are actually "out to get you." Always check the facts before assuming the worst. Obviously, if a person is being cruel or vindictive, util-ising this tool would be inappropriate.

> Your friend does not invite you to her wedding. You are devastated. You call and ask her why. She tells you that she was very hurt that you did not invite her to your birthday dinner and now she wants to hurt you back.

In this case, you should not use the tool "**depersonalise**" because her actions are meant to hurt you personally. However, to move past your devastation you may need to use other tools such as "**find a solution**" (page 257) or "**do the difficult**" (page 197).

In summary, remember that like you, people are busy with their own agendas and do not actively set out to make you unhappy. Even the most loving, successful, put together person can make a mistake. This tool will help you to take out the personal hurt from the equation and look at the situation in a more realistic way.

The following exercise will assist you to see situations in a less personal way from now on.

EXERCISE 28

Fill out possible personalised and depersonalised thoughts for the scenarios below.

1. A co-worker is talking loudly on the phone which prevents you from concentrating.
   a) Personalised thought: *He does not want me to be successful so he is disturbing my concentration.*
   b) Depersonalised thought: *He is so excited about the deal he is closing that he is oblivious to his surroundings including me.*

2. Your friend does not acknowledge your birthday.
   a) Personalised thought: _______________
   b) Depersonalised thought:_______________

3. A family member does not take you into his/her confidence.
   a) Personalised thought: _______________
   b) Depersonalised thought: _______________

4. A relative does not buy a product you are selling for work.
    a) Personalised thought: _________________________________
    b) Depersonalised thought: _______________________________

5. You are not asked by a close friend to go on holiday with
    them.
    a) Personalised thought: _________________________________
    b) Depersonalised thought: _______________________________

6. You did not get a pay rise at work.
    a) Personalised thought: _________________________________
    b) Depersonalised thought: _______________________________

7. Your spouse/partner goes out for an evening when you are
    sick at home.
    a) Personalised thought: _________________________________
    b) Depersonalised thought:_______________________________

Find a solution: behavioural tool

"I choose to solutionise. I will find a solution by taking advice or doing research."

Frequently, when we encounter a problem, we feel overwhelmed and anxious. This may lead us to give up because the problem seems insurmountable. However, when you begin to look for a solution, your anxiety will slowly reduce.

To solve a problem you may need (A) to take advice or (B) to do further research.

A — Taking advice

One way of attempting to find a solution is to ask somebody who is experienced in the problem area for advice. Many people believe that asking for advice is shameful and that the ideal way of operating is to be self-sufficient. Believe me, there is nothing shameful about needing advice. All the greatest minds in the world had mentors who were key to their success.

EXERCISE 29

Do you find it difficult to ask for advice?　　　　　　　YES/NO

If you answered "no," who do you generally call on for advice?

If you answered "yes," why do you think this is so?

- > You are shy
- > You do not trust anybody
- > You do not want to expose your ignorance
- > There are no intelligent people around
- > You are too proud
- > You worry you will lose face
- > You believe in self-sufficiency
- > Other: ____________________________________

Having circled one or more of the above options, think of ways you can rectify the situation. Write them down.

Advantages of taking advice

Taking advice can save you a lot of time. Why reinvent the wheel when somebody can direct you to a method that works?

You will be amazed at how much people around you know. Even people who lack formal education have a wealth of experience and knowledge. By asking for advice, you are also going to get emotional support (even if only indirectly). Suddenly, you are no longer alone, and there is somebody to assist you.

Who to ask?

There is a wide range of people you could ask. Here is a short list of some of them:

> family member
> business consultant
> colleague
> partner
> psychologist
> expert in the relevant field

> friend
> religious leader

Criteria of whom to ask

There are only two criteria to bear in mind before deciding whom you will ask. At times, it is beneficial to get several opinions.

> The person you ask must have your benefit at heart. It is no good asking a competitor or antagonist.
> You must respect the person you ask and be willing to give their words consideration.

B — Doing further research

When a process breaks down, it is often a result of insufficient groundwork. Thus, rather than giving up, spacing out or catastrophising, it is preferable to go back to the drawing board. You may need to read books, go on a course, refer to old notes, or travel to obtain the answers you are seeking. Doing further research can be done individually or in collaboration with others. Collaboration will frequently incorporate asking for advice.

> Tim is an architect who specialises in corporate designs. When he submits a proposal for a building, it is often knocked back. This is commonplace where design is involved because the first suggestion is the artist's idea and needs to be approved by the customer.
>
> In the early stages of his career, Tim would give up and withdraw from a job if his design was not accepted immediately. With years of experience behind him, Tim now knows that design is a collaborative process that occurs

over time. Currently, if a proposal is not accepted, he will go back to the drawing board, do additional research and submit an improved design.

> Minnie is in year 11 at school. There is a lot of work to do at this level and her teachers drive her hard. When she first consulted with me, she described how she would cry if her essay earned a poor mark.

After a few sessions, Minnie grasped that her teachers were preparing her for her final exams. She changed her perception. Now when she receives a poor mark, she meets with the relevant teacher to learn how she can improve.

> Joe has a new job as a graduate lawyer. He was overwhelmed by the amount of work allocated to him plus the complexity. For a while, he wanted to give up and flunk out because it felt so overwhelming.

After learning that there is no shame in asking for advice and assistance, he approached a few senior lawyers. To his happy surprise, he found that they understood his situation completely, having gone through it themselves. They were helpful, supportive and non-judgmental.

EXERCISE 30

Imagine that you have submitted a work-related proposal and it is sent back to you asking you to amend and improve it. (If you are at school, imagine you have submitted a school project instead. If you are at home full-time, imagine a family member criticises your cooking.)

Do you think you would?

> give up
> space out
> change your job
> fear the worst
> give in
> run away
> scream at the manager/teacher/family member
> other

Explain how doing any of these things would be helpful to you.

Would you ever think about re-working the proposal until it is acceptable?   YES/NO

If you answered "yes," how would you go about doing it?

If you answered "no," what is the reason?

> You do not believe you'd get a second chance
> You cannot persevere
> You need immediate recognition
> You do not believe that your work could ever be deficient
> You wouldn't give the manager the satisfaction
> You're prepared to try everything only once
> Other

Grounding: calming tool

Grounding is a form of mindfulness that utilises your five senses to help you notice what is happening right here, right now.

In any given situation, ask yourself:

> > What am I seeing?
> > What am I hearing?
> > What am I touching?
> > What am I smelling?
> > What am I tasting?

Grounding helps you to stop, think and take in the moment.

Let's say you are washing dishes. Take a moment to ask yourself:

> > What am I seeing? — soapy suds
> > What am I hearing? — the water splash
> > What am I touching? — warm soapy water
> > What am I smelling? — the lemon of the soap
> > What am I tasting? — the steak from dinner

All through the day, there are opportunities for grounding. When you cook, dress, shower, or sit on the train…the list is endless.

EXERCISE 31

Stop right now and ground yourself by asking and answering:

> > What am I seeing?
> > What am I hearing?
> > What am I touching?
> > What am I smelling?
> > What am I tasting?

Day	M	T	W	T	F	S	S
Overall Anxiety Rating for the day (0-10)							
1. EXERCISE							
How long?							
Anxiety level before (0-10)							
Anxiety level after (0-10)							
2. BREATHING							
How long?							
Anxiety level before (0-10)							
Anxiety level after (0-10)							
3. RELAXATION							
How long?							
Anxiety level before (0-10)							
Anxiety level after (0-10)							
4. PERVASIVE PESSIMISTIC THINKING							
How often this type of thought occurred							
Belief in thoughts before challenging (0-10)							
Belief in thoughts after challenging (0-10)							
5. CATASTROPHIC THINKING							
How often this type of thought occurred							
Belief in thoughts before challenging (0-10)							
Belief in thoughts after challenging (0-10)							

Day	M	T	W	T	F	S	S
6. PERMANENT PESSIMISTIC THINKING							
How often this type of thought occurred							
Belief in thoughts before challenging (0-10)							
Belief in thoughts after challenging (0-10)							
7. MINDFULNESS **(FORMAL, GROUNDING, INFORMAL MINDFULNESS)**							
How long?							
Anxiety level before (0-10)							
Anxiety level after (0-10)							
8. ROMANTIC THINKING							
How often this type of thought occurred							
Belief in thoughts before challenging (0-10)							
Belief in thoughts after challenging (0-10)							
9. NEGATIVE JUDGMENTAL THINKING							
How often this type of thought occurred							
Belief in thoughts before challenging (0-10)							
Belief in thoughts after challenging (0-10)							
10. CAN'T LET GO THINKING							
How often this type of thought occurred							
Belief in thoughts before challenging (0-10)							
Belief in thoughts after challenging (0-10)							
11. MEDITATION							
How long?							
Anxiety level before (0-10)							
Anxiety level after (0-10)							

Date: ______________

Anxiety Management Worksheet

The purpose of this worksheet is to help you to see every stressful event as an opportunity for
1. greater understanding of yourself, your anxiety and the people around you, and
2. practicing tools to manage your anxiety.

Step One: An Event

Briefly describe an event when you became anxious. Give such details as time, place and people involved, and end with "That's when I began to work myself up…"

____

____

____

____

Rate your anxiety on a scale of 0 to 100%: ☐ %

E

Step Two: The Working-Up Process

Learn about your working up process by identifying your thoughts, feelings, behaviours and bodily reactions during the event.
Tick the ones that most resonate with you.

B

Undermining Beliefs

I fear that I have lost...

☐ approval
☐ control
☐ co-operation
☐ face
☐ respect
☐ success
☐ trust
☐ validation
☐ love

This event proves that I am...

☐ stupid
☐ abnormal
☐ incompetent
☐ lazy
☐ irresponsible
☐ a total failure
☐ undisciplined
☐ untogether
☐ useless

I worry that I will suffer...

☐ mental collapse
☐ illness
☐ financial hardship

What I want is...

☐ total control
☐ respect
☐ success
☐ perfection
☐ comfort
☐ fairness
☐ tranquility
☐ all the answers
☐ for life to go smoothly
☐ to be all things to all people

Self-destructive Behaviour

Active

☐ get violent
☐ swear
☐ slam doors
☐ run away
☐ overeat
☐ harm myself
☐ criticise

Passive

☐ take it too seriously
☐ give up
☐ wallow in self pity
☐ sulk
☐ space out
☐ procrastinate
☐ give in
☐ be controlled

Intense Feelings

Angry feelings

☐ hateful
☐ aggravated
☐ annoyed
☐ hostile
☐ outraged
☐ punitive
☐ resentful
☐ vengeful

Fearful feelings

☐ helpless
☐ hopeless
☐ disappointed
☐ sad

☐ attacked
☐ worn out
☐ rejected
☐ jealous
☐ afraid
☐ exploited
☐ lonely
☐ abandoned
☐ guilty
☐ insulted
☐ confused
☐ disillusioned
☐ misunderstood
☐ trapped

Bodily Reactions (limbic system)

I am uncomfortable because I am experiencing...

☐ tremors
☐ nausea
☐ sweaty palms
☐ stomach-ache
☐ pounding heart
☐ general tension
☐ fatigue
☐ imagination on fire
☐ headache
☐ dry mouth
☐ jaw clenching
☐ shortness of breath

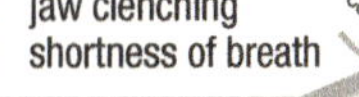

B   **F**   **L**

Step Three: The Working-Down Process

Begin with, "Suddenly I realised that I was anxious and that I had choices..." This is the step of self-leadership and trust in one's ability to handle the situation.

Choose helpful thoughts:

I choose to depersonalise
There is no intention to hurt me. He is doing the best he can with the tools he has at the moment.

I choose realism over romanticism
Life presents many obstacles. I lower or raise standards as needed.

There is no right or wrong
Unless it is a moral issue, I will see it simply as a difference of opinion and/or taste.

I choose the total view of positivity
Even though this event is negative, the total view of his behaviour is positive.

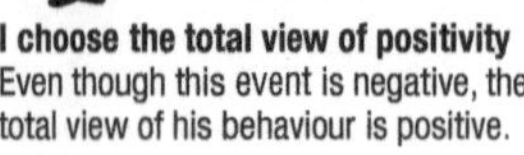

I surrender control
Since I cannot change this situation, I choose to let go of it.

I choose to put this event in perspective This event is not a catastrophe because it is not life threatening. It can be viewed as a trivial life event, a normal life problem that needs to be solved not dramatised.

I choose to view this event as average, falling within the normal range
This event is not exceptional; many people have gone through this.

It's temporary - "this too shall pass"
Life is constantly changing and moving through phases and this situation will also change.

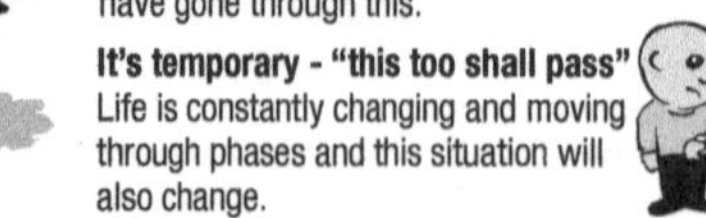

Fears or facts?
Why fear? It may not happen!

I choose to focus on this as a learning experience
Every problem that comes my way is an opportunity for me to learn about my strengths and weaknesses, others and life.

Feel soothing emotions:

I choose to feel warm, loving emotions. I do this by focusing on my heart and letting love, trust forgiveness, compassion, hope or gratitude fill my heart space.

Behave constructively:

I choose to work in part acts:
I will break the overwhelming job into manageable parts.

Do the difficult:
I will face what I fear and act with self-discipline.

I choose to solutionise:
I will find a solution by taking advice or doing research.

Prioritise myself:
I will keep my life balanced by meeting friends, doing exercise or laughing.

Compartmentalise:
I will not let this event cloud my whole day; I will focus on something else now.

Utilise calming strategies:

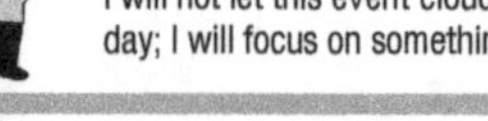

When I:
- relax,
- breathe deeply,
- go for a run,
- shower,
- lie down,
- read,
- watch TV,
- climb into a mental helicopter,
- practice mindfulness/meditation,

my mind and body calm down.

Step Four: The Self Motivation Process

Endorse yourself for any growth no matter how small.

In the past I would have...

____

____

But this time I...

____

____

Tick off the traits that you strengthened when you worked down your anxiety:

- ☐ generosity
- ☐ kindness
- ☐ compassion
- ☐ consideration
- ☐ helpfulness
- ☐ respectfulness
- ☐ honesty
- ☐ fairness
- ☐ patience
- ☐ peacefulness
- ☐ self-discipline
- ☐ forgiveness
- ☐ courage
- ☐ responsibility
- ☐ reliability
- ☐ loyalty
- ☐ love
- ☐ humility

Rate your anxiety on a scale of 0 to 100%:

________ %

O

W

Date: ___________

Anxiety Management Worksheet

The purpose of this worksheet is to help you to see every stressful event as an opportunity for
1. greater understanding of yourself, your anxiety and the people around you, and
2. practicing tools to manage your anxiety.

Step One: An Event

Briefly describe an event when you became anxious. Give such details as time, place and people involved, and end with "That's when I began to work myself up…"

E

Rate your anxiety on a scale of 0 to 100%: ______ %

Step Two: The Working-Up Process

Learn about your working up process by identifying your thoughts, feelings, behaviours and bodily reactions during the event.
Tick the ones that most resonate with you.

Undermining Beliefs

B

I fear that I have lost...
- ☐ approval
- ☐ control
- ☐ co-operation
- ☐ face
- ☐ respect
- ☐ success
- ☐ trust
- ☐ validation
- ☐ love

This event proves that I am...
- ☐ stupid
- ☐ abnormal
- ☐ incompetent
- ☐ lazy
- ☐ irresponsible
- ☐ a total failure
- ☐ undisciplined
- ☐ untogether
- ☐ useless

I worry that I will suffer...
- ☐ mental collapse
- ☐ illness
- ☐ financial hardship

What I want is...
- ☐ total control
- ☐ respect
- ☐ success
- ☐ perfection
- ☐ comfort
- ☐ fairness
- ☐ tranquility
- ☐ all the answers
- ☐ for life to go smoothly
- ☐ to be all things to all people

Self-destructive Behaviour

Active
- ☐ get violent
- ☐ swear
- ☐ slam doors
- ☐ run away
- ☐ overeat
- ☐ harm myself
- ☐ criticise

Passive
- ☐ take it too seriously
- ☐ give up
- ☐ wallow in self pity
- ☐ sulk
- ☐ space out
- ☐ procrastinate
- ☐ give in
- ☐ be controlled

Intense Feelings

Angry feelings
- ☐ hateful
- ☐ aggravated
- ☐ annoyed
- ☐ hostile
- ☐ outraged
- ☐ punitive
- ☐ resentful
- ☐ vengeful
- ☐ attacked
- ☐ worn out
- ☐ rejected
- ☐ jealous
- ☐ afraid
- ☐ exploited
- ☐ lonely
- ☐ abandoned
- ☐ guilty

Fearful feelings
- ☐ helpless
- ☐ hopeless
- ☐ disappointed
- ☐ sad
- ☐ insulted
- ☐ confused
- ☐ disillusioned
- ☐ misunderstood
- ☐ trapped

Bodily Reactions (limbic system)

I am uncomfortable because I am experiencing...
- ☐ tremors
- ☐ nausea
- ☐ sweaty palms
- ☐ stomach-ache
- ☐ pounding heart
- ☐ general tension
- ☐ fatigue
- ☐ imagination on fire
- ☐ headache
- ☐ dry mouth
- ☐ jaw clenching
- ☐ shortness of breath

Continued over

B   **F**   **L**

Step Three: The Working-Down Process

Begin with, "Suddenly I realised that I was anxious and that I had choices..." This is the step of self-leadership and trust in one's ability to handle the situation.

Choose helpful thoughts:

I choose to depersonalise
There is no intention to hurt me. He is doing the best he can with the tools he has at the moment.

I choose realism over romanticism
Life presents many obstacles. I lower or raise standards as needed.

There is no right or wrong
Unless it is a moral issue, I will see it simply as a difference of opinion and/or taste.

I choose the total view of positivity
Even though this event is negative, the total view of his behaviour is positive.

I surrender control
Since I cannot change this situation, I choose to let go of it.

I choose to put this event in perspective This event is not a catastrophe because it is not life threatening. It can be viewed as a trivial life event, a normal life problem that needs to be solved not dramatised.

I choose to view this event as average, falling within the normal range
This event is not exceptional; many people have gone through this.

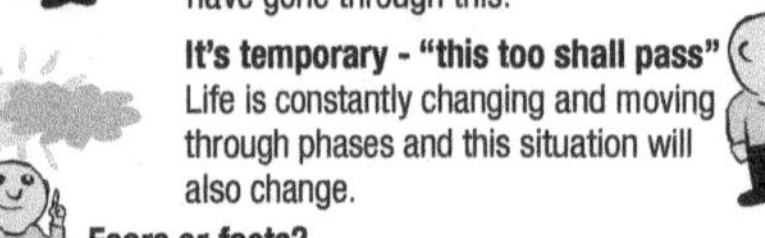

It's temporary - "this too shall pass"
Life is constantly changing and moving through phases and this situation will also change.

Fears or facts?
Why fear? It may not happen!

I choose to focus on this as a learning experience
Every problem that comes my way is an opportunity for me to learn about my strengths and weaknesses, others and life.

Feel soothing emotions:

I choose to feel warm, loving emotions. I do this by focusing on my heart and letting love, trust forgiveness, compassion, hope or gratitude fill my heart space.

Behave constructively:

I choose to work in part acts:
I will break the overwhelming job into manageable parts.

Do the difficult:
I will face what I fear and act with self-discipline.

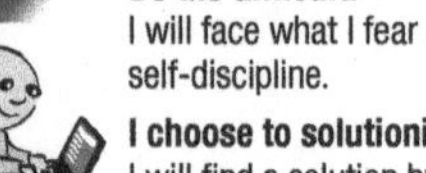

I choose to solutionise:
I will find a solution by taking advice or doing research.

Prioritise myself:
I will keep my life balanced by meeting friends, doing exercise or laughing.

Compartmentalise:
I will not let this event cloud my whole day; I will focus on something else now.

Utilise calming strategies:

When I:
- relax,
- breathe deeply,
- go for a run,
- shower,
- lie down,
- read,
- watch TV,
- climb into a mental helicopter,
- practice mindfulness/meditation,

my mind and body calm down.

Step Four: The Self Motivation Process

Endorse yourself for any growth no matter how small.

In the past I would have...

____

____

But this time I...

____

____

Tick off the traits that you strengthened when you worked down your anxiety:

☐ generosity   ☐ peacefulness
☐ kindness   ☐ self-discipline
☐ compassion   ☐ forgiveness
☐ consideration   ☐ courage
☐ helpfulness   ☐ responsibility
☐ respectfulness   ☐ reliability
☐ honesty   ☐ loyalty
☐ fairness   ☐ love
☐ patience   ☐ humility

Rate your anxiety on a scale of 0 to 100%:

________ %

O

W

Date: ___________

Anxiety Management Worksheet

The purpose of this worksheet is to help you to see every stressful event as an opportunity for
1. greater understanding of yourself, your anxiety and the people around you, and
2. practicing tools to manage your anxiety.

Step One: An Event

Briefly describe an event when you became anxious. Give such details as time, place and people involved, and end with "That's when I began to work myself up..."

____

____

____

_______________________________________ Rate your anxiety on a scale of 0 to 100%: [____] %

E

Step Two: The Working-Up Process

Learn about your working up process by identifying your thoughts, feelings, behaviours and bodily reactions during the event.

Tick the ones that most resonate with you.

Undermining Beliefs

B

I fear that I have lost...

- ☐ approval
- ☐ control
- ☐ co-operation
- ☐ face
- ☐ respect
- ☐ success
- ☐ trust
- ☐ validation
- ☐ love

This event proves that I am...

- ☐ stupid
- ☐ abnormal
- ☐ incompetent
- ☐ lazy
- ☐ irresponsible
- ☐ a total failure
- ☐ undisciplined
- ☐ untogether
- ☐ useless

I worry that I will suffer...

- ☐ mental collapse
- ☐ illness
- ☐ financial hardship

What I want is...

- ☐ total control
- ☐ respect
- ☐ success
- ☐ perfection
- ☐ comfort
- ☐ fairness
- ☐ tranquility
- ☐ all the answers
- ☐ for life to go smoothly
- ☐ to be all things to all people

Self-destructive Behaviour

Active

- ☐ get violent
- ☐ swear
- ☐ slam doors
- ☐ run away
- ☐ overeat
- ☐ harm myself
- ☐ criticise

Passive

- ☐ take it too seriously
- ☐ give up
- ☐ wallow in self pity
- ☐ sulk
- ☐ space out
- ☐ procrastinate
- ☐ give in
- ☐ be controlled

Intense Feelings

Angry feelings

- ☐ hateful
- ☐ aggravated
- ☐ annoyed
- ☐ hostile
- ☐ outraged
- ☐ punitive
- ☐ resentful
- ☐ vengeful

Fearful feelings

- ☐ helpless
- ☐ hopeless
- ☐ disappointed
- ☐ sad

- ☐ attacked
- ☐ worn out
- ☐ rejected
- ☐ jealous
- ☐ afraid
- ☐ exploited
- ☐ lonely
- ☐ abandoned
- ☐ guilty
- ☐ insulted
- ☐ confused
- ☐ disillusioned
- ☐ misunderstood
- ☐ trapped

Bodily Reactions (limbic system)

I am uncomfortable because I am experiencing...

- ☐ tremors
- ☐ nausea
- ☐ sweaty palms
- ☐ stomach-ache
- ☐ pounding heart
- ☐ general tension
- ☐ fatigue
- ☐ imagination on fire
- ☐ headache
- ☐ dry mouth
- ☐ jaw clenching
- ☐ shortness of breath

Continued over

B   **F**   **L**

Step Three: The Working-Down Process

Begin with, "Suddenly I realised that I was anxious and that I had choices..." This is the step of self-leadership and trust in one's ability to handle the situation.

Choose helpful thoughts:

I choose to depersonalise
There is no intention to hurt me. He is doing the best he can with the tools he has at the moment.

I choose realism over romanticism
Life presents many obstacles. I lower or raise standards as needed.

There is no right or wrong
Unless it is a moral issue, I will see it simply as a difference of opinion and/or taste.

I choose the total view of positivity
Even though this event is negative, the total view of his behaviour is positive.

I surrender control
Since I cannot change this situation, I choose to let go of it.

I choose to put this event in perspective This event is not a catastrophe because it is not life threatening. It can be viewed as a trivial life event, a normal life problem that needs to be solved not dramatised.

I choose to view this event as average, falling within the normal range
This event is not exceptional; many people have gone through this.

It's temporary - "this too shall pass"
Life is constantly changing and moving through phases and this situation will also change.

Fears or facts?
Why fear? It may not happen!

I choose to focus on this as a learning experience
Every problem that comes my way is an opportunity for me to learn about my strengths and weaknesses, others and life.

Feel soothing emotions:

I choose to feel warm, loving emotions. I do this by focusing on my heart and letting love, trust forgiveness, compassion, hope or gratitude fill my heart space.

Behave constructively:

I choose to work in part acts:
I will break the overwhelming job into manageable parts.

Do the difficult:
I will face what I fear and act with self-discipline.

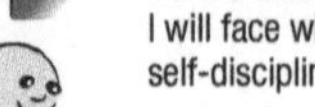

I choose to solutionise:
I will find a solution by taking advice or doing research.

Prioritise myself:
I will keep my life balanced by meeting friends, doing exercise or laughing.

Compartmentalise:
I will not let this event cloud my whole day; I will focus on something else now.

Utilise calming strategies:

When I:
- relax,
- breathe deeply,
- go for a run,
- shower,
- lie down,
- read,
- watch TV,
- climb into a mental helicopter,
- practice mindfulness/meditation,

  my mind and body calm down.

Step Four: The Self Motivation Process

Endorse yourself for any growth no matter how small.

In the past I would have...

____

____

But this time I...

____

____

Tick off the traits that you strengthened when you worked down your anxiety:

☐ generosity	☐ peacefulness		
☐ kindness	☐ self-discipline		
☐ compassion	☐ forgiveness		
☐ consideration	☐ courage		
☐ helpfulness	☐ responsibility		
☐ respectfulness	☐ reliability		
☐ honesty	☐ loyalty		
☐ fairness	☐ love		
☐ patience	☐ humility		

Rate your anxiety on a scale of 0 to 100%:

____ %

o

w

Date: ___________

Anxiety Management Worksheet

The purpose of this worksheet is to help you to see every stressful event as an opportunity for
1. greater understanding of yourself, your anxiety and the people around you, and
2. practicing tools to manage your anxiety.

Step One: An Event

Briefly describe an event when you became anxious. Give such details as time, place and people involved, and end with "That's when I began to work myself up…"

____

____

____

_______________________________ Rate your anxiety on a scale of 0 to 100%: [   ] %

E

Step Two: The Working-Up Process

Learn about your working up process by identifying your thoughts, feelings, behaviours and bodily reactions during the event.

Tick the ones that most resonate with you.

Undermining Beliefs

B

I fear that I have lost...
- ☐ approval
- ☐ control
- ☐ co-operation
- ☐ face
- ☐ respect
- ☐ success
- ☐ trust
- ☐ validation
- ☐ love

This event proves that I am...
- ☐ stupid
- ☐ abnormal
- ☐ incompetent
- ☐ lazy
- ☐ irresponsible
- ☐ a total failure
- ☐ undisciplined
- ☐ untogether
- ☐ useless

I worry that I will suffer...
- ☐ mental collapse
- ☐ illness
- ☐ financial hardship

What I want is...
- ☐ total control
- ☐ respect
- ☐ success
- ☐ perfection
- ☐ comfort
- ☐ fairness
- ☐ tranquility
- ☐ all the answers
- ☐ for life to go smoothly
- ☐ to be all things to all people

Self-destructive Behaviour

Active
- ☐ get violent
- ☐ swear
- ☐ slam doors
- ☐ run away
- ☐ overeat
- ☐ harm myself
- ☐ criticise

Passive
- ☐ take it too seriously
- ☐ give up
- ☐ wallow in self pity
- ☐ sulk
- ☐ space out
- ☐ procrastinate
- ☐ give in
- ☐ be controlled

Intense Feelings

Angry feelings
- ☐ hateful
- ☐ aggravated
- ☐ annoyed
- ☐ hostile
- ☐ outraged
- ☐ punitive
- ☐ resentful
- ☐ vengeful

Fearful feelings
- ☐ helpless
- ☐ hopeless
- ☐ disappointed
- ☐ sad

- ☐ attacked
- ☐ worn out
- ☐ rejected
- ☐ jealous
- ☐ afraid
- ☐ exploited
- ☐ lonely
- ☐ abandoned
- ☐ guilty
- ☐ insulted
- ☐ confused
- ☐ disillusioned
- ☐ misunderstood
- ☐ trapped

Bodily Reactions (limbic system)

I am uncomfortable because I am experiencing...
- ☐ tremors
- ☐ nausea
- ☐ sweaty palms
- ☐ stomach-ache
- ☐ pounding heart
- ☐ general tension
- ☐ fatigue
- ☐ imagination on fire
- ☐ headache
- ☐ dry mouth
- ☐ jaw clenching
- ☐ shortness of breath

Continued over

B   **F**   **L**

Step Three: The Working-Down Process

Begin with, "Suddenly I realised that I was anxious and that I had choices..." This is the step of self-leadership and trust in one's ability to handle the situation.

Choose helpful thoughts:

I choose to depersonalise
There is no intention to hurt me. He is doing the best he can with the tools he has at the moment.

I choose realism over romanticism
Life presents many obstacles. I lower or raise standards as needed.

There is no right or wrong
Unless it is a moral issue, I will see it simply as a difference of opinion and/or taste.

I choose the total view of positivity
Even though this event is negative, the total view of his behaviour is positive.

I surrender control
Since I cannot change this situation, I choose to let go of it.

I choose to put this event in perspective This event is not a catastrophe because it is not life threatening. It can be viewed as a trivial life event, a normal life problem that needs to be solved not dramatised.

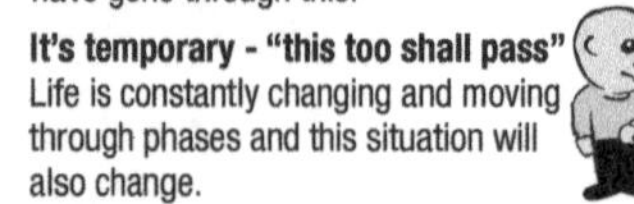

I choose to view this event as average, falling within the normal range
This event is not exceptional; many people have gone through this.

It's temporary - "this too shall pass"
Life is constantly changing and moving through phases and this situation will also change.

Fears or facts?
Why fear? It may not happen!

I choose to focus on this as a learning experience
Every problem that comes my way is an opportunity for me to learn about my strengths and weaknesses, others and life..

Feel soothing emotions:

I choose to feel warm, loving emotions. I do this by focusing on my heart and letting love, trust forgiveness, compassion, hope or gratitude fill my heart space.

Behave constructively:

I choose to work in part acts:
I will break the overwhelming job into manageable parts.

Do the difficult:
I will face what I fear and act with self-discipline.

I choose to solutionise:
I will find a solution by taking advice or doing research.

Prioritise myself:
I will keep my life balanced by meeting friends, doing exercise or laughing.

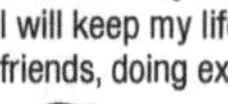

Compartmentalise:
I will not let this event cloud my whole day; I will focus on something else now.

Utilise calming strategies:

When I:
- relax,
- breathe deeply,
- go for a run,
- shower,
- lie down,
- read,
- watch TV,
- climb into a mental helicopter,
- practice mindfulness/meditation,

my mind and body calm down.

Step Four: The Self Motivation Process

Endorse yourself for any growth no matter how small.

In the past I would have...

____

____

But this time I...

____

____

Tick off the traits that you strengthened when you worked down your anxiety:

☐	generosity	☐	peacefulness
☐	kindness	☐	self-discipline
☐	compassion	☐	forgiveness
☐	consideration	☐	courage
☐	helpfulness	☐	responsibility
☐	respectfulness	☐	reliability
☐	honesty	☐	loyalty
☐	fairness	☐	love
☐	patience	☐	humility

Rate your anxiety on a scale of 0 to 100%:

[____]%

Anxiety Management Worksheet

The purpose of this worksheet is to help you to see every stressful event as an opportunity for
1. greater understanding of yourself, your anxiety and the people around you, and
2. practicing tools to manage your anxiety.

Step One: An Event

Briefly describe an event when you became anxious. Give such details as time, place and people involved, and end with "That's when I began to work myself up…"

____

____

____

____ Rate your anxiety on a scale of 0 to 100%: ☐ %

E

Step Two: The Working-Up Process

Learn about your working up process by identifying your thoughts, feelings, behaviours and bodily reactions during the event.
Tick the ones that most resonate with you.

Undermining Beliefs

B

I fear that I have lost…
- ☐ approval
- ☐ control
- ☐ co-operation
- ☐ face
- ☐ respect
- ☐ success
- ☐ trust
- ☐ validation
- ☐ love

This event proves that I am…
- ☐ stupid
- ☐ abnormal
- ☐ incompetent
- ☐ lazy
- ☐ irresponsible
- ☐ a total failure
- ☐ undisciplined
- ☐ untogether
- ☐ useless

I worry that I will suffer…
- ☐ mental collapse
- ☐ illness
- ☐ financial hardship

What I want is…
- ☐ total control
- ☐ respect
- ☐ success
- ☐ perfection
- ☐ comfort
- ☐ fairness
- ☐ tranquility
- ☐ all the answers
- ☐ for life to go smoothly
- ☐ to be all things to all people

Self-destructive Behaviour

Active
- ☐ get violent
- ☐ swear
- ☐ slam doors
- ☐ run away
- ☐ overeat
- ☐ harm myself
- ☐ criticise

Passive
- ☐ take it too seriously
- ☐ give up
- ☐ wallow in self pity
- ☐ sulk
- ☐ space out
- ☐ procrastinate
- ☐ give in
- ☐ be controlled

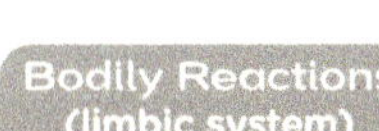

Intense Feelings

Angry feelings
- ☐ hateful
- ☐ aggravated
- ☐ annoyed
- ☐ hostile
- ☐ outraged
- ☐ punitive
- ☐ resentful
- ☐ vengeful
- ☐ attacked
- ☐ worn out
- ☐ rejected
- ☐ jealous
- ☐ afraid
- ☐ exploited
- ☐ lonely
- ☐ abandoned
- ☐ guilty

Fearful feelings
- ☐ helpless
- ☐ hopeless
- ☐ disappointed
- ☐ sad
- ☐ insulted
- ☐ confused
- ☐ disillusioned
- ☐ misunderstood
- ☐ trapped

Bodily Reactions (limbic system)

I am uncomfortable because I am experiencing…
- ☐ tremors
- ☐ nausea
- ☐ sweaty palms
- ☐ stomach-ache
- ☐ pounding heart
- ☐ general tension
- ☐ fatigue
- ☐ imagination on fire
- ☐ headache
- ☐ dry mouth
- ☐ jaw clenching
- ☐ shortness of breath

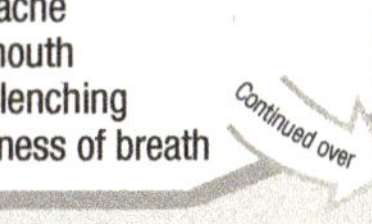

Continued over

B   **F**   **L**

Step Three: The Working-Down Process

Begin with, "Suddenly I realised that I was anxious and that I had choices…" This is the step of self-leadership and trust in one's ability to handle the situation.

Choose helpful thoughts:

I choose to depersonalise
There is no intention to hurt me. He is doing the best he can with the tools he has at the moment.

I choose realism over romanticism
Life presents many obstacles. I lower or raise standards as needed.

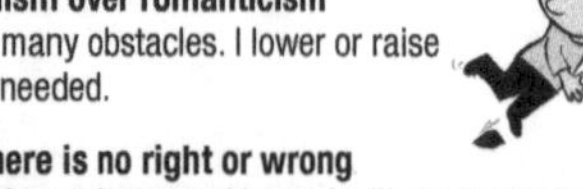

There is no right or wrong
Unless it is a moral issue, I will see it simply as a difference of opinion and/or taste.

I choose the total view of positivity
Even though this event is negative, the total view of his behaviour is positive.

I surrender control
Since I cannot change this situation, I choose to let go of it.

I choose to put this event in perspective
This event is not a catastrophe because it is not life threatening. It can be viewed as a trivial life event, a normal life problem that needs to be solved not dramatised.

I choose to view this event as average, falling within the normal range
This event is not exceptional; many people have gone through this.

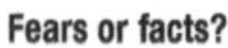

It's temporary - "this too shall pass"
Life is constantly changing and moving through phases and this situation will also change.

Fears or facts?
Why fear? It may not happen!

I choose to focus on this as a learning experience
Every problem that comes my way is an opportunity for me to learn about my strengths and weaknesses, others and life.

Feel soothing emotions:

I choose to feel warm, loving emotions. I do this by focusing on my heart and letting love, trust forgiveness, compassion, hope or gratitude fill my heart space.

Behave constructively:

I choose to work in part acts:
I will break the overwhelming job into manageable parts.

Do the difficult:
I will face what I fear and act with self-discipline.

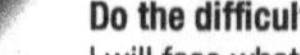

I choose to solutionise:
I will find a solution by taking advice or doing research.

Prioritise myself:
I will keep my life balanced by meeting friends, doing exercise or laughing.

Compartmentalise:
I will not let this event cloud my whole day; I will focus on something else now.

Utilise calming strategies:

When I:
- relax,
- breathe deeply,
- go for a run,
- shower,
- lie down,
- read,
- watch TV,
- climb into a mental helicopter,
- practice mindfulness/meditation,

my mind and body calm down.

Step Four: The Self Motivation Process

Endorse yourself for any growth no matter how small.

In the past I would have…
____

____

But this time I…
____

____

Tick off the traits that you strengthened when you worked down your anxiety:

☐ generosity	☐ peacefulness
☐ kindness	☐ self-discipline
☐ compassion	☐ forgiveness
☐ consideration	☐ courage
☐ helpfulness	☐ responsibility
☐ respectfulness	☐ reliability
☐ honesty	☐ loyalty
☐ fairness	☐ love
☐ patience	☐ humility

Rate your anxiety on a scale of 0 to 100%:

[ ] %

O

W

Date: ___________

Anxiety Management Worksheet

The purpose of this worksheet is to help you to see every stressful event as an opportunity for
1. greater understanding of yourself, your anxiety and the people around you, and
2. practicing tools to manage your anxiety.

Step One: An Event

Briefly describe an event when you became anxious. Give such details as time, place and people involved, and end with "That's when I began to work myself up…"

E

Rate your anxiety on a scale of 0 to 100%: ____ %

Step Two: The Working-Up Process

Learn about your working up process by identifying your thoughts, feelings, behaviours and bodily reactions during the event.

Tick the ones that most resonate with you.

Undermining Beliefs

B

I fear that I have lost…

- ☐ approval
- ☐ control
- ☐ co-operation
- ☐ face
- ☐ respect
- ☐ success
- ☐ trust
- ☐ validation
- ☐ love

This event proves that I am…

- ☐ stupid
- ☐ abnormal
- ☐ incompetent
- ☐ lazy
- ☐ irresponsible
- ☐ a total failure
- ☐ undisciplined
- ☐ untogether
- ☐ useless

I worry that I will suffer…

- ☐ mental collapse
- ☐ illness
- ☐ financial hardship

What I want is…

- ☐ total control
- ☐ respect
- ☐ success
- ☐ perfection
- ☐ comfort
- ☐ fairness
- ☐ tranquility
- ☐ all the answers
- ☐ for life to go smoothly
- ☐ to be all things to all people

Self-destructive Behaviour

Active 
- ☐ get violent
- ☐ swear
- ☐ slam doors
- ☐ run away
- ☐ overeat
- ☐ harm myself
- ☐ criticise

Passive
- ☐ take it too seriously
- ☐ give up
- ☐ wallow in self pity
- ☐ sulk
- ☐ space out
- ☐ procrastinate
- ☐ give in
- ☐ be controlled

B

Intense Feelings

Angry feelings
- ☐ hateful
- ☐ aggravated
- ☐ annoyed
- ☐ hostile
- ☐ outraged
- ☐ punitive
- ☐ resentful
- ☐ vengeful

Fearful feelings
- ☐ helpless
- ☐ hopeless
- ☐ disappointed
- ☐ sad
- ☐ attacked
- ☐ worn out
- ☐ rejected
- ☐ jealous
- ☐ afraid
- ☐ exploited
- ☐ lonely
- ☐ abandoned
- ☐ guilty
- ☐ insulted
- ☐ confused
- ☐ disillusioned
- ☐ misunderstood
- ☐ trapped

F

Bodily Reactions (limbic system)

I am uncomfortable because I am experiencing…

- ☐ tremors
- ☐ nausea
- ☐ sweaty palms
- ☐ stomach-ache
- ☐ pounding heart
- ☐ general tension
- ☐ fatigue
- ☐ imagination on fire
- ☐ headache
- ☐ dry mouth
- ☐ jaw clenching
- ☐ shortness of breath

Continued over

L

Step Three: The Working-Down Process

Begin with, "Suddenly I realised that I was anxious and that I had choices…" This is the step of self-leadership and trust in one's ability to handle the situation.

Choose helpful thoughts:

I choose to depersonalise
There is no intention to hurt me. He is doing the best he can with the tools he has at the moment.

I choose realism over romanticism
Life presents many obstacles. I lower or raise standards as needed.

There is no right or wrong
Unless it is a moral issue, I will see it simply as a difference of opinion and/or taste.

I choose the total view of positivity
Even though this event is negative, the total view of his behaviour is positive.

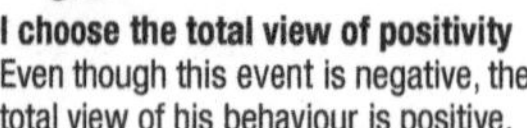

I surrender control
Since I cannot change this situation, I choose to let go of it.

I choose to put this event in perspective This event is not a catastrophe because it is not life threatening. It can be viewed as a trivial life event, a normal life problem that needs to be solved not dramatised.

I choose to view this event as average, falling within the normal range
This event is not exceptional; many people have gone through this.

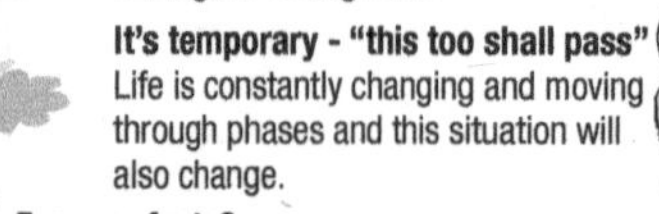

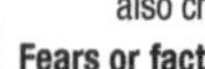

It's temporary - "this too shall pass"
Life is constantly changing and moving through phases and this situation will also change.

Fears or facts?
Why fear? It may not happen!

I choose to focus on this as a learning experience
Every problem that comes my way is an opportunity for me to learn about my strengths and weaknesses, others and life.

Feel soothing emotions:

I choose to feel warm, loving emotions. I do this by focusing on my heart and letting love, trust forgiveness, compassion, hope or gratitude fill my heart space.

Behave constructively:

I choose to work in part acts:
I will break the overwhelming job into manageable parts.

Do the difficult:
I will face what I fear and act with self-discipline.

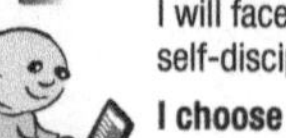

I choose to solutionise:
I will find a solution by taking advice or doing research.

Prioritise myself:
I will keep my life balanced by meeting friends, doing exercise or laughing.

Compartmentalise:
I will not let this event cloud my whole day; I will focus on something else now.

Utilise calming strategies:

When I:
- relax,
- breathe deeply,
- go for a run,
- shower,
- lie down,
- read,
- watch TV,
- climb into a mental helicopter,
- practice mindfulness/meditation,

my mind and body calm down.

Step Four: The Self Motivation Process

Endorse yourself for any growth no matter how small.

In the past I would have...

____

____

But this time I...

____

____

Tick off the traits that you strengthened when you worked down your anxiety:

☐ generosity	☐ peacefulness		
☐ kindness	☐ self-discipline		
☐ compassion	☐ forgiveness		
☐ consideration	☐ courage		
☐ helpfulness	☐ responsibility		
☐ respectfulness	☐ reliability		
☐ honesty	☐ loyalty		
☐ fairness	☐ love		
☐ patience	☐ humility		

Rate your anxiety on a scale of 0 to 100%:

______ %

Date: __________

Anxiety Management Worksheet

The purpose of this worksheet is to help you to see every stressful event as an opportunity for
1. greater understanding of yourself, your anxiety and the people around you, and
2. practicing tools to manage your anxiety.

Step One: An Event

Briefly describe an event when you became anxious. Give such details as time, place and people involved, and end with "That's when I began to work myself up…"

____

____

____

_______________________________________ Rate your anxiety on a scale of 0 to 100%: ☐ %

E

Step Two: The Working-Up Process

Learn about your working up process by identifying your thoughts, feelings, behaviours and bodily reactions during the event.
Tick the ones that most resonate with you.

B

Undermining Beliefs

I fear that I have lost...

☐ approval
☐ control
☐ co-operation
☐ face
☐ respect
☐ success
☐ trust
☐ validation
☐ love

This event proves that I am...

☐ stupid
☐ abnormal
☐ incompetent
☐ lazy
☐ irresponsible
☐ a total failure
☐ undisciplined
☐ untogether
☐ useless

I worry that I will suffer...

☐ mental collapse
☐ illness
☐ financial hardship

What I want is...

☐ total control
☐ respect
☐ success
☐ perfection
☐ comfort
☐ fairness
☐ tranquility
☐ all the answers
☐ for life to go smoothly
☐ to be all things to all people

Self-destructive Behaviour

Active
☐ get violent
☐ swear
☐ slam doors
☐ run away
☐ overeat
☐ harm myself
☐ criticise

Passive
☐ take it too seriously
☐ give up
☐ wallow in self pity
☐ sulk
☐ space out
☐ procrastinate
☐ give in
☐ be controlled

Intense Feelings

Angry feelings
☐ hateful
☐ aggravated
☐ annoyed
☐ hostile
☐ outraged
☐ punitive
☐ resentful
☐ vengeful
☐ attacked
☐ worn out
☐ rejected
☐ jealous
☐ afraid
☐ exploited
☐ lonely
☐ abandoned
☐ guilty

Fearful feelings
☐ helpless
☐ hopeless
☐ disappointed
☐ sad
☐ insulted
☐ confused
☐ disillusioned
☐ misunderstood
☐ trapped

Bodily Reactions (limbic system)

I am uncomfortable because I am experiencing...

☐ tremors
☐ nausea
☐ sweaty palms
☐ stomach-ache
☐ pounding heart
☐ general tension
☐ fatigue
☐ imagination on fire
☐ headache
☐ dry mouth
☐ jaw clenching
☐ shortness of breath

Continued over

B   **F**   **L**

Step Three: The Working-Down Process

Begin with, "Suddenly I realised that I was anxious and that I had choices..." This is the step of self-leadership and trust in one's ability to handle the situation.

Choose helpful thoughts:

I choose to depersonalise
There is no intention to hurt me. He is doing the best he can with the tools he has at the moment.

I choose realism over romanticism
Life presents many obstacles. I lower or raise standards as needed.

There is no right or wrong
Unless it is a moral issue, I will see it simply as a difference of opinion and/or taste.

I choose the total view of positivity
Even though this event is negative, the total view of his behaviour is positive.

I surrender control
Since I cannot change this situation, I choose to let go of it.

I choose to put this event in perspective This event is not a catastrophe because it is not life threatening. It can be viewed as a trivial life event, a normal life problem that needs to be solved not dramatised.

I choose to view this event as average, falling within the normal range
This event is not exceptional; many people have gone through this.

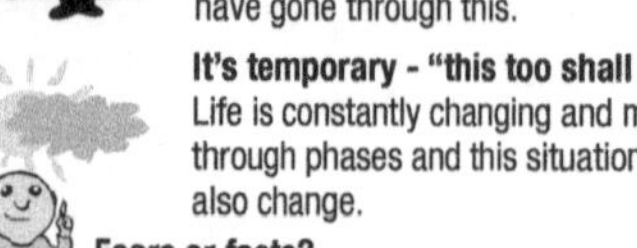

It's temporary - "this too shall pass"
Life is constantly changing and moving through phases and this situation will also change.

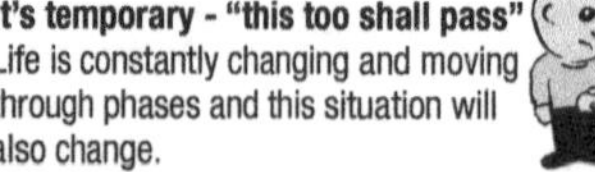

Fears or facts?
Why fear? It may not happen!

I choose to focus on this as a learning experience
Every problem that comes my way is an opportunity for me to learn about my strengths and weaknesses, others and life.

Feel soothing emotions:

I choose to feel warm, loving emotions. I do this by focusing on my heart and letting love, trust forgiveness, compassion, hope or gratitude fill my heart space.

Behave constructively:

I choose to work in part acts:
I will break the overwhelming job into manageable parts.

Do the difficult:
I will face what I fear and act with self-discipline.

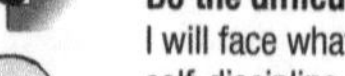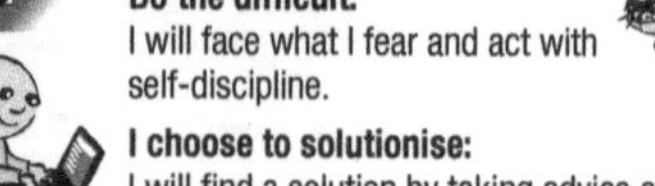

I choose to solutionise:
I will find a solution by taking advice or doing research.

Prioritise myself:
I will keep my life balanced by meeting friends, doing exercise or laughing.

Compartmentalise:
I will not let this event cloud my whole day; I will focus on something else now.

Utilise calming strategies:

When I:
- relax,
- breathe deeply,
- go for a run,
- shower,
- lie down,
- read,
- watch TV,
- climb into a mental helicopter,
- practice mindfulness/meditation,

my mind and body calm down.

Step Four: The Self Motivation Process

Endorse yourself for any growth no matter how small.

In the past I would have...

____

____

But this time I...

____

____

Tick off the traits that you strengthened when you worked down your anxiety:

- ☐ generosity
- ☐ kindness
- ☐ compassion
- ☐ consideration
- ☐ helpfulness
- ☐ respectfulness
- ☐ honesty
- ☐ fairness
- ☐ patience

- ☐ peacefulness
- ☐ self-discipline
- ☐ forgiveness
- ☐ courage
- ☐ responsibility
- ☐ reliability
- ☐ loyalty
- ☐ love
- ☐ humility

Rate your anxiety on a scale of 0 to 100%:

☐ %

O

W

Week 10

This week, the focus is on the following three tools:

1. Not exceptional: thinking tool
2. Part acts: behavioural tool
3. Informal mindfulness: calming tool

Not exceptional: thinking tool

"I choose to view this event as average, falling within the normal range. This event is not exceptional; many people have gone through this."

Please fill out the exercise below. This will assist you to identify whether or not you feel exceptional. I will then explain the tool, and what it means, giving you the opportunity to re-evaluate where you stand at the end.

EXERCISE 32

Do you ever feel that you are different to other people?   YES/NO

If you answered "yes," in what ways?

Do you ever think that your work/home/relationship situation is exceptionally bad (ie worse than most other peoples')?   YES/NO

If you answered "yes," in what ways?

After an upsetting event occurs, we often feel additionally upset because we believe that what just occurred is unique to us. For instance, you may think that you are the only person who gets highly anxious at times. Consequently you feel worse than if you presumed that many people feel anxious in similar life situations and moments.

This tool is here to remind you that it is unlikely that you are the first, or only, person who has experienced the event that is upsetting you right now. Strengthen yourself by believing that this event is natural (not abnormal) and that other people have been, or are going through, the same.

For the purposes of this tool, there are two options. The first is that you feel normal, part of the human race, like everybody else. The second option is that you feel exceptional, an exception to the rule. Exceptional means that you feel different in some way.

When you believe that you are the exception, this will result in you feeling different, misunderstood, alone, helpless or abnormal. Conversely, when you know that what you are going through is a common problem, you will no longer feel different or alone. Moreover you can turn to people who have been through the same thing for support and solutions.

This is a major strength in group therapy or supportive groups. There are groups for mums with new babies, recently divorced dads, people trying to lose weight, alcoholics, step mothers and any other human experience you could think of. Hospitals run groups for patients who are suffering from the same illness. Cancer councils train volunteers who have experienced cancer, and recovered, to visit and strengthen people living with cancer. Today the web is filled with forums made up of people from all over the world who share their experiences. What a relief it is to discover that you are not the only new mum who gets angry when the baby will not settle or that you are not the only divorced dad who feels bereft at leaving his children.

When you have a problem, that is bad enough and you will need to work through it. For instance, if you are a father who has moved out of the family home, you may feel sad and lost. It will take time and emotional work to move forward. Without this tool, your problems multiply. Thinking you are the only person going through these adjustments creates a second problem. You now additionally feel sorry for yourself, lonely, misunderstood and guilty. However, when you meet a group of fathers who are going through the identical issues, the second problem falls away and you only have the first one to deal with.

Even when an incident is exceptional, there will always be a group who has experienced the same thing. For example, let us say you require a mastectomy. Nobody in your social circle has had one. The problem (mastectomy) may be exceptional at this moment among your family and friends but, rest assured, many other women have had a mastectomy and felt very similar to the way you feel now.

The bell curve effectively explains this tool. Understanding the bell curve will help you see that even if you are "different," "eccentric" or "out of the box," you are still part of the normal human race. "Normal" covers a huge range.

Below is a diagram of a bell curve of intelligence. (24) It shows the range of scores people gain on intelligence tests.

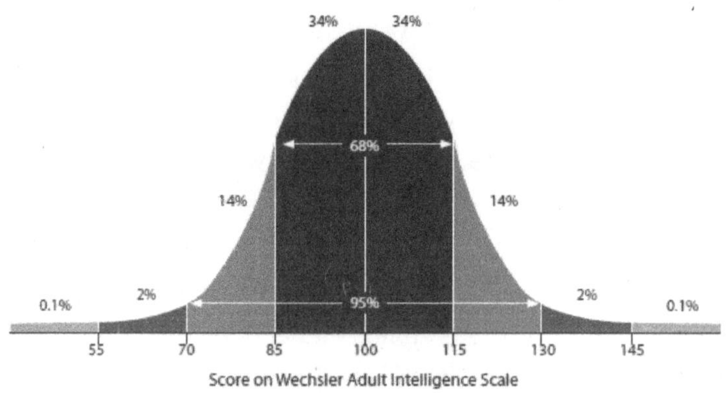

The range of IQ scores is large, 0–150. Most people are likely to score between 85 points and 115 points (68% of people). The range of very high and very low scores however, is small. Fewer than 2% score above 130 points or below a score of 70. Thus 96% of us fall within the normal range.

If we were to do a bell curve in relation to height, it would look identical: 68% of people would be of average height (the blue section). Average height is different for men and women. The average height for women is between 150 and 170 centimetres. For men, the average height is between 165 and 185 centimetres.

Only 2% of the population would be extremely short, around 145 cm tall (the brown section), but they would still be considered to fall within the normal range. They would not be classified as dwarves. Similarly a person who is over 190 cm tall would be classified as very tall, but would still fall within the normal range and not a "giant".

Dwarfs and giants do exist. They have a medical diagnosis and their height is always associated with other signs and symptoms. They comprise 1% of the population, that is, 1 in 1000 people fall at the tails of the bell curve. The bell curve, therefore also shows that it is "normal" to have a small number of people experience something unusual.

The bell curve in this case is being used to explain a concept, namely, that you fit in to the human race. It is important that you think you are normal and that your problems fit into a normal range. If you believe that you are alone, abnormal, or a freak, you will feel much, much worse. This tool also teaches you to view your problem as a normal life event that could, and does happen to many other people.

Several of my clients have reacted negatively to this tool. One felt they were being reduced to a statistic. Another believed that she would lose her individuality if she stopped feeling that she was exceptional. Others enjoyed the idea of being exceptional and feeling different, because they did not want to "fit into a box".

Rest assured, the bell curve does not remove individuality. As explained, very short and very tall people (plus every height in between) exist. No two people are alike. However, whatever your height, you need to understand that you fall within the normal range. You will always be unique as an individual but your characteristics fall within a normal range. Similarly, events that happen to you will have individual variations but will belong in the normal range of events. Except in extremely rare circumstances, we all have experiences that are universal and fall within the normal range.

Self esteem

People with low self-esteem typically compare themselves to others. When you compare yourself, you will frequently feel inferior because there will always be somebody who is smarter, richer or thinner than you. One common suggestion made to help with these comparisons is to only look at those people who are less smart, less rich and fatter than you.

My recommendation instead is that you use the bell curve to feel better about yourself. The bell curve shows that each individual occupies a different place (percentile). Work on accepting that you have a unique place, a unique purpose and a unique destiny in the world that only you can fulfil. Once you do this, your self-esteem will rise.

The composition of an orchestra illustrates this point clearly. An orchestra makes beautiful music because many different instruments contribute their unique and distinctive sounds. The piano sounds different to the violins, which sound different to the wind instruments and cymbals. I once watched an orchestra play a piece where the cymbals were only used once, at the crescendo. All the violinists worked hard throughout, playing non-stop at an incredible speed while the man playing the cymbals sat and waited for his moment. When it came, it brought a sound that elevated the whole piece. The violinists appeared to be more "important" than the cymbals. However, the symphony would not have been complete without the clashing of the cymbals. In other words, every instrument is vital in order to produce a complete and wonderful sound.

An orchestra is analogous to a social group/community. Each of us makes a unique contribution to the world. You may be the busy violinist or the occasional cymbal clasher. You have that function because of your unique blend of height, weight, intelligence, age and "musical" expertise. There is no use comparing yourself to anybody else. Whether you are the violinist, or the percussionist, you will be on the bell curve.

When you embrace your individuality and strive to be the best cymbal clasher ever, you will feel good about yourself, less anxious and happier.

Arrogance

Some arrogant individuals like to believe that they are exceptional. When someone boasts that they are the smartest, the tallest or the richest, their arrogance is obvious. However, their arrogance is less obvious when they boast about negative things.

Common arrogant expressions are:

> You think you have it hard? My work is more back breaking than yours.
> You do not know what pain is. When I get a headache I cannot move for three days.

> My husband is the most uncommunicative man in the world.

> My son is, for sure, the wildest boy in his age group.

Whatever your motivation to holding on to feeling exceptional, I encourage you to let go of it. You will feel much happier and calmer when you accept that you fit in the normal range and that your life is following the natural path.

EXERCISE 33

Having learned this tool, do you still think that you are exceptional?　　　　　　　　　　　　　　　　　　YES/NO

If you answered "yes," please elaborate:

Do you still think that your anxiety-provoking situation is exceptional?　　　　　　　　　　　　　　　　　　YES/NO

If you answered "yes," please elaborate:

If you have answered "yes" to either of the above, then this tool is not applicable to your situation.

Can you think of another tool that would be better suited to your predicament?

Is it possible that you are holding on to believing that you/your situation is exceptional because it makes you feel good?

This tool is only applicable when an occurrence is not exceptional but you *believe* that it is, and the belief is causing you stress. When a situation is indeed exceptional (eg an abusive situation), measures must be taken immediately to change/stop/move away from the situation. You might need the advice of a friend or objective third party to clarify whether or not the situation is indeed exceptional.

Daily monitoring diary

From this week onwards, you will be able to note down every time that you notice yourself thinking that you and/or your situation is exceptional. Challenge these thoughts by presenting the facts or asking a qualified professional. Your anxiety will reduce noticeably when you see yourself and your situation as within the average range.

Part acts: behavioural tool

"I choose to work in part acts. I will solve the problem one step at a time."

Major sources of stress and anxiety are large projects that need to be completed or big problems that need to be solved. Facing a large project or problem can often lead to feelings of being over-whelmed and helpless. This tool teaches you to tackle an over-whelming challenge one chunk at a time. As you work through each bite-sized chunk, your anxiety will reduce.

Let us say that you are moving house. When you see the large number of items that require packing you may feel overwhelmed. You may even procrastinate and avoid the task. Once you break the task into parts, however you will feel empowered to make a start. Working in part acts, in this example, would mean packing up one room at a time, not the whole house. Or it would mean packing one box at a time, not the whole wardrobe.

There are many philosophies in life that support this value. AA and its offshoots talk about taking it "one day at a time". There is also a Japanese philosophy that states (this is not a direct quote): "If a road is 1000 steps, each small step you take is one step closer to the end."

EXERCISE 34

How do you feel about this philosophy?

Have you ever applied this philosophy?   YES/NO

> If yes, in what situations?

Describe how it helped reduce your anxiety?

Write down any similar philosophies that you find useful?

EXERCISE 35

This exercise will help you to practise breaking large projects into parts. Projects can be broken up into tasks or time frames or both. Please describe how you could break up each of the projects below into solvable, part acts.

You are moving house in one week.

I would break the house into six parts (areas) and do one area per day. Sunday — pack up spare bedroom. Monday — pack up study. Tuesday — pack up living room. Wednesday — pack up dining room. Thursday — pack up outdoors and bathroom, except essentials. Friday — pack up my bedroom, except essentials.

1. You are planning your wedding with dinner for 100 people which is taking place in a year's time.

----

2. You have been asked to write a 50 page report in a week.

3. You are required to plan a four-week holiday for you and your family.

4. You got drunk and were rude to a group of your friends and you need to make amends to all of them.

5. You have acquired a new smart phone and have no idea how it works. How will you learn to use it in the most stress free manner?

6. You have moved to a new city and need to drive to a new location on the first day. You do not have a GPS.

7. You are unemployed and need to find a job.

Informal mindfulness: calming tool

Informal mindfulness practice can be done anywhere and at any time. The aim is to make you aware of how you think and act as well as what is happening in the present moment.

You do not need to take time out of your regular daily activities to be mindful in this way. Nor do you need a special room or space in which to do it. All you need to do is simply become more aware of what you are doing in the moment. Everyday activities provide excellent opportunities to practice informal mindfulness including sitting on the train, walking or closing a door.

> When you close a door, for example, be mindful of closing it with intention. This may mean making sure it does not slam or create any noise or, on the contrary, you deliberately slam it.

> When you cook, be mindful of how you spice the food. Think about the taste you are trying to create.

> When you are sitting at your desk be mindful of your posture. If your posture is poor, mindfully correct it.

As you are reading this page now, become aware of how you are reading. Are you reading slowly and with concentration or are you skimming through? Do you understand the content or do you feel confused? How are you sitting? Where are your hands? Write down your observations.

DAILY MONITORING DIARY WEEK ENDING ______________

Day	M	T	W	T	F	S	S
Overall Anxiety Rating for the day (0-10)							
1. EXERCISE							
How long?							
Anxiety level before (0-10)							
Anxiety level after (0-10)							
2. BREATHING							
How long?							
Anxiety level before (0-10)							
Anxiety level after (0-10)							
3. RELAXATION							
How long?							
Anxiety level before (0-10)							
Anxiety level after (0-10)							
4. PERVASIVE PESSIMISTIC THINKING							
How often this type of thought occurred							
Belief in thoughts before challenging (0-10)							
Belief in thoughts after challenging (0-10)							
5. CATASTROPHIC THINKING							
How often this type of thought occurred							
Belief in thoughts before challenging (0-10)							
Belief in thoughts after challenging (0-10)							
6. PERMANENT PESSIMISTIC THINKING							
How often this type of thought occurred							
Belief in thoughts before challenging (0-10)							
Belief in thoughts after challenging (0-10)							

Day	M	T	W	T	F	S	S
7. MINDFULNESS (FORMAL, GROUNDING, INFORMAL MINDFULNESS)							
How long?							
Anxiety level before (0-10)							
Anxiety level after (0-10)							
8. ROMANTIC THINKING							
How often this type of thought occurred							
Belief in thoughts before challenging (0-10)							
Belief in thoughts after challenging (0-10)							
9. NEGATIVE JUDGEMENTAL THINKING							
How often this type of thought occurred							
Belief in thoughts before challenging (0-10)							
Belief in thoughts after challenging (0-10)							
10. CAN'T LET GO THINKING							
How often this type of thought occurred							
Belief in thoughts before challenging (0-10)							
Belief in thoughts after challenging (0-10)							
11. MEDITATION							
How long?							
Anxiety level before (0-10)							
Anxiety level after (0-10)							
12. EXCEPTIONAL THINKING							
How often this type of thought occurred							
Belief in thoughts before challenging (0-10)							
Belief in thoughts after challenging (0-10)							

Date: ___________

Anxiety Management Worksheet

The purpose of this worksheet is to help you to see every stressful event as an opportunity for
1. greater understanding of yourself, your anxiety and the people around you, and
2. practicing tools to manage your anxiety.

Step One: An Event

Briefly describe an event when you became anxious. Give such details as time, place and people involved, and end with "That's when I began to work myself up..."

____

____

____

____ Rate your anxiety on a scale of 0 to 100%: [ ] %

E

Step Two: The Working-Up Process

Learn about your working up process by identifying your thoughts, feelings, behaviours and bodily reactions during the event.
Tick the ones that most resonate with you.

Undermining Beliefs

B

I fear that I have lost...

- ☐ approval
- ☐ control
- ☐ co-operation
- ☐ face
- ☐ respect
- ☐ success
- ☐ trust
- ☐ validation
- ☐ love

This event proves that I am...

- ☐ stupid
- ☐ abnormal
- ☐ incompetent
- ☐ lazy
- ☐ irresponsible
- ☐ a total failure
- ☐ undisciplined
- ☐ untogether
- ☐ useless

I worry that I will suffer...

- ☐ mental collapse
- ☐ illness
- ☐ financial hardship

What I want is...

- ☐ total control
- ☐ respect
- ☐ success
- ☐ perfection
- ☐ comfort
- ☐ fairness
- ☐ tranquility
- ☐ all the answers
- ☐ for life to go smoothly
- ☐ to be all things to all people

Self-destructive Behaviour

Active

- ☐ get violent
- ☐ swear
- ☐ slam doors
- ☐ run away
- ☐ overeat
- ☐ harm myself
- ☐ criticise

Passive

- ☐ take it too seriously
- ☐ give up
- ☐ wallow in self pity
- ☐ sulk
- ☐ space out
- ☐ procrastinate
- ☐ give in
- ☐ be controlled

Intense Feelings

Angry feelings

- ☐ hateful
- ☐ aggravated
- ☐ annoyed
- ☐ hostile
- ☐ outraged
- ☐ punitive
- ☐ resentful
- ☐ vengeful

Fearful feelings

- ☐ helpless
- ☐ hopeless
- ☐ disappointed
- ☐ sad
- ☐ attacked
- ☐ worn out
- ☐ rejected
- ☐ jealous
- ☐ afraid
- ☐ exploited
- ☐ lonely
- ☐ abandoned
- ☐ guilty
- ☐ insulted
- ☐ confused
- ☐ disillusioned
- ☐ misunderstood
- ☐ trapped

Bodily Reactions (limbic system)

I am uncomfortable because I am experiencing...

- ☐ tremors
- ☐ nausea
- ☐ sweaty palms
- ☐ stomach-ache
- ☐ pounding heart
- ☐ general tension
- ☐ fatigue
- ☐ imagination on fire
- ☐ headache
- ☐ dry mouth
- ☐ jaw clenching
- ☐ shortness of breath

B   **F**   **L**

Step Three: The Working-Down Process

Begin with, "Suddenly I realised that I was anxious and that I had choices..." This is the step of self-leadership and trust in one's ability to handle the situation.

Choose helpful thoughts:

I choose to depersonalise
There is no intention to hurt me. He is doing the best he can with the tools he has at the moment.

I choose realism over romanticism
Life presents many obstacles. I lower or raise standards as needed.

There is no right or wrong
Unless it is a moral issue, I will see it simply as a difference of opinion and/or taste.

I choose the total view of positivity
Even though this event is negative, the total view of his behaviour is positive.

I surrender control
Since I cannot change this situation, I choose to let go of it.

I choose to put this event in perspective This event is not a catastrophe because it is not life threatening. It can be viewed as a trivial life event, a normal life problem that needs to be solved not dramatised.

I choose to view this event as average, falling within the normal range
This event is not exceptional; many people have gone through this.

It's temporary - "this too shall pass"
Life is constantly changing and moving through phases and this situation will also change.

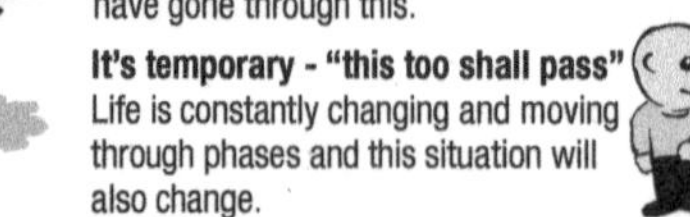

Fears or facts?
Why fear? It may not happen!

I choose to focus on this as a learning experience
Every problem that comes my way is an opportunity for me to learn about my strengths and weaknesses, others and life.

Feel soothing emotions:

I choose to feel warm, loving emotions. I do this by focusing on my heart and letting love, trust forgiveness, compassion, hope or gratitude fill my heart space.

Behave constructively:

I choose to work in part acts:
I will break the overwhelming job into manageable parts.

Do the difficult:
I will face what I fear and act with self-discipline.

I choose to solutionise:
I will find a solution by taking advice or doing research.

Prioritise myself:
I will keep my life balanced by meeting friends, doing exercise or laughing.

Compartmentalise:
I will not let this event cloud my whole day; I will focus on something else now.

Utilise calming strategies:

When I:
• relax,
• breathe deeply,
• go for a run,
• shower,
• lie down,
• read,
• watch TV,
• climb into a mental helicopter,
• practice mindfulness/meditation,
my mind and body calm down.

Step Four: The Self Motivation Process

Endorse yourself for any growth no matter how small.

In the past I would have...

____

____

But this time I...

____

____

Tick off the traits that you strengthened when you worked down your anxiety:

☐ generosity ☐ peacefulness
☐ kindness ☐ self-discipline
☐ compassion ☐ forgiveness
☐ consideration ☐ courage
☐ helpfulness ☐ responsibility
☐ respectfulness ☐ reliability
☐ honesty ☐ loyalty
☐ fairness ☐ love
☐ patience ☐ humility

Rate your anxiety on a scale of 0 to 100%:

[____]%

O

W

Date: ___________

Anxiety Management Worksheet

The purpose of this worksheet is to help you to see every stressful event as an opportunity for
1. greater understanding of yourself, your anxiety and the people around you, and
2. practicing tools to manage your anxiety.

Step One: An Event

Briefly describe an event when you became anxious. Give such details as time, place and people involved, and end with "That's when I began to work myself up..."

____

____

____

_______________________________________ Rate your anxiety on a scale of 0 to 100%: [______] %

E

Step Two: The Working-Up Process

Learn about your working up process by identifying your thoughts, feelings, behaviours and bodily reactions during the event.

Tick the ones that most resonate with you.

Undermining Beliefs

B

I fear that I have lost...
- ☐ approval
- ☐ control
- ☐ co-operation
- ☐ face
- ☐ respect
- ☐ success
- ☐ trust
- ☐ validation
- ☐ love

This event proves that I am...
- ☐ stupid
- ☐ abnormal
- ☐ incompetent
- ☐ lazy
- ☐ irresponsible
- ☐ a total failure
- ☐ undisciplined
- ☐ untogether
- ☐ useless

I worry that I will suffer...
- ☐ mental collapse
- ☐ illness
- ☐ financial hardship

What I want is...
- ☐ total control
- ☐ respect
- ☐ success
- ☐ perfection
- ☐ comfort
- ☐ fairness
- ☐ tranquility
- ☐ all the answers
- ☐ for life to go smoothly
- ☐ to be all things to all people

Self-destructive Behaviour

Active
- ☐ get violent
- ☐ swear
- ☐ slam doors
- ☐ run away
- ☐ overeat
- ☐ harm myself
- ☐ criticise

Passive
- ☐ take it too seriously
- ☐ give up
- ☐ wallow in self pity
- ☐ sulk
- ☐ space out
- ☐ procrastinate
- ☐ give in
- ☐ be controlled

Intense Feelings

Angry feelings
- ☐ hateful
- ☐ aggravated
- ☐ annoyed
- ☐ hostile
- ☐ outraged
- ☐ punitive
- ☐ resentful
- ☐ vengeful

Fearful feelings
- ☐ helpless
- ☐ hopeless
- ☐ disappointed
- ☐ sad

- ☐ attacked
- ☐ worn out
- ☐ rejected
- ☐ jealous
- ☐ afraid
- ☐ exploited
- ☐ lonely
- ☐ abandoned
- ☐ guilty
- ☐ insulted
- ☐ confused
- ☐ disillusioned
- ☐ misunderstood
- ☐ trapped

Bodily Reactions (limbic system)

I am uncomfortable because I am experiencing...
- ☐ tremors
- ☐ nausea
- ☐ sweaty palms
- ☐ stomach-ache
- ☐ pounding heart
- ☐ general tension
- ☐ fatigue
- ☐ imagination on fire
- ☐ headache
- ☐ dry mouth
- ☐ jaw clenching
- ☐ shortness of breath

Continued over

B   **F**   **L**

Step Three: The Working-Down Process

Begin with, "Suddenly I realised that I was anxious and that I had choices..." This is the step of self-leadership and trust in one's ability to handle the situation.

Choose helpful thoughts:

I choose to depersonalise
There is no intention to hurt me. He is doing the best he can with the tools he has at the moment.

I choose realism over romanticism
Life presents many obstacles. I lower or raise standards as needed. 

There is no right or wrong
Unless it is a moral issue, I will see it simply as a difference of opinion and/or taste.

I choose the total view of positivity
Even though this event is negative, the total view of his behaviour is positive. 

I surrender control
Since I cannot change this situation, I choose to let go of it.

I choose to put this event in perspective This event is not a catastrophe because it is not life threatening. It can be viewed as a trivial life event, a normal life problem that needs to be solved not dramatised. 

I choose to view this event as average, falling within the normal range
This event is not exceptional; many people have gone through this.

It's temporary - "this too shall pass"
Life is constantly changing and moving through phases and this situation will also change.

Fears or facts?
Why fear? It may not happen!

I choose to focus on this as a learning experience
Every problem that comes my way is an opportunity for me to learn about my strengths and weaknesses, others and life. 

Feel soothing emotions:

I choose to feel warm, loving emotions. I do this by focusing on my heart and letting love, trust forgiveness, compassion, hope or gratitude fill my heart space.

Behave constructively:

I choose to work in part acts:
I will break the overwhelming job into manageable parts.

Do the difficult:
I will face what I fear and act with self-discipline. 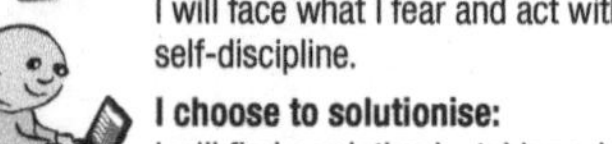

I choose to solutionise:
I will find a solution by taking advice or doing research.

Prioritise myself:
I will keep my life balanced by meeting friends, doing exercise or laughing. 

Compartmentalise:
I will not let this event cloud my whole day; I will focus on something else now.

Utilise calming strategies:

When I:
- relax,
- breathe deeply,
- go for a run,
- shower,
- lie down,
- read,
- watch TV,
- climb into a mental helicopter,
- practice mindfulness/meditation,

my mind and body calm down.

Step Four: The Self Motivation Process

Endorse yourself for any growth no matter how small.

In the past I would have...

____

____

But this time I...

____

____

Tick off the traits that you strengthened when you worked down your anxiety:

☐ generosity	☐ peacefulness
☐ kindness	☐ self-discipline
☐ compassion	☐ forgiveness
☐ consideration	☐ courage
☐ helpfulness	☐ responsibility
☐ respectfulness	☐ reliability
☐ honesty	☐ loyalty
☐ fairness	☐ love
☐ patience	☐ humility

Rate your anxiety on a scale of 0 to 100%:

[ ] %

O

W

Date: ___________

Anxiety Management Worksheet

The purpose of this worksheet is to help you to see every stressful event as an opportunity for
1. greater understanding of yourself, your anxiety and the people around you, and
2. practicing tools to manage your anxiety.

Step One: An Event

Briefly describe an event when you became anxious. Give such details as time, place and people involved, and end with "That's when I began to work myself up…"

____

____

____

____ Rate your anxiety on a scale of 0 to 100%: [____] %

E

Step Two: The Working-Up Process

Learn about your working up process by identifying your thoughts, feelings, behaviours and bodily reactions during the event.
Tick the ones that most resonate with you.

Undermining Beliefs

B

I fear that I have lost...

- ☐ approval
- ☐ control
- ☐ co-operation
- ☐ face
- ☐ respect
- ☐ success
- ☐ trust
- ☐ validation
- ☐ love

This event proves that I am...

- ☐ stupid
- ☐ abnormal
- ☐ incompetent
- ☐ lazy
- ☐ irresponsible
- ☐ a total failure
- ☐ undisciplined
- ☐ untogether
- ☐ useless

I worry that I will suffer...

- ☐ mental collapse
- ☐ illness
- ☐ financial hardship

What I want is...

- ☐ total control
- ☐ respect
- ☐ success
- ☐ perfection
- ☐ comfort
- ☐ fairness
- ☐ tranquility
- ☐ all the answers
- ☐ for life to go smoothly
- ☐ to be all things to all people

Self-destructive Behaviour

Active

- ☐ get violent
- ☐ swear
- ☐ slam doors
- ☐ run away
- ☐ overeat
- ☐ harm myself
- ☐ criticise

Passive

- ☐ take it too seriously
- ☐ give up
- ☐ wallow in self pity
- ☐ sulk
- ☐ space out
- ☐ procrastinate
- ☐ give in
- ☐ be controlled

Intense Feelings

Angry feelings

- ☐ hateful
- ☐ aggravated
- ☐ annoyed
- ☐ hostile
- ☐ outraged
- ☐ punitive
- ☐ resentful
- ☐ vengeful
- ☐ attacked
- ☐ worn out
- ☐ rejected
- ☐ jealous
- ☐ afraid
- ☐ exploited
- ☐ lonely
- ☐ abandoned
- ☐ guilty
- ☐ insulted

Fearful feelings

- ☐ helpless
- ☐ hopeless
- ☐ disappointed
- ☐ sad
- ☐ confused
- ☐ disillusioned
- ☐ misunderstood
- ☐ trapped

Bodily Reactions (limbic system)

I am uncomfortable because I am experiencing...

- ☐ tremors
- ☐ nausea
- ☐ sweaty palms
- ☐ stomach-ache
- ☐ pounding heart
- ☐ general tension
- ☐ fatigue
- ☐ imagination on fire
- ☐ headache
- ☐ dry mouth
- ☐ jaw clenching
- ☐ shortness of breath

B   **F**   **L**

Step Three: The Working-Down Process

Begin with, "Suddenly I realised that I was anxious and that I had choices..." This is the step of self-leadership and trust in one's ability to handle the situation.

Choose helpful thoughts:

I choose to depersonalise
There is no intention to hurt me. He is doing the best he can with the tools he has at the moment.

I choose realism over romanticism
Life presents many obstacles. I lower or raise standards as needed.

There is no right or wrong
Unless it is a moral issue, I will see it simply as a difference of opinion and/or taste.

I choose the total view of positivity
Even though this event is negative, the total view of his behaviour is positive.

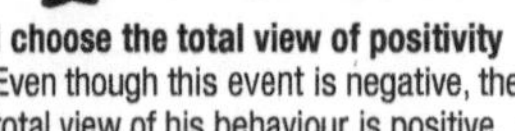

I surrender control
Since I cannot change this situation, I choose to let go of it.

I choose to put this event in perspective This event is not a catastrophe because it is not life threatening. It can be viewed as a trivial life event, a normal life problem that needs to be solved not dramatised.

I choose to view this event as average, falling within the normal range
This event is not exceptional; many people have gone through this.

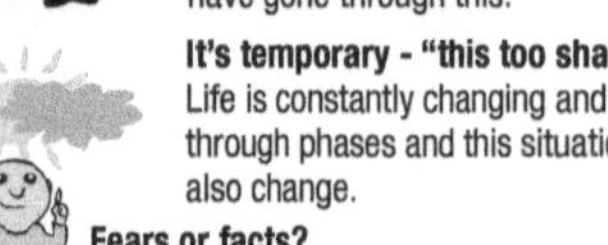

It's temporary - "this too shall pass"
Life is constantly changing and moving through phases and this situation will also change.

Fears or facts?
Why fear? It may not happen!

I choose to focus on this as a learning experience
Every problem that comes my way is an opportunity for me to learn about my strengths and weaknesses, others and life.

Feel soothing emotions:

I choose to feel warm, loving emotions. I do this by focusing on my heart and letting love, trust forgiveness, compassion, hope or gratitude fill my heart space.

Behave constructively:

I choose to work in part acts:
I will break the overwhelming job into manageable parts.

Do the difficult:
I will face what I fear and act with self-discipline.

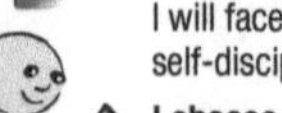

I choose to solutionise:
I will find a solution by taking advice or doing research.

Prioritise myself:
I will keep my life balanced by meeting friends, doing exercise or laughing.

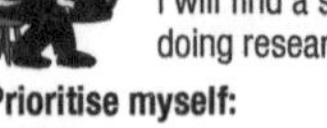

Compartmentalise:
I will not let this event cloud my whole day; I will focus on something else now.

Utilise calming strategies:

When I:
- relax,
- breathe deeply,
- go for a run,
- shower,
- lie down,
- read,
- watch TV,
- climb into a mental helicopter,
- practice mindfulness/meditation,

my mind and body calm down.

Step Four: The Self Motivation Process

Endorse yourself for any growth no matter how small.

In the past I would have...
____

____

But this time I...
____

____

Tick off the traits that you strengthened when you worked down your anxiety:

☐ generosity	☐ peacefulness
☐ kindness	☐ self-discipline
☐ compassion	☐ forgiveness
☐ consideration	☐ courage
☐ helpfulness	☐ responsibility
☐ respectfulness	☐ reliability
☐ honesty	☐ loyalty
☐ fairness	☐ love
☐ patience	☐ humility

Rate your anxiety on a scale of 0 to 100%:

______ %

O

W

Date: ____________

Anxiety Management Worksheet

The purpose of this worksheet is to help you to see every stressful event as an opportunity for
1. greater understanding of yourself, your anxiety and the people around you, and
2. practicing tools to manage your anxiety.

Step One: An Event

Briefly describe an event when you became anxious. Give such details as time, place and people involved, and end with "That's when I began to work myself up..."

____

____

____

____ Rate your anxiety on a scale of 0 to 100%: [   ] %

E

Step Two: The Working-Up Process

Learn about your working up process by identifying your thoughts, feelings, behaviours and bodily reactions during the event.
Tick the ones that most resonate with you.

Undermining Beliefs

B

I fear that I have lost...
- ☐ approval
- ☐ control
- ☐ co-operation
- ☐ face
- ☐ respect
- ☐ success
- ☐ trust
- ☐ validation
- ☐ love

This event proves that I am...
- ☐ stupid
- ☐ abnormal
- ☐ incompetent
- ☐ lazy
- ☐ irresponsible
- ☐ a total failure
- ☐ undisciplined
- ☐ untogether
- ☐ useless

I worry that I will suffer...
- ☐ mental collapse
- ☐ illness
- ☐ financial hardship

What I want is...
- ☐ total control
- ☐ respect
- ☐ success
- ☐ perfection
- ☐ comfort
- ☐ fairness
- ☐ tranquility
- ☐ all the answers
- ☐ for life to go smoothly
- ☐ to be all things to all people

Self-destructive Behaviour

Active
- ☐ get violent
- ☐ swear
- ☐ slam doors
- ☐ run away
- ☐ overeat
- ☐ harm myself
- ☐ criticise

Passive
- ☐ take it too seriously
- ☐ give up
- ☐ wallow in self pity
- ☐ sulk
- ☐ space out
- ☐ procrastinate
- ☐ give in
- ☐ be controlled

Intense Feelings

Angry feelings
- ☐ hateful
- ☐ aggravated
- ☐ annoyed
- ☐ hostile
- ☐ outraged
- ☐ punitive
- ☐ resentful
- ☐ vengeful

Fearful feelings
- ☐ helpless
- ☐ hopeless
- ☐ disappointed
- ☐ sad
- ☐ attacked
- ☐ worn out
- ☐ rejected
- ☐ jealous
- ☐ afraid
- ☐ exploited
- ☐ lonely
- ☐ abandoned
- ☐ guilty
- ☐ insulted
- ☐ confused
- ☐ disillusioned
- ☐ misunderstood
- ☐ trapped

Bodily Reactions (limbic system)

I am uncomfortable because I am experiencing...
- ☐ tremors
- ☐ nausea
- ☐ sweaty palms
- ☐ stomach-ache
- ☐ pounding heart
- ☐ general tension
- ☐ fatigue
- ☐ imagination on fire
- ☐ headache
- ☐ dry mouth
- ☐ jaw clenching
- ☐ shortness of breath

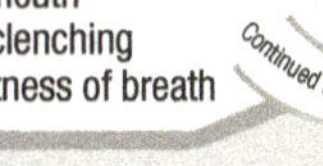

B   **F**   **L**

Copyright Renee Mill 2014

Step Three: The Working-Down Process

Begin with, "Suddenly I realised that I was anxious and that I had choices..." This is the step of self-leadership and trust in one's ability to handle the situation.

Choose helpful thoughts:

I choose to depersonalise
There is no intention to hurt me. He is doing the best he can with the tools he has at the moment.

I choose realism over romanticism
Life presents many obstacles. I lower or raise standards as needed.

There is no right or wrong
Unless it is a moral issue, I will see it simply as a difference of opinion and/or taste.

I choose the total view of positivity
Even though this event is negative, the total view of his behaviour is positive.

I surrender control
Since I cannot change this situation, I choose to let go of it.

I choose to put this event in perspective
This event is not a catastrophe because it is not life threatening. It can be viewed as a trivial life event, a normal life problem that needs to be solved not dramatised.

I choose to view this event as average, falling within the normal range
This event is not exceptional; many people have gone through this.

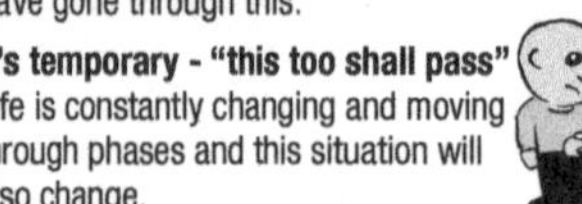

It's temporary - "this too shall pass"
Life is constantly changing and moving through phases and this situation will also change.

Fears or facts?
Why fear? It may not happen!

I choose to focus on this as a learning experience
Every problem that comes my way is an opportunity for me to learn about my strengths and weaknesses, others and life.

Feel soothing emotions:

I choose to feel warm, loving emotions. I do this by focusing on my heart and letting love, trust forgiveness, compassion, hope or gratitude fill my heart space.

Behave constructively:

I choose to work in part acts:
I will break the overwhelming job into manageable parts.

Do the difficult:
I will face what I fear and act with self-discipline.

I choose to solutionise:
I will find a solution by taking advice or doing research.

Prioritise myself:
I will keep my life balanced by meeting friends, doing exercise or laughing.

Compartmentalise:
I will not let this event cloud my whole day; I will focus on something else now.

Utilise calming strategies:

When I:
- relax,
- breathe deeply,
- go for a run,
- shower,
- lie down,
- read,
- watch TV,
- climb into a mental helicopter,
- practice mindfulness/meditation,

my mind and body calm down.

Step Four: The Self Motivation Process

Endorse yourself for any growth no matter how small.

In the past I would have...

____

____

But this time I...

____

____

Tick off the traits that you strengthened when you worked down your anxiety:

- ☐ generosity
- ☐ kindness
- ☐ compassion
- ☐ consideration
- ☐ helpfulness
- ☐ respectfulness
- ☐ honesty
- ☐ fairness
- ☐ patience
- ☐ peacefulness
- ☐ self-discipline
- ☐ forgiveness
- ☐ courage
- ☐ responsibility
- ☐ reliability
- ☐ loyalty
- ☐ love
- ☐ humility

Rate your anxiety on a scale of 0 to 100%:

________%

O

W

Date: ___________

Anxiety Management Worksheet

The purpose of this worksheet is to help you to see every stressful event as an opportunity for
1. greater understanding of yourself, your anxiety and the people around you, and
2. practicing tools to manage your anxiety.

Step One: An Event

Briefly describe an event when you became anxious. Give such details as time, place and people involved, and end with "That's when I began to work myself up..."

____

____

____

____   Rate your anxiety on a scale of 0 to 100%: ________ %

E

Step Two: The Working-Up Process

Learn about your working up process by identifying your thoughts, feelings, behaviours and bodily reactions during the event.
Tick the ones that most resonate with you.

Undermining Beliefs

B

I fear that I have lost...
- ☐ approval
- ☐ control
- ☐ co-operation
- ☐ face
- ☐ respect
- ☐ success
- ☐ trust
- ☐ validation
- ☐ love

This event proves that I am...
- ☐ stupid
- ☐ abnormal
- ☐ incompetent
- ☐ lazy
- ☐ irresponsible
- ☐ a total failure
- ☐ undisciplined
- ☐ untogether
- ☐ useless

I worry that I will suffer...
- ☐ mental collapse
- ☐ illness
- ☐ financial hardship

What I want is...
- ☐ total control
- ☐ respect
- ☐ success
- ☐ perfection
- ☐ comfort
- ☐ fairness
- ☐ tranquility
- ☐ all the answers
- ☐ for life to go smoothly
- ☐ to be all things to all people

Self-destructive Behaviour

Active
- ☐ get violent
- ☐ swear
- ☐ slam doors
- ☐ run away
- ☐ overeat
- ☐ harm myself
- ☐ criticise

Passive
- ☐ take it too seriously
- ☐ give up
- ☐ wallow in self pity
- ☐ sulk
- ☐ space out
- ☐ procrastinate
- ☐ give in
- ☐ be controlled

Intense Feelings

Angry feelings
- ☐ hateful
- ☐ aggravated
- ☐ annoyed
- ☐ hostile
- ☐ outraged
- ☐ punitive
- ☐ resentful
- ☐ vengeful

Fearful feelings
- ☐ helpless
- ☐ hopeless
- ☐ disappointed
- ☐ sad
- ☐ attacked
- ☐ worn out
- ☐ rejected
- ☐ jealous
- ☐ afraid
- ☐ exploited
- ☐ lonely
- ☐ abandoned
- ☐ guilty
- ☐ insulted
- ☐ confused
- ☐ disillusioned
- ☐ misunderstood
- ☐ trapped

Bodily Reactions (limbic system)

I am uncomfortable because I am experiencing...
- ☐ tremors
- ☐ nausea
- ☐ sweaty palms
- ☐ stomach-ache
- ☐ pounding heart
- ☐ general tension
- ☐ fatigue
- ☐ imagination on fire
- ☐ headache
- ☐ dry mouth
- ☐ jaw clenching
- ☐ shortness of breath

Continued over

B   **F**   **L**

Step Three: The Working-Down Process

Begin with, "Suddenly I realised that I was anxious and that I had choices..." This is the step of self-leadership and trust in one's ability to handle the situation.

Choose helpful thoughts:

I choose to depersonalise
There is no intention to hurt me. He is doing the best he can with the tools he has at the moment.

I choose realism over romanticism
Life presents many obstacles. I lower or raise standards as needed.

There is no right or wrong
Unless it is a moral issue, I will see it simply as a difference of opinion and/or taste.

I choose the total view of positivity
Even though this event is negative, the total view of his behaviour is positive.

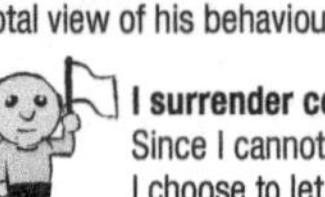

I surrender control
Since I cannot change this situation, I choose to let go of it.

I choose to put this event in perspective
This event is not a catastrophe because it is not life threatening. It can be viewed as a trivial life event, a normal life problem that needs to be solved not dramatised.

I choose to view this event as average, falling within the normal range
This event is not exceptional; many people have gone through this.

It's temporary - "this too shall pass"
Life is constantly changing and moving through phases and this situation will also change.

Fears or facts?
Why fear? It may not happen!

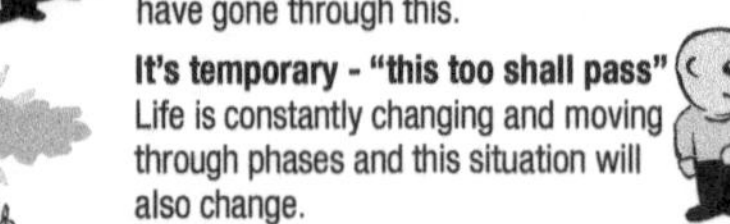

I choose to focus on this as a learning experience
Every problem that comes my way is an opportunity for me to learn about my strengths and weaknesses, others and life.

Feel soothing emotions:

I choose to feel warm, loving emotions. I do this by focusing on my heart and letting love, trust forgiveness, compassion, hope or gratitude fill my heart space.

Behave constructively:

I choose to work in part acts:
I will break the overwhelming job into manageable parts.

Do the difficult:
I will face what I fear and act with self-discipline.

I choose to solutionise:
I will find a solution by taking advice or doing research.

Prioritise myself:
I will keep my life balanced by meeting friends, doing exercise or laughing.

Compartmentalise:
I will not let this event cloud my whole day; I will focus on something else now.

Utilise calming strategies:

When I:
- relax,
- breathe deeply,
- go for a run,
- shower,
- lie down,
- read,
- watch TV,
- climb into a mental helicopter,
- practice mindfulness/meditation,

my mind and body calm down.

Step Four: The Self Motivation Process

Endorse yourself for any growth no matter how small.

In the past I would have...

____

____

But this time I...

____

____

Tick off the traits that you strengthened when you worked down your anxiety:

☐ generosity	☐ peacefulness
☐ kindness	☐ self-discipline
☐ compassion	☐ forgiveness
☐ consideration	☐ courage
☐ helpfulness	☐ responsibility
☐ respectfulness	☐ reliability
☐ honesty	☐ loyalty
☐ fairness	☐ love
☐ patience	☐ humility

Rate your anxiety on a scale of 0 to 100%:

_______ %

O

W

Date: ______________

Anxiety Management Worksheet

The purpose of this worksheet is to help you to see every stressful event as an opportunity for
1. greater understanding of yourself, your anxiety and the people around you, and
2. practicing tools to manage your anxiety.

Step One: An Event

Briefly describe an event when you became anxious. Give such details as time, place and people involved, and end with "That's when I began to work myself up..."

____

____ **E**

____

____ Rate your anxiety on a scale of 0 to 100%: [ ] %

Step Two: The Working-Up Process

Learn about your working up process by identifying your thoughts, feelings, behaviours and bodily reactions during the event.
Tick the ones that most resonate with you.

Undermining Beliefs

B

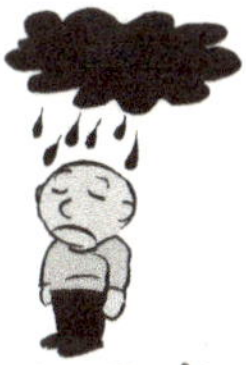

I fear that I have lost...
- ☐ approval
- ☐ control
- ☐ co-operation
- ☐ face
- ☐ respect
- ☐ success
- ☐ trust
- ☐ validation
- ☐ love

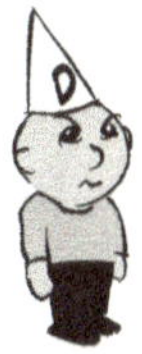

This event proves that I am...
- ☐ stupid
- ☐ abnormal
- ☐ incompetent
- ☐ lazy
- ☐ irresponsible
- ☐ a total failure
- ☐ undisciplined
- ☐ untogether
- ☐ useless

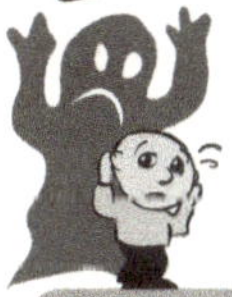

I worry that I will suffer...
- ☐ mental collapse
- ☐ illness
- ☐ financial hardship

What I want is...
- ☐ total control
- ☐ respect
- ☐ success
- ☐ perfection
- ☐ comfort
- ☐ fairness
- ☐ tranquility
- ☐ all the answers
- ☐ for life to go smoothly
- ☐ to be all things to all people

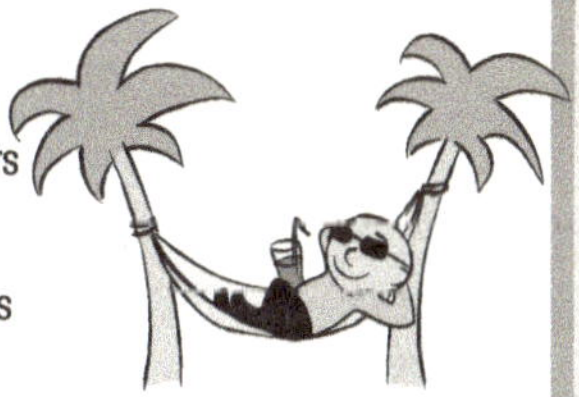

Self-destructive Behaviour

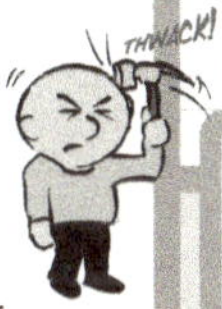

Active
- ☐ get violent
- ☐ swear
- ☐ slam doors
- ☐ run away
- ☐ overeat
- ☐ harm myself
- ☐ criticise

Passive
- ☐ take it too seriously
- ☐ give up
- ☐ wallow in self pity
- ☐ sulk
- ☐ space out
- ☐ procrastinate
- ☐ give in
- ☐ be controlled

Intense Feelings

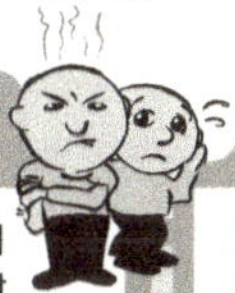

Angry feelings
- ☐ hateful
- ☐ aggravated
- ☐ annoyed
- ☐ hostile
- ☐ outraged
- ☐ punitive
- ☐ resentful
- ☐ vengeful

Fearful feelings
- ☐ helpless
- ☐ hopeless
- ☐ disappointed
- ☐ sad
- ☐ attacked
- ☐ worn out
- ☐ rejected
- ☐ jealous
- ☐ afraid
- ☐ exploited
- ☐ lonely
- ☐ abandoned
- ☐ guilty
- ☐ insulted
- ☐ confused
- ☐ disillusioned
- ☐ misunderstood
- ☐ trapped

Bodily Reactions (limbic system)

I am uncomfortable because I am experiencing... 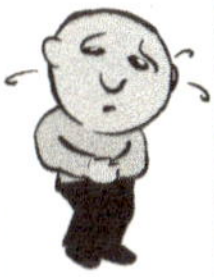
- ☐ tremors
- ☐ nausea
- ☐ sweaty palms
- ☐ stomach-ache
- ☐ pounding heart
- ☐ general tension
- ☐ fatigue
- ☐ imagination on fire
- ☐ headache
- ☐ dry mouth
- ☐ jaw clenching
- ☐ shortness of breath

Continued over

B   **F**   **L**

Step Three: The Working-Down Process

Begin with, "Suddenly I realised that I was anxious and that I had choices..." This is the step of self-leadership and trust in one's ability to handle the situation.

Choose helpful thoughts:

I choose to depersonalise
There is no intention to hurt me. He is doing the best he can with the tools he has at the moment.

I choose realism over romanticism
Life presents many obstacles. I lower or raise standards as needed.

There is no right or wrong
Unless it is a moral issue, I will see it simply as a difference of opinion and/or taste.

I choose the total view of positivity
Even though this event is negative, the total view of his behaviour is positive.

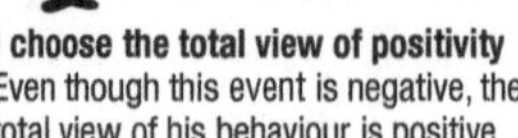

I surrender control
Since I cannot change this situation, I choose to let go of it.

I choose to put this event in perspective This event is not a catastrophe because it is not life threatening. It can be viewed as a trivial life event, a normal life problem that needs to be solved not dramatised.

I choose to view this event as average, falling within the normal range
This event is not exceptional; many people have gone through this.

It's temporary - "this too shall pass"
Life is constantly changing and moving through phases and this situation will also change.

Fears or facts?
Why fear? It may not happen!

I choose to focus on this as a learning experience
Every problem that comes my way is an opportunity for me to learn about my strengths and weaknesses, others and life.

Feel soothing emotions:

I choose to feel warm, loving emotions. I do this by focusing on my heart and letting love, trust forgiveness, compassion, hope or gratitude fill my heart space.

Behave constructively:

I choose to work in part acts:
I will break the overwhelming job into manageable parts.

Do the difficult:
I will face what I fear and act with self-discipline.

I choose to solutionise:
I will find a solution by taking advice or doing research.

Prioritise myself:
I will keep my life balanced by meeting friends, doing exercise or laughing.

Compartmentalise:
I will not let this event cloud my whole day; I will focus on something else now.

Utilise calming strategies:

When I:
• relax,
• breathe deeply,
• go for a run,
• shower,
• lie down,
• read,
• watch TV,
• climb into a mental helicopter,
• practice mindfulness/meditation,
my mind and body calm down.

Step Four: The Self Motivation Process

Endorse yourself for any growth no matter how small.

In the past I would have...

____

____

But this time I...

____

____

Tick off the traits that you strengthened when you worked down your anxiety:

☐ generosity	☐ peacefulness	
☐ kindness	☐ self-discipline	
☐ compassion	☐ forgiveness	
☐ consideration	☐ courage	
☐ helpfulness	☐ responsibility	
☐ respectfulness	☐ reliability	
☐ honesty	☐ loyalty	
☐ fairness	☐ love	
☐ patience	☐ humility	

Rate your anxiety on a scale of 0 to 100%:

☐ %

O

W

Date: ___________

Anxiety Management Worksheet

The purpose of this worksheet is to help you to see every stressful event as an opportunity for
1. greater understanding of yourself, your anxiety and the people around you, and
2. practicing tools to manage your anxiety.

Step One: An Event

Briefly describe an event when you became anxious. Give such details as time, place and people involved, and end with "That's when I began to work myself up…"

____

____

____

_________________________ Rate your anxiety on a scale of 0 to 100%: [   ] %

E

Step Two: The Working-Up Process

Learn about your working up process by identifying your thoughts, feelings, behaviours and bodily reactions during the event.
Tick the ones that most resonate with you.

Undermining Beliefs

B

I fear that I have lost...
- ☐ approval
- ☐ control
- ☐ co-operation
- ☐ face
- ☐ respect
- ☐ success
- ☐ trust
- ☐ validation
- ☐ love

This event proves that I am...
- ☐ stupid
- ☐ abnormal
- ☐ incompetent
- ☐ lazy
- ☐ irresponsible
- ☐ a total failure
- ☐ undisciplined
- ☐ untogether
- ☐ useless

I worry that I will suffer...
- ☐ mental collapse
- ☐ illness
- ☐ financial hardship

What I want is...
- ☐ total control
- ☐ respect
- ☐ success
- ☐ perfection
- ☐ comfort
- ☐ fairness
- ☐ tranquility
- ☐ all the answers
- ☐ for life to go smoothly
- ☐ to be all things to all people

Self-destructive Behaviour

Active
- ☐ get violent
- ☐ swear
- ☐ slam doors
- ☐ run away
- ☐ overeat
- ☐ harm myself
- ☐ criticise

Passive
- ☐ take it too seriously
- ☐ give up
- ☐ wallow in self pity
- ☐ sulk
- ☐ space out
- ☐ procrastinate
- ☐ give in
- ☐ be controlled

Intense Feelings

Angry feelings
- ☐ hateful
- ☐ aggravated
- ☐ annoyed
- ☐ hostile
- ☐ outraged
- ☐ punitive
- ☐ resentful
- ☐ vengeful

Fearful feelings
- ☐ helpless
- ☐ hopeless
- ☐ disappointed
- ☐ sad
- ☐ attacked
- ☐ worn out
- ☐ rejected
- ☐ jealous
- ☐ afraid
- ☐ exploited
- ☐ lonely
- ☐ abandoned
- ☐ guilty
- ☐ insulted
- ☐ confused
- ☐ disillusioned
- ☐ misunderstood
- ☐ trapped

Bodily Reactions (limbic system)

I am uncomfortable because I am experiencing...
- ☐ tremors
- ☐ nausea
- ☐ sweaty palms
- ☐ stomach-ache
- ☐ pounding heart
- ☐ general tension
- ☐ fatigue
- ☐ imagination on fire
- ☐ headache
- ☐ dry mouth
- ☐ jaw clenching
- ☐ shortness of breath

Continued over

B   **F**   **L**

Step Three: The Working-Down Process

Begin with, "Suddenly I realised that I was anxious and that I had choices..." This is the step of self-leadership and trust in one's ability to handle the situation.

Choose helpful thoughts:

I choose to depersonalise
There is no intention to hurt me. He is doing the best he can with the tools he has at the moment.

I choose realism over romanticism
Life presents many obstacles. I lower or raise standards as needed.

There is no right or wrong
Unless it is a moral issue, I will see it simply as a difference of opinion and/or taste.

I choose the total view of positivity
Even though this event is negative, the total view of his behaviour is positive.

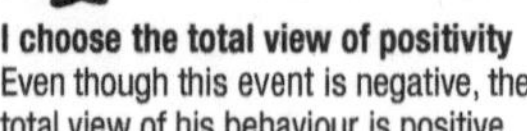

I surrender control
Since I cannot change this situation, I choose to let go of it.

I choose to put this event in perspective This event is not a catastrophe because it is not life threatening. It can be viewed as a trivial life event, a normal life problem that needs to be solved not dramatised.

I choose to view this event as average, falling within the normal range
This event is not exceptional; many people have gone through this.

It's temporary - "this too shall pass"
Life is constantly changing and moving through phases and this situation will also change.

Fears or facts?
Why fear? It may not happen!

I choose to focus on this as a learning experience
Every problem that comes my way is an opportunity for me to learn about my strengths and weaknesses, others and life.

Feel soothing emotions:

I choose to feel warm, loving emotions. I do this by focusing on my heart and letting love, trust forgiveness, compassion, hope or gratitude fill my heart space.

Behave constructively:

I choose to work in part acts:
I will break the overwhelming job into manageable parts.

Do the difficult:
I will face what I fear and act with self-discipline.

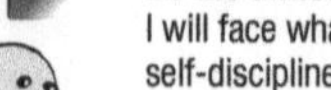

I choose to solutionise:
I will find a solution by taking advice or doing research.

Prioritise myself:
I will keep my life balanced by meeting friends, doing exercise or laughing.

Compartmentalise:
I will not let this event cloud my whole day; I will focus on something else now.

Utilise calming strategies:

When I:
- relax,
- breathe deeply,
- go for a run,
- shower,
- lie down,
- read,
- watch TV,
- climb into a mental helicopter,
- practice mindfulness/meditation,

  my mind and body calm down.

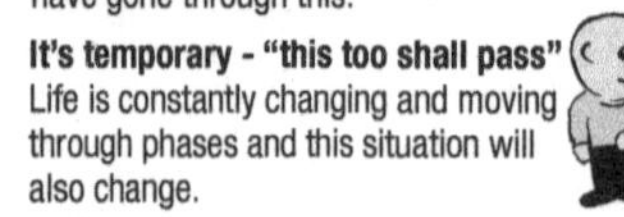
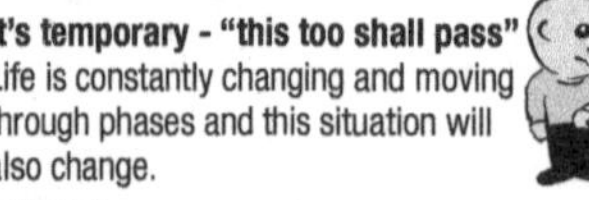

Step Four: The Self Motivation Process

Endorse yourself for any growth no matter how small.

In the past I would have...

____

____

But this time I...

____

____

Tick off the traits that you strengthened when you worked down your anxiety:

☐ generosity	☐ peacefulness	
☐ kindness	☐ self-discipline	
☐ compassion	☐ forgiveness	
☐ consideration	☐ courage	
☐ helpfulness	☐ responsibility	
☐ respectfulness	☐ reliability	
☐ honesty	☐ loyalty	
☐ fairness	☐ love	
☐ patience	☐ humility	

Rate your anxiety on a scale of 0 to 100%:

☐ %

O

W

Week 11

1. Week eleven is here, only two more weeks to go. By now you should be feeling much better, even anxiety free. This does not mean you should stop. On the contrary, it is vital that you keep going and complete the 90 days to ensure lasting change. Moreover, there are still some very useful tools to learn including: Fears or facts: thinking tool
2. Mental helicopter: behavioural tool
3. Visualisation: calming tool

Fears or facts: thinking tool

Why fear? It may not happen!

An important premise of CBT is that irrational thoughts lead to fear and anxiety. A primary tool of CBT is to gather facts to prove that these thoughts are not rational. The aim is to replace the irrational thoughts with rational thoughts which are based on facts. This is what lessens your fear. A common question utilised in CBT is "What is the evidence?" What facts do you have to confirm your fear? For instance, where is the proof that you will definitely make a fool of yourself when you deliver your speech?

The idea that is emphasised with this tool is that fears are not always facts. Fears may feel real but until they are confirmed by reality, they are simply that — fears. Humans tend to ruminate about possible negative outcomes, and women seem to do it more than men. We tend to forget the old but true cliché that 90% of the things we worry about never actually materialise.

Compare this to a child who is afraid of the dark. She imagines that there are things that are waiting in the cupboard to pounce when in fact nothing of the sort exists.

As adults we do this, too. Let us say, for example, that your manager asks you to swap desks with a newcomer; you then start to imagine that after the desk, you will be asked to relinquish your senior position in the company to the newcomer and ultimately, you will be answering to the newcomer. The starting off point was being asked to swap desks; your fears push you to take it to an end-point where you would have to answer to the newcomer. Many other "end-points" exist in possibility but you have chosen the one that reflects your fears. Until the boss actually tells you that you are demoted in relation to the newcomer, it is only your fear that leads you to believe that you will be demoted.

The following exercise is here to assist you to hold on calmly through scary moments. Before you succumb to worry and despair, this tool will assist you to wait until you have the facts before jumping to conclusions.

EXERCISE 37

For the scenarios presented below, write out possible fearful thoughts and then calm yourself by repeating the wording of this tool.

Your manager asks you to swap desks.

    a) Fearful thought: *"I will soon be answering to the newcomer."*

    b) Calming thought: *"Why waste energy on worry and fear? Until the boss tells me otherwise, I will continue in my job as before, albeit at a new desk."*

1. You find a lump on your hand:
   a) Fearful thought: _______________
   b) Calming thought: _______________

2. Your boss calls you to his office unexpectedly:
   a) Fearful thought: _______________
   b) Calming thought: _______________

3. A police car is just behind you and initiates the siren:
   a) Fearful thought: _______________
   b) Calming thought: _______________

4. Your partner does not eat the soup you specially prepared:
   a) Fearful thought: _______________
   b) Calming thought: _______________

5. Your best friend's car has gone in for repairs for a month:
   a) Fearful thought: _______________
   b) Calming thought: _______________

6. Your company has merged with another, larger company:
   a) Fearful thought: _______________________________
   b) Calming thought: _______________________________

7. A fellow passenger on the bus moves from the seat next to you to the back of the bus:
   a) Fearful thought: _______________________________
   b) Calming thought: _______________________________

8. Your partner is late and is not answering his/her phone.
   a) Fearful thought: _______________________________
   b) Calming thought: _______________________________

EXERCISE 38

Have you ever predicted a negative outcome that proved to be incorrect?   YES/NO

If you answered "yes," what was it and how did it turn out in reality?

____

____

____

____

____

This tool is particularly helpful when it is difficult to move from a negative thought to a positive one. Sometimes we are so convinced that there will be a negative outcome that our brain cannot process a positive possibility. When you try to think more positively, your brain responds as if it is a "trick" question and may become even more sceptical.

This tool moves you from a negative thought to a neutral thought. You are not trying to disprove your fears. You are simply putting possible conclusions on hold or in the "too hard basket". You are also reassuring yourself that you will be free to start worrying when you have evidence that your fear is a fact.

For example, when you discover a lump on your hand, it is nearly impossible to try and convince yourself that it is nothing. After all, a lump is a lump and should not be there. However, it is possible to move into a neutral position. You say, *"Why fear the worst, it may not be the truth. Until the doctor gives me a reliable diagnosis, I will think about other things and not focus on it."*

Climbing into a mental helicopter: behavioural tool

This is a great tool to use when you begin to work yourself up and are not in a position to physically exit a situation. The helicopter is the vehicle of choice because it can hover above a situation. In other words it is present but not right in the middle of the situation.

> You are sitting in a board meeting. There is a lot of tension between team members. You do not want to be dragged into the tension. You will be presenting your proposal shortly and want to stay calm.
>
> You have few options. You cannot leave the room as that would be unprofessional. You cannot do deep breathing or relaxation as that would be inappropriate. What you can do is visualise yourself climbing into a mental helicopter. Imagine your tense feelings hovering above, not being caught up in the tension.

This is an effective tool because your body and conscious rational mind are fully present in the moment and able to perform with excellence, while your potentially damaging emotions are at a distance.

> You are at a family dinner. Your mother-in-law is picking on your husband. You want to interfere, to stick up for him or to leave. However, you know it will upset the rest of the family, including your husband, who is used to his mother's ways. While sitting at the table, climb into your mental helicopter. Let all your judgments and animosity hover above while you display warmth and enthusiasm to the rest of the family.

Note: Climbing into a mental helicopter is not spacing out or disassociating. It is making an active choice to put your emotions out of centre. They are there, you are aware of them, you can tap into them at any time. However, for peace and calm, you choose to keep them in the helicopter until it is an appropriate time to deal with them.

Visualisation (also called mental rehearsal): calming tool

When you were a child, you had an active imagination and could see yourself being anybody that you wanted including Superman. Unfortunately, as adults many of us become realists and do not use our imagination enough.

Your imagination is extremely potent. Research has shown that when you imagine yourself moving a muscle, your neurons in your brain will fire exactly as if you were actually moving that muscle. There is the case of an Olympic diver who broke a hip and was in a plaster cast for four months. Of course, this meant she could not practise her dives and all she could do was keep her upper body strong with exercise. However, that was not all she could do. Every day she would imagine herself executing the most perfect dive. After the cast was removed, she discovered that her diving had improved enormously and she was able to perform dives in reality as well as she had performed them in her imagination.

Your imagination can assist you to become the calm person you aspire to be. For instance, say you are afraid of speaking at business meetings. Every day, take ten minutes to visualise yourself in a business meeting and calmly asserting your point of view. The trick here is not to see yourself getting it wrong and then improving because that will also cause your neurons to fire. You should only visualise yourself as you want to be. Moreover, you can only visualise yourself changing and improving. You cannot imagine that anybody else will change, such as, your stern boss becoming softer after you mentally rehearse.

You can utilise visualisation for any situation. The more you practise, the more you will create the person you want to be.

Visualisation and relaxation

You can utilise visualisation at any time. However, sometimes the biggest change manifests when you utilise visualisation while being deeply relaxed. When you are in a relaxed state, your mind is receptive to new ideas and to making changes. Your defences are down.

Let us say that you are afraid of spiders. You cannot visualise yourself feeling safe in their presence. It is too hard for your brain to accept the image of you being calm as your fear neurons are firing. However, when you are totally relaxed, there is no fear and consequently your imagination can now be stretched in any direction that you want.

Progressive muscle relaxation

A very effective method of relaxation is called progressive muscle relaxation.

EXERCISE 39

1. Close your eyes. Get comfortable in your chair. Uncross your legs and separate your fingers.

2. Think of your toes. Think of each one in turn and as you do so your toes will begin to feel heavy. Now think of your feet, the soles of your feet, the balls of your feet and the upper skin. Feel your feet grow heavy. Feel all the tension drain out through the tips of your toes.

3. Now think of your heels and then your ankles until your whole feet, from top to bottom feel heavy and feel like they are sinking into the floor.

4. Moving upwards, focus on the calves of your legs, first the right one then the next. Calves are frequently tense so focus on letting the tension drain out through your feet and the tips of your toes.

5. Think about your knees and feel them grow heavy. Continue moving up, feel your thighs grow heavy and sink deeply into the chair. Any remaining tension can drain downwards through your toes.

6. Your whole leg is relaxed and heavy now from your hips to the tips of your toes. Focus on your hips and feel them grow heavy. Feel your whole pelvic area grow heavy. Next feel your stomach and lower back grow heavy as they become more and more deeply relaxed.

7. Continue moving upwards, feeling the relaxation spreading to your chest and upper back and even your shoulders. Feel your shoulders relax as the tension in them drains through your fingers. Turn your focus to your upper arms and then your lower arms and feel them slowly become heavy as all the tension drains through your fingers. Feel your hands and fingers relax.

8. You are now relaxed from your shoulders down. Moving upwards, turn your attention to your neck, which holds a huge amount of strain. Let the tension drain out. Then move upwards to your jaw. Unclench your jaw. Let your tongue and teeth be loose. Allow your cheeks to be soft and unscrew your eyelids. Your whole face is relaxed by now, only your scalp remains. Focus on your scalp and feel it relax completely.

9. You are now deeply relaxed, deeper and deeper. From today onwards, every time that you do progressive muscle relaxation, you will find it easier and easier to relax and you will go into a deeper and deeper state of relaxation.

Once you are deeply relaxed, your mind will be open to positive visualisations. You are now ready to mentally rehearse. Mental rehearsal utilises your imagination to program your subconscious to feel confident in your ability.

Master mental rehearsal

I use the image of a violinist to demonstrate the use of mental rehearsal technique to lower performance anxiety. However, the technique is effective for any person suffering from any type of anxiety including specific phobias.

EXERCISE 40

1. Arrange for ten uninterrupted minutes alone in a quiet setting. Be alert and not sleepy.

2. You may sit or lie down. Either way, ensure that your back is straight and you feel comfortable.

3. Close your eyes. Focus on your breathing. Breathe in slowly and fully through your nose, and breathe out slowly through your mouth.

4. Execute a total body scan: check all your muscles from head to toe and release any tension that you find.

5. Select a visual reference point from memory such as your musical instrument.

6. Warm up. Imagine yourself playing scales and warming up. Can you hear yourself? Can you feel your fingers limbering up?

7. Imagine yourself performing. Go step by step from your entrance, getting seated, cuing the music, following the music phrase by phrase, etc.

8. Go through a piece without making a mistake. If you make a mistake just ignore it and keep on playing perfectly.

9. Bring in all your senses. Hear the music but also feel the wood of your violin. Make your mental rehearsal as vivid and lifelike as possible.

10. Play around with different approaches. Envision different famous venues and concert halls. Try out a new repertoire.

11. Test yourself. Record yourself playing a piece. Rate yourself. Then do seven mental rehearsals of the same piece. Record yourself again and review again. After eight sessions of mental rehearsal, you will notice a huge improvement in your playing and confidence.

12. When you are satisfied with the performance, pick a more challenging piece that you have not mastered and mentally rehearse it.

Time and practice gives you control over your imagination which is critical to confidence, and ability, to perform well under pressure. When you have finished, bring yourself slowly out of your "trance" by counting backwards from ten.

Like all relaxation methods, the more you practise, the more likely a calm state becomes your norm.

DAILY MONITORING DIARY WEEK ENDING _________________________

Day	M	T	W	T	F	S	S
Overall Anxiety Rating for the day (0-10)							
1. EXERCISE							
How long?							
Anxiety level before (0-10)							
Anxiety level after (0-10)							
2. BREATHING							
How long?							
Anxiety level before (0-10)							
Anxiety level after (0-10)							
3. RELAXATION							
How long?							
Anxiety level before (0-10)							
Anxiety level after (0-10)							
4. PERVASIVE PESSIMISTIC THINKING							
How often this type of thought occurred							
Belief in thoughts before challenging (0-10)							
Belief in thoughts after challenging (0-10)							

Day	M	T	W	T	F	S	S
5. CATASTROPHIC THINKING							
How often this type of thought occurred							
Belief in thoughts before challenging (0-10)							
Belief in thoughts after challenging (0-10)							
6. PERMANENT PESSIMISTIC THINKING							
How often this type of thought occurred							
Belief in thoughts before challenging (0-10)							
Belief in thoughts after challenging (0-10)							
7. MINDFULNESS (FORMAL, GROUNDING, INFORMAL MINDFULNESS)							
How long?							
Anxiety level before (0-10)							
Anxiety level after (0-10)							
8. ROMANTIC THINKING							
How often this type of thought occurred							
Belief in thoughts before challenging (0-10)							
Belief in thoughts after challenging (0-10)							

Day	M	T	W	T	F	S	S
9. NEGATIVE JUDGEMENTAL THINKING							
How often this type of thought occurred							
Belief in thoughts before challenging (0-10)							
Belief in thoughts after challenging (0-10)							
10. CAN'T LET GO THINKING							
How often this type of thought occurred							
Belief in thoughts before challenging (0-10)							
Belief in thoughts after challenging (0-10)							
11. MEDITATION							
How long?							
Anxiety level before (0-10)							
Anxiety level after (0-10)							
12. EXCEPTIONAL THINKING							
How often this type of thought occurred							
Belief in thoughts before challenging (0-10)							
Belief in thoughts after challenging (0-10)							

Date: ___________

Anxiety Management Worksheet

The purpose of this worksheet is to help you to see every stressful event as an opportunity for
1. greater understanding of yourself, your anxiety and the people around you, and
2. practicing tools to manage your anxiety.

Step One: An Event

Briefly describe an event when you became anxious. Give such details as time, place and people involved, and end with "That's when I began to work myself up…"

____

____

____

____ Rate your anxiety on a scale of 0 to 100%: [   ] %

E

Step Two: The Working-Up Process

Learn about your working up process by identifying your thoughts, feelings, behaviours and bodily reactions during the event.
Tick the ones that most resonate with you.

B

Undermining Beliefs

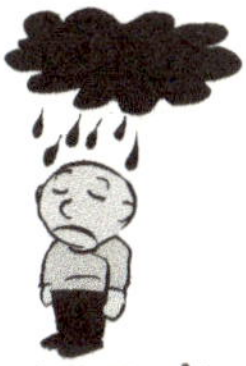

I fear that I have lost...
- ☐ approval
- ☐ control
- ☐ co-operation
- ☐ face
- ☐ respect
- ☐ success
- ☐ trust
- ☐ validation
- ☐ love

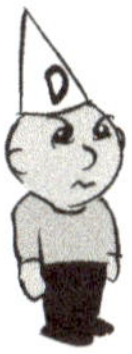

This event proves that I am...
- ☐ stupid
- ☐ abnormal
- ☐ incompetent
- ☐ lazy
- ☐ irresponsible
- ☐ a total failure
- ☐ undisciplined
- ☐ untogether
- ☐ useless

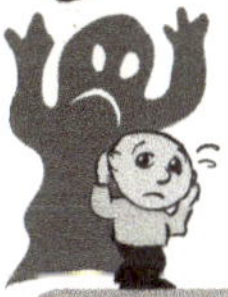

I worry that I will suffer...
- ☐ mental collapse
- ☐ illness
- ☐ financial hardship

What I want is...
- ☐ total control
- ☐ respect
- ☐ success
- ☐ perfection
- ☐ comfort
- ☐ fairness
- ☐ tranquility
- ☐ all the answers
- ☐ for life to go smoothly
- ☐ to be all things to all people

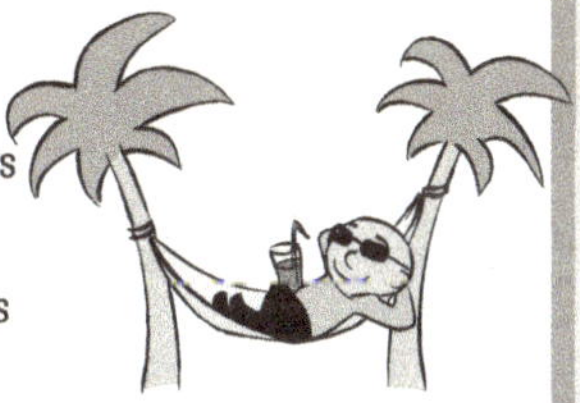

Self-destructive Behaviour

Active
- ☐ get violent
- ☐ swear
- ☐ slam doors
- ☐ run away
- ☐ overeat
- ☐ harm myself
- ☐ criticise

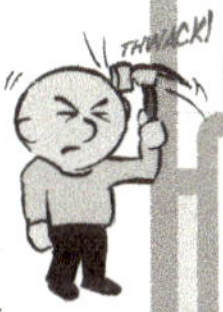

Passive
- ☐ take it too seriously
- ☐ give up
- ☐ wallow in self pity
- ☐ sulk
- ☐ space out
- ☐ procrastinate
- ☐ give in
- ☐ be controlled

Intense Feelings

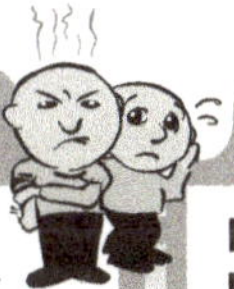

Angry feelings
- ☐ hateful
- ☐ aggravated
- ☐ annoyed
- ☐ hostile
- ☐ outraged
- ☐ punitive
- ☐ resentful
- ☐ vengeful

Fearful feelings
- ☐ helpless
- ☐ hopeless
- ☐ disappointed
- ☐ sad

- ☐ attacked
- ☐ worn out
- ☐ rejected
- ☐ jealous
- ☐ afraid
- ☐ exploited
- ☐ lonely
- ☐ abandoned
- ☐ guilty
- ☐ insulted
- ☐ confused
- ☐ disillusioned
- ☐ misunderstood
- ☐ trapped

Bodily Reactions (limbic system)

I am uncomfortable because I am experiencing...
- ☐ tremors
- ☐ nausea
- ☐ sweaty palms
- ☐ stomach-ache
- ☐ pounding heart
- ☐ general tension
- ☐ fatigue
- ☐ imagination on fire
- ☐ headache
- ☐ dry mouth
- ☐ jaw clenching
- ☐ shortness of breath

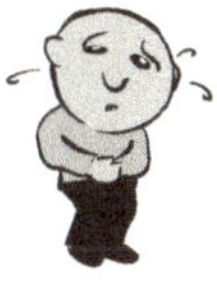

Continued over

B   F   L

Step Three: The Working-Down Process

Begin with, "Suddenly I realised that I was anxious and that I had choices..." This is the step of self-leadership and trust in one's ability to handle the situation.

Choose helpful thoughts:

I choose to depersonalise
There is no intention to hurt me. He is doing the best he can with the tools he has at the moment.

I choose realism over romanticism
Life presents many obstacles. I lower or raise standards as needed.

There is no right or wrong
Unless it is a moral issue, I will see it simply as a difference of opinion and/or taste.

I choose the total view of positivity
Even though this event is negative, the total view of his behaviour is positive.

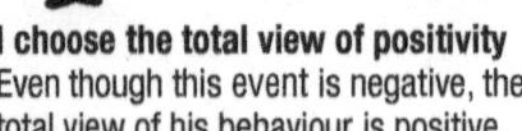

I surrender control
Since I cannot change this situation, I choose to let go of it.

I choose to put this event in perspective This event is not a catastrophe because it is not life threatening. It can be viewed as a trivial life event, a normal life problem that needs to be solved not dramatised.

I choose to view this event as average, falling within the normal range
This event is not exceptional; many people have gone through this.

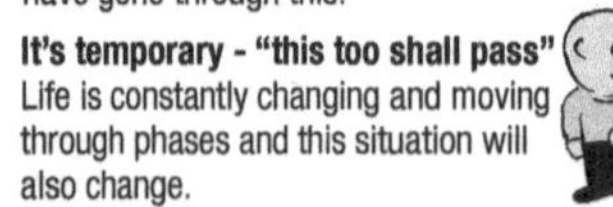

It's temporary - "this too shall pass"
Life is constantly changing and moving through phases and this situation will also change.

Fears or facts?
Why fear? It may not happen!

I choose to focus on this as a learning experience
Every problem that comes my way is an opportunity for me to learn about my strengths and weaknesses, others and life.

Feel soothing emotions:

I choose to feel warm, loving emotions. I do this by focusing on my heart and letting love, trust forgiveness, compassion, hope or gratitude fill my heart space.

Behave constructively:

I choose to work in part acts:
I will break the overwhelming job into manageable parts.

Do the difficult:
I will face what I fear and act with self-discipline.

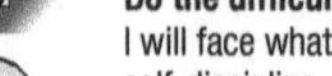

I choose to solutionise:
I will find a solution by taking advice or doing research.

Prioritise myself:
I will keep my life balanced by meeting friends, doing exercise or laughing.

Compartmentalise:
I will not let this event cloud my whole day; I will focus on something else now.

Utilise calming strategies:

When I:
- relax,
- breathe deeply,
- go for a run,
- shower,
- lie down,
- read,
- watch TV,
- climb into a mental helicopter,
- practice mindfulness/meditation,

my mind and body calm down.

Step Four: The Self Motivation Process

Endorse yourself for any growth no matter how small.

In the past I would have...

____

____

But this time I...

____

____

Tick off the traits that you strengthened when you worked down your anxiety:

☐	generosity	☐	peacefulness
☐	kindness	☐	self-discipline
☐	compassion	☐	forgiveness
☐	consideration	☐	courage
☐	helpfulness	☐	responsibility
☐	respectfulness	☐	reliability
☐	honesty	☐	loyalty
☐	fairness	☐	love
☐	patience	☐	humility

Rate your anxiety
on a scale of
0 to 100%:

[______] %

Date: ___________

Anxiety Management Worksheet

The purpose of this worksheet is to help you to see every stressful event as an opportunity for
1. greater understanding of yourself, your anxiety and the people around you, and
2. practicing tools to manage your anxiety.

Step One: An Event

Briefly describe an event when you became anxious. Give such details as time, place and people involved, and end with "That's when I began to work myself up…"

____

____

____

____   Rate your anxiety on a scale of 0 to 100%: [   ] %

E

Step Two: The Working-Up Process

Learn about your working up process by identifying your thoughts, feelings, behaviours and bodily reactions during the event.
Tick the ones that most resonate with you.

B

Undermining Beliefs

I fear that I have lost...
- ☐ approval
- ☐ control
- ☐ co-operation
- ☐ face
- ☐ respect
- ☐ success
- ☐ trust
- ☐ validation
- ☐ love

This event proves that I am...
- ☐ stupid
- ☐ abnormal
- ☐ incompetent
- ☐ lazy
- ☐ irresponsible
- ☐ a total failure
- ☐ undisciplined
- ☐ untogether
- ☐ useless

I worry that I will suffer...
- ☐ mental collapse
- ☐ illness
- ☐ financial hardship

What I want is...
- ☐ total control
- ☐ respect
- ☐ success
- ☐ perfection
- ☐ comfort
- ☐ fairness
- ☐ tranquility
- ☐ all the answers
- ☐ for life to go smoothly
- ☐ to be all things to all people

Self-destructive Behaviour

Active
- ☐ get violent
- ☐ swear
- ☐ slam doors
- ☐ run away
- ☐ overeat
- ☐ harm myself
- ☐ criticise

Passive
- ☐ take it too seriously
- ☐ give up
- ☐ wallow in self pity
- ☐ sulk
- ☐ space out
- ☐ procrastinate
- ☐ give in
- ☐ be controlled

Intense Feelings

Angry feelings
- ☐ hateful
- ☐ aggravated
- ☐ annoyed
- ☐ hostile
- ☐ outraged
- ☐ punitive
- ☐ resentful
- ☐ vengeful

Fearful feelings
- ☐ helpless
- ☐ hopeless
- ☐ disappointed
- ☐ sad
- ☐ attacked
- ☐ worn out
- ☐ rejected
- ☐ jealous
- ☐ afraid
- ☐ exploited
- ☐ lonely
- ☐ abandoned
- ☐ guilty
- ☐ insulted
- ☐ confused
- ☐ disillusioned
- ☐ misunderstood
- ☐ trapped

Bodily Reactions (limbic system)

I am uncomfortable because I am experiencing...
- ☐ tremors
- ☐ nausea
- ☐ sweaty palms
- ☐ stomach-ache
- ☐ pounding heart
- ☐ general tension
- ☐ fatigue
- ☐ imagination on fire
- ☐ headache
- ☐ dry mouth
- ☐ jaw clenching
- ☐ shortness of breath

Continued over

B   **F**   **L**

Step Three: The Working-Down Process

Begin with, "Suddenly I realised that I was anxious and that I had choices..." This is the step of self-leadership and trust in one's ability to handle the situation.

Choose helpful thoughts:

I choose to depersonalise
There is no intention to hurt me. He is doing the best he can with the tools he has at the moment.

I choose realism over romanticism
Life presents many obstacles. I lower or raise standards as needed.

There is no right or wrong
Unless it is a moral issue, I will see it simply as a difference of opinion and/or taste.

I choose the total view of positivity
Even though this event is negative, the total view of his behaviour is positive.

I surrender control
Since I cannot change this situation, I choose to let go of it.

I choose to put this event in perspective This event is not a catastrophe because it is not life threatening. It can be viewed as a trivial life event, a normal life problem that needs to be solved not dramatised.

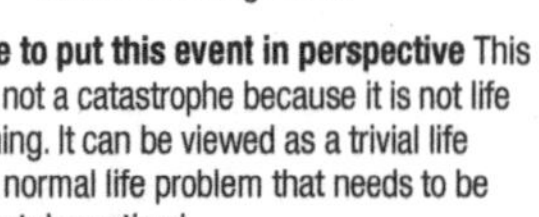

I choose to view this event as average, falling within the normal range
This event is not exceptional; many people have gone through this.

It's temporary - "this too shall pass"
Life is constantly changing and moving through phases and this situation will also change.

Fears or facts?
Why fear? It may not happen!

I choose to focus on this as a learning experience
Every problem that comes my way is an opportunity for me to learn about my strengths and weaknesses, others and life.

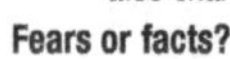

Feel soothing emotions:

I choose to feel warm, loving emotions. I do this by focusing on my heart and letting love, trust forgiveness, compassion, hope or gratitude fill my heart space.

Behave constructively:

I choose to work in part acts:
I will break the overwhelming job into manageable parts.

Do the difficult:
I will face what I fear and act with self-discipline.

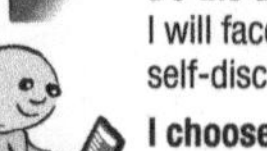

I choose to solutionise:
I will find a solution by taking advice or doing research.

Prioritise myself:
I will keep my life balanced by meeting friends, doing exercise or laughing.

Compartmentalise:
I will not let this event cloud my whole day; I will focus on something else now.

Utilise calming strategies:

When I:
- relax,
- breathe deeply,
- go for a run,
- shower,
- lie down,
- read,
- watch TV,
- climb into a mental helicopter,
- practice mindfulness/meditation,

my mind and body calm down.

Step Four: The Self Motivation Process

Endorse yourself for any growth no matter how small.

In the past I would have...

____

____

But this time I...

____

____

Tick off the traits that you strengthened when you worked down your anxiety:

☐ generosity	☐ peacefulness
☐ kindness	☐ self-discipline
☐ compassion	☐ forgiveness
☐ consideration	☐ courage
☐ helpfulness	☐ responsibility
☐ respectfulness	☐ reliability
☐ honesty	☐ loyalty
☐ fairness	☐ love
☐ patience	☐ humility

Rate your anxiety on a scale of 0 to 100%:

________ %

O

W

Date: _____________

Anxiety Management Worksheet

The purpose of this worksheet is to help you to see every stressful event as an opportunity for
1. greater understanding of yourself, your anxiety and the people around you, and
2. practicing tools to manage your anxiety.

Step One: An Event

Briefly describe an event when you became anxious. Give such details as time, place and people involved, and end with "That's when I began to work myself up…"

____

____

____

______________________________ Rate your anxiety on a scale of 0 to 100%: [   ] %

E

Step Two: The Working-Up Process

Learn about your working up process by identifying your thoughts, feelings, behaviours and bodily reactions during the event.
Tick the ones that most resonate with you.

Undermining Beliefs

B

I fear that I have lost...

- ☐ approval
- ☐ control
- ☐ co-operation
- ☐ face
- ☐ respect
- ☐ success
- ☐ trust
- ☐ validation
- ☐ love

This event proves that I am...

- ☐ stupid
- ☐ abnormal
- ☐ incompetent
- ☐ lazy
- ☐ irresponsible
- ☐ a total failure
- ☐ undisciplined
- ☐ untogether
- ☐ useless

I worry that I will suffer...

- ☐ mental collapse
- ☐ illness
- ☐ financial hardship

What I want is...

- ☐ total control
- ☐ respect
- ☐ success
- ☐ perfection
- ☐ comfort
- ☐ fairness
- ☐ tranquility
- ☐ all the answers
- ☐ for life to go smoothly
- ☐ to be all things to all people

Self-destructive Behaviour

Active
- ☐ get violent
- ☐ swear
- ☐ slam doors
- ☐ run away
- ☐ overeat
- ☐ harm myself
- ☐ criticise

Passive
- ☐ take it too seriously
- ☐ give up
- ☐ wallow in self pity
- ☐ sulk
- ☐ space out
- ☐ procrastinate
- ☐ give in
- ☐ be controlled

Intense Feelings

Angry feelings
- ☐ hateful
- ☐ aggravated
- ☐ annoyed
- ☐ hostile
- ☐ outraged
- ☐ punitive
- ☐ resentful
- ☐ vengeful
- ☐ attacked
- ☐ worn out
- ☐ rejected
- ☐ jealous
- ☐ afraid
- ☐ exploited
- ☐ lonely
- ☐ abandoned
- ☐ guilty
- ☐ insulted

Fearful feelings
- ☐ helpless
- ☐ hopeless
- ☐ disappointed
- ☐ sad
- ☐ confused
- ☐ disillusioned
- ☐ misunderstood
- ☐ trapped

Bodily Reactions (limbic system)

I am uncomfortable because I am experiencing...
- ☐ tremors
- ☐ nausea
- ☐ sweaty palms
- ☐ stomach-ache
- ☐ pounding heart
- ☐ general tension
- ☐ fatigue
- ☐ imagination on fire
- ☐ headache
- ☐ dry mouth
- ☐ jaw clenching
- ☐ shortness of breath

Continued over

B   **F**   **L**

Step Three: The Working-Down Process

Begin with, "Suddenly I realised that I was anxious and that I had choices..." This is the step of self-leadership and trust in one's ability to handle the situation.

Choose helpful thoughts:

I choose to depersonalise
There is no intention to hurt me. He is doing the best he can with the tools he has at the moment.

I choose realism over romanticism
Life presents many obstacles. I lower or raise standards as needed.

There is no right or wrong
Unless it is a moral issue, I will see it simply as a difference of opinion and/or taste.

I choose the total view of positivity
Even though this event is negative, the total view of his behaviour is positive.

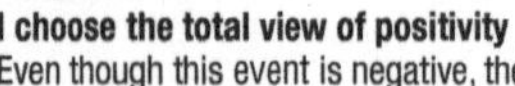

I surrender control
Since I cannot change this situation, I choose to let go of it.

I choose to put this event in perspective This event is not a catastrophe because it is not life threatening. It can be viewed as a trivial life event, a normal life problem that needs to be solved not dramatised.

I choose to view this event as average, falling within the normal range
This event is not exceptional; many people have gone through this.

It's temporary - "this too shall pass"
Life is constantly changing and moving through phases and this situation will also change.

Fears or facts?
Why fear? It may not happen!

I choose to focus on this as a learning experience
Every problem that comes my way is an opportunity for me to learn about my strengths and weaknesses, others and life.

Feel soothing emotions:

I choose to feel warm, loving emotions. I do this by focusing on my heart and letting love, trust forgiveness, compassion, hope or gratitude fill my heart space.

Behave constructively:

I choose to work in part acts:
I will break the overwhelming job into manageable parts.

Do the difficult:
I will face what I fear and act with self-discipline.

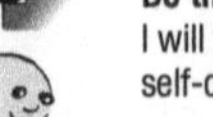
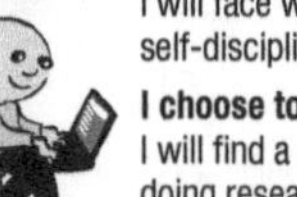

I choose to solutionise:
I will find a solution by taking advice or doing research.

Prioritise myself:
I will keep my life balanced by meeting friends, doing exercise or laughing.

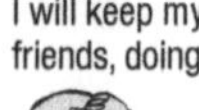

Compartmentalise:
I will not let this event cloud my whole day; I will focus on something else now.

Utilise calming strategies:

When I:
- relax,
- breathe deeply,
- go for a run,
- shower,
- lie down,
- read,
- watch TV,
- climb into a mental helicopter,
- practice mindfulness/meditation,

my mind and body calm down.

Step Four: The Self Motivation Process

Endorse yourself for any growth no matter how small.

In the past I would have...

____

____

But this time I...

____

____

Tick off the traits that you strengthened when you worked down your anxiety:

☐ generosity	☐ peacefulness
☐ kindness	☐ self-discipline
☐ compassion	☐ forgiveness
☐ consideration	☐ courage
☐ helpfulness	☐ responsibility
☐ respectfulness	☐ reliability
☐ honesty	☐ loyalty
☐ fairness	☐ love
☐ patience	☐ humility

Rate your anxiety on a scale of 0 to 100%:

____ %

O

W

Date: _______________

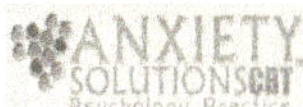

Anxiety Management Worksheet

The purpose of this worksheet is to help you to see every stressful event as an opportunity for
1. greater understanding of yourself, your anxiety and the people around you, and
2. practicing tools to manage your anxiety.

Step One: An Event

Briefly describe an event when you became anxious. Give such details as time, place and people involved, and end with "That's when I began to work myself up..."

____

____   **E**

____

____ Rate your anxiety on a scale of 0 to 100%: [   ] %

Step Two: The Working-Up Process

Learn about your working up process by identifying your thoughts, feelings, behaviours and bodily reactions during the event.
Tick the ones that most resonate with you.

Undermining Beliefs

B

I fear that I have lost...
- ☐ approval
- ☐ control
- ☐ co-operation
- ☐ face
- ☐ respect
- ☐ success
- ☐ trust
- ☐ validation
- ☐ love

This event proves that I am...
- ☐ stupid
- ☐ abnormal
- ☐ incompetent
- ☐ lazy
- ☐ irresponsible
- ☐ a total failure
- ☐ undisciplined
- ☐ untogether
- ☐ useless

I worry that I will suffer...
- ☐ mental collapse
- ☐ illness
- ☐ financial hardship

What I want is...
- ☐ total control
- ☐ respect
- ☐ success
- ☐ perfection
- ☐ comfort
- ☐ fairness
- ☐ tranquility
- ☐ all the answers
- ☐ for life to go smoothly
- ☐ to be all things to all people

Self-destructive Behaviour

Active
- ☐ get violent
- ☐ swear
- ☐ slam doors
- ☐ run away
- ☐ overeat
- ☐ harm myself
- ☐ criticise

Passive
- ☐ take it too seriously
- ☐ give up
- ☐ wallow in self pity
- ☐ sulk
- ☐ space out
- ☐ procrastinate
- ☐ give in
- ☐ be controlled

Intense Feelings

Angry feelings
- ☐ hateful
- ☐ aggravated
- ☐ annoyed
- ☐ hostile
- ☐ outraged
- ☐ punitive
- ☐ resentful
- ☐ vengeful
- ☐ attacked
- ☐ worn out
- ☐ rejected
- ☐ jealous
- ☐ afraid
- ☐ exploited
- ☐ lonely
- ☐ abandoned
- ☐ guilty

Fearful feelings
- ☐ helpless
- ☐ hopeless
- ☐ disappointed
- ☐ sad
- ☐ insulted
- ☐ confused
- ☐ disillusioned
- ☐ misunderstood
- ☐ trapped

Bodily Reactions (limbic system)

I am uncomfortable because I am experiencing... 
- ☐ tremors
- ☐ nausea
- ☐ sweaty palms
- ☐ stomach-ache
- ☐ pounding heart
- ☐ general tension
- ☐ fatigue
- ☐ imagination on fire
- ☐ headache
- ☐ dry mouth
- ☐ jaw clenching
- ☐ shortness of breath

B   **F**   **L**

Step Three: The Working-Down Process

Begin with, "Suddenly I realised that I was anxious and that I had choices..." This is the step of self-leadership and trust in one's ability to handle the situation.

Choose helpful thoughts:

I choose to depersonalise
There is no intention to hurt me. He is doing the best he can with the tools he has at the moment.

I choose realism over romanticism
Life presents many obstacles. I lower or raise standards as needed.

There is no right or wrong
Unless it is a moral issue, I will see it simply as a difference of opinion and/or taste.

I choose the total view of positivity
Even though this event is negative, the total view of his behaviour is positive.

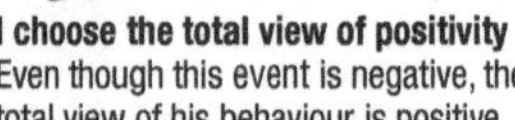

I surrender control
Since I cannot change this situation, I choose to let go of it.

I choose to put this event in perspective This event is not a catastrophe because it is not life threatening. It can be viewed as a trivial life event, a normal life problem that needs to be solved not dramatised.

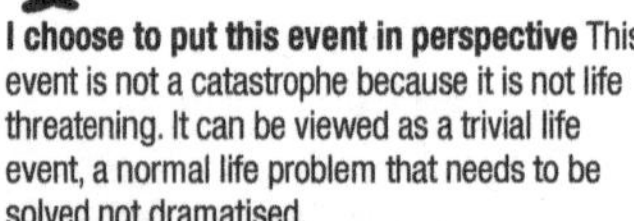
I choose to view this event as average, falling within the normal range
This event is not exceptional; many people have gone through this.

It's temporary - "this too shall pass"
Life is constantly changing and moving through phases and this situation will also change.

Fears or facts?
Why fear? It may not happen!

I choose to focus on this as a learning experience
Every problem that comes my way is an opportunity for me to learn about my strengths and weaknesses, others and life.

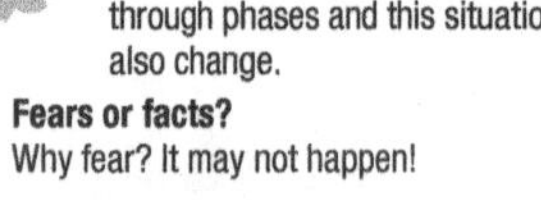

Feel soothing emotions:

I choose to feel warm, loving emotions. I do this by focusing on my heart and letting love, trust forgiveness, compassion, hope or gratitude fill my heart space.

Behave constructively:

I choose to work in part acts:
I will break the overwhelming job into manageable parts.

Do the difficult:
I will face what I fear and act with self-discipline.

I choose to solutionise:
I will find a solution by taking advice or doing research.

Prioritise myself:
I will keep my life balanced by meeting friends, doing exercise or laughing.

Compartmentalise:
I will not let this event cloud my whole day; I will focus on something else now.

Utilise calming strategies:

When I:
- relax,
- breathe deeply,
- go for a run,
- shower,
- lie down,
- read,
- watch TV,
- climb into a mental helicopter,
- practice mindfulness/meditation,

my mind and body calm down.

Step Four: The Self Motivation Process

Endorse yourself for any growth no matter how small.

In the past I would have...

____

____

But this time I...

____

____

Tick off the traits that you strengthened when you worked down your anxiety:

☐ generosity	☐ peacefulness
☐ kindness	☐ self-discipline
☐ compassion	☐ forgiveness
☐ consideration	☐ courage
☐ helpfulness	☐ responsibility
☐ respectfulness	☐ reliability
☐ honesty	☐ loyalty
☐ fairness	☐ love
☐ patience	☐ humility

Rate your anxiety on a scale of 0 to 100%:

________%

Anxiety Management Worksheet

The purpose of this worksheet is to help you to see every stressful event as an opportunity for
1. greater understanding of yourself, your anxiety and the people around you, and
2. practicing tools to manage your anxiety.

Step One: An Event

Briefly describe an event when you became anxious. Give such details as time, place and people involved, and end with "That's when I began to work myself up…"

____

____

____

_______________________________ Rate your anxiety on a scale of 0 to 100%: [ ] %

E

Step Two: The Working-Up Process

Learn about your working up process by identifying your thoughts, feelings, behaviours and bodily reactions during the event.
Tick the ones that most resonate with you.

Undermining Beliefs

B

I fear that I have lost...

- ☐ approval
- ☐ success
- ☐ control
- ☐ trust
- ☐ co-operation
- ☐ validation
- ☐ face
- ☐ love
- ☐ respect

This event proves that I am...

- ☐ stupid
- ☐ a total failure
- ☐ abnormal
- ☐ undisciplined
- ☐ incompetent
- ☐ untogether
- ☐ lazy
- ☐ useless
- ☐ irresponsible

I worry that I will suffer...

- ☐ mental collapse
- ☐ illness
- ☐ financial hardship

What I want is...

- ☐ total control
- ☐ tranquility
- ☐ respect
- ☐ all the answers
- ☐ success
- ☐ for life to go smoothly
- ☐ perfection
- ☐ comfort
- ☐ to be all things to all people
- ☐ fairness

Self-destructive Behaviour

Active

- ☐ get violent
- ☐ swear
- ☐ slam doors
- ☐ run away
- ☐ overeat
- ☐ harm myself
- ☐ criticise

Passive

- ☐ take it too seriously
- ☐ give up
- ☐ wallow in self pity
- ☐ sulk
- ☐ space out
- ☐ procrastinate
- ☐ give in
- ☐ be controlled

Intense Feelings

Angry feelings

- ☐ hateful
- ☐ attacked
- ☐ aggravated
- ☐ worn out
- ☐ annoyed
- ☐ rejected
- ☐ hostile
- ☐ jealous
- ☐ outraged
- ☐ afraid
- ☐ punitive
- ☐ exploited
- ☐ resentful
- ☐ lonely
- ☐ vengeful
- ☐ abandoned

Fearful feelings

- ☐ guilty
- ☐ helpless
- ☐ insulted
- ☐ hopeless
- ☐ confused
- ☐ disappointed
- ☐ disillusioned
- ☐ sad
- ☐ misunderstood
- ☐ trapped

Bodily Reactions (limbic system)

I am uncomfortable because I am experiencing...

- ☐ tremors
- ☐ nausea
- ☐ sweaty palms
- ☐ stomach-ache
- ☐ pounding heart
- ☐ general tension
- ☐ fatigue
- ☐ imagination on fire
- ☐ headache
- ☐ dry mouth
- ☐ jaw clenching
- ☐ shortness of breath

Continued over

B **F** **L**

Step Three: The Working-Down Process

Begin with, "Suddenly I realised that I was anxious and that I had choices..." This is the step of self-leadership and trust in one's ability to handle the situation.

Choose helpful thoughts:

I choose to depersonalise
There is no intention to hurt me. He is doing the best he can with the tools he has at the moment.

I choose realism over romanticism
Life presents many obstacles. I lower or raise standards as needed.

There is no right or wrong
Unless it is a moral issue, I will see it simply as a difference of opinion and/or taste.

I choose the total view of positivity
Even though this event is negative, the total view of his behaviour is positive.

I surrender control
Since I cannot change this situation, I choose to let go of it.

I choose to put this event in perspective This event is not a catastrophe because it is not life threatening. It can be viewed as a trivial life event, a normal life problem that needs to be solved not dramatised.

I choose to view this event as average, falling within the normal range
This event is not exceptional; many people have gone through this.

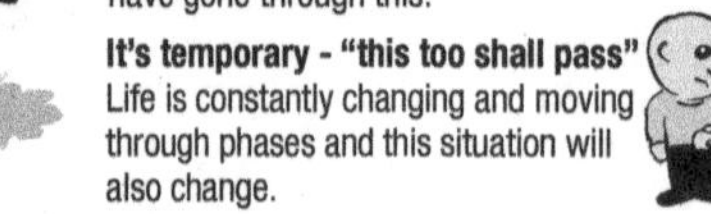

It's temporary - "this too shall pass"
Life is constantly changing and moving through phases and this situation will also change.

Fears or facts?
Why fear? It may not happen!

I choose to focus on this as a learning experience
Every problem that comes my way is an opportunity for me to learn about my strengths and weaknesses, others and life.

Feel soothing emotions:

I choose to feel warm, loving emotions. I do this by focusing on my heart and letting love, trust forgiveness, compassion, hope or gratitude fill my heart space.

Behave constructively:

I choose to work in part acts:
I will break the overwhelming job into manageable parts.

Do the difficult:
I will face what I fear and act with self-discipline.

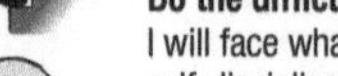
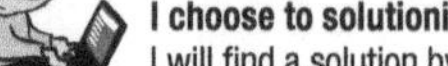

I choose to solutionise:
I will find a solution by taking advice or doing research.

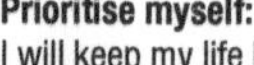

Prioritise myself:
I will keep my life balanced by meeting friends, doing exercise or laughing.

Compartmentalise:
I will not let this event cloud my whole day; I will focus on something else now.

Utilise calming strategies:

When I:
- relax,
- breathe deeply,
- go for a run,
- shower,
- lie down,
- read,
- watch TV,
- climb into a mental helicopter,
- practice mindfulness/meditation,

my mind and body calm down.

Step Four: The Self Motivation Process

Endorse yourself for any growth no matter how small.

In the past I would have...

____

____

But this time I...

____

____

Tick off the traits that you strengthened when you worked down your anxiety:

☐ generosity	☐ peacefulness	
☐ kindness	☐ self-discipline	
☐ compassion	☐ forgiveness	
☐ consideration	☐ courage	
☐ helpfulness	☐ responsibility	
☐ respectfulness	☐ reliability	
☐ honesty	☐ loyalty	
☐ fairness	☐ love	
☐ patience	☐ humility	

Rate your anxiety on a scale of 0 to 100%:

⬇

__________ %

O

W

Date: _______________

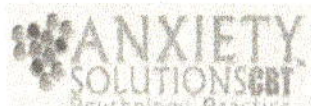

Anxiety Management Worksheet

The purpose of this worksheet is to help you to see every stressful event as an opportunity for
1. greater understanding of yourself, your anxiety and the people around you, and
2. practicing tools to manage your anxiety.

Step One: An Event

Briefly describe an event when you became anxious. Give such details as time, place and people involved, and end with "That's when I began to work myself up..."

____

____

____

____ Rate your anxiety on a scale of 0 to 100%: [   ] %

E

Step Two: The Working-Up Process

Learn about your working up process by identifying your thoughts, feelings, behaviours and bodily reactions during the event.

Tick the ones that most resonate with you.

Undermining Beliefs

B

I fear that I have lost...

- ☐ approval
- ☐ control
- ☐ co-operation
- ☐ face
- ☐ respect
- ☐ success
- ☐ trust
- ☐ validation
- ☐ love

This event proves that I am...

- ☐ stupid
- ☐ abnormal
- ☐ incompetent
- ☐ lazy
- ☐ irresponsible
- ☐ a total failure
- ☐ undisciplined
- ☐ untogether
- ☐ useless

I worry that I will suffer...

- ☐ mental collapse
- ☐ illness
- ☐ financial hardship

What I want is...

- ☐ total control
- ☐ respect
- ☐ success
- ☐ perfection
- ☐ comfort
- ☐ fairness
- ☐ tranquility
- ☐ all the answers
- ☐ for life to go smoothly
- ☐ to be all things to all people

Self-destructive Behaviour

Active

- ☐ get violent
- ☐ swear
- ☐ slam doors
- ☐ run away
- ☐ overeat
- ☐ harm myself
- ☐ criticise

Passive

- ☐ take it too seriously
- ☐ give up
- ☐ wallow in self pity
- ☐ sulk
- ☐ space out
- ☐ procrastinate
- ☐ give in
- ☐ be controlled

Intense Feelings

Angry feelings

- ☐ hateful
- ☐ aggravated
- ☐ annoyed
- ☐ hostile
- ☐ outraged
- ☐ punitive
- ☐ resentful
- ☐ vengeful

Fearful feelings

- ☐ helpless
- ☐ hopeless
- ☐ disappointed
- ☐ sad
- ☐ attacked
- ☐ worn out
- ☐ rejected
- ☐ jealous
- ☐ afraid
- ☐ exploited
- ☐ lonely
- ☐ abandoned
- ☐ guilty
- ☐ insulted
- ☐ confused
- ☐ disillusioned
- ☐ misunderstood
- ☐ trapped

Bodily Reactions (limbic system)

I am uncomfortable because I am experiencing...

- ☐ tremors
- ☐ nausea
- ☐ sweaty palms
- ☐ stomach-ache
- ☐ pounding heart
- ☐ general tension
- ☐ fatigue
- ☐ imagination on fire
- ☐ headache
- ☐ dry mouth
- ☐ jaw clenching
- ☐ shortness of breath

Continued over

B   **F**   **L**

Step Three: The Working-Down Process

Begin with, "Suddenly I realised that I was anxious and that I had choices..." This is the step of self-leadership and trust in one's ability to handle the situation.

Choose helpful thoughts:

I choose to depersonalise
There is no intention to hurt me. He is doing the best he can with the tools he has at the moment.

I choose realism over romanticism
Life presents many obstacles. I lower or raise standards as needed.

There is no right or wrong
Unless it is a moral issue, I will see it simply as a difference of opinion and/or taste.

I choose the total view of positivity
Even though this event is negative, the total view of his behaviour is positive.

I surrender control
Since I cannot change this situation, I choose to let go of it.

I choose to put this event in perspective This event is not a catastrophe because it is not life threatening. It can be viewed as a trivial life event, a normal life problem that needs to be solved not dramatised.

I choose to view this event as average, falling within the normal range
This event is not exceptional; many people have gone through this.

It's temporary - "this too shall pass"
Life is constantly changing and moving through phases and this situation will also change.

Fears or facts?
Why fear? It may not happen!

I choose to focus on this as a learning experience
Every problem that comes my way is an opportunity for me to learn about my strengths and weaknesses, others and life.

Feel soothing emotions:

I choose to feel warm, loving emotions. I do this by focusing on my heart and letting love, trust forgiveness, compassion, hope or gratitude fill my heart space.

Behave constructively:

I choose to work in part acts:
I will break the overwhelming job into manageable parts.

Do the difficult:
I will face what I fear and act with self-discipline.

I choose to solutionise:
I will find a solution by taking advice or doing research.

Prioritise myself:
I will keep my life balanced by meeting friends, doing exercise or laughing.

Compartmentalise:
I will not let this event cloud my whole day; I will focus on something else now.

Utilise calming strategies:

When I:
- relax,
- breathe deeply,
- go for a run,
- shower,
- lie down,
- read,
- watch TV,
- climb into a mental helicopter,
- practice mindfulness/meditation,

my mind and body calm down.

Step Four: The Self Motivation Process

Endorse yourself for any growth no matter how small.

In the past I would have...

____

____

But this time I...

____

____

Tick off the traits that you strengthened when you worked down your anxiety:

- ☐ generosity
- ☐ kindness
- ☐ compassion
- ☐ consideration
- ☐ helpfulness
- ☐ respectfulness
- ☐ honesty
- ☐ fairness
- ☐ patience
- ☐ peacefulness
- ☐ self-discipline
- ☐ forgiveness
- ☐ courage
- ☐ responsibility
- ☐ reliability
- ☐ loyalty
- ☐ love
- ☐ humility

Rate your anxiety on a scale of 0 to 100%:

☐ %

O

W

Date: _______________

Anxiety Management Worksheet

The purpose of this worksheet is to help you to see every stressful event as an opportunity for
1. greater understanding of yourself, your anxiety and the people around you, and
2. practicing tools to manage your anxiety.

Step One: An Event

Briefly describe an event when you became anxious. Give such details as time, place and people involved, and end with "That's when I began to work myself up…"

____

____

____

_______________________________________ Rate your anxiety on a scale of 0 to 100%: [   ] %

E

Step Two: The Working-Up Process

Learn about your working up process by identifying your thoughts, feelings, behaviours and bodily reactions during the event.
Tick the ones that most resonate with you.

B

Undermining Beliefs

I fear that I have lost...
- ☐ approval
- ☐ control
- ☐ co-operation
- ☐ face
- ☐ respect
- ☐ success
- ☐ trust
- ☐ validation
- ☐ love

This event proves that I am...
- ☐ stupid
- ☐ abnormal
- ☐ incompetent
- ☐ lazy
- ☐ irresponsible
- ☐ a total failure
- ☐ undisciplined
- ☐ untogether
- ☐ useless

I worry that I will suffer...
- ☐ mental collapse
- ☐ illness
- ☐ financial hardship

What I want is...
- ☐ total control
- ☐ respect
- ☐ success
- ☐ perfection
- ☐ comfort
- ☐ fairness
- ☐ tranquility
- ☐ all the answers
- ☐ for life to go smoothly
- ☐ to be all things to all people

Self-destructive Behaviour

Active
- ☐ get violent
- ☐ swear
- ☐ slam doors
- ☐ run away
- ☐ overeat
- ☐ harm myself
- ☐ criticise

Passive
- ☐ take it too seriously
- ☐ give up
- ☐ wallow in self pity
- ☐ sulk
- ☐ space out
- ☐ procrastinate
- ☐ give in
- ☐ be controlled

Intense Feelings

Angry feelings
- ☐ hateful
- ☐ aggravated
- ☐ annoyed
- ☐ hostile
- ☐ outraged
- ☐ punitive
- ☐ resentful
- ☐ vengeful

Fearful feelings
- ☐ helpless
- ☐ hopeless
- ☐ disappointed
- ☐ sad
- ☐ attacked
- ☐ worn out
- ☐ rejected
- ☐ jealous
- ☐ afraid
- ☐ exploited
- ☐ lonely
- ☐ abandoned
- ☐ guilty
- ☐ insulted
- ☐ confused
- ☐ disillusioned
- ☐ misunderstood
- ☐ trapped

Bodily Reactions (limbic system)

I am uncomfortable because I am experiencing...
- ☐ tremors
- ☐ nausea
- ☐ sweaty palms
- ☐ stomach-ache
- ☐ pounding heart
- ☐ general tension
- ☐ fatigue
- ☐ imagination on fire
- ☐ headache
- ☐ dry mouth
- ☐ jaw clenching
- ☐ shortness of breath

Continued over

B   **F**   **L**

Step Three: The Working-Down Process

Begin with, "Suddenly I realised that I was anxious and that I had choices..." This is the step of self-leadership and trust in one's ability to handle the situation.

Choose helpful thoughts:

I choose to depersonalise
There is no intention to hurt me. He is doing the best he can with the tools he has at the moment.

I choose realism over romanticism
Life presents many obstacles. I lower or raise standards as needed.

There is no right or wrong
Unless it is a moral issue, I will see it simply as a difference of opinion and/or taste.

I choose the total view of positivity
Even though this event is negative, the total view of his behaviour is positive.

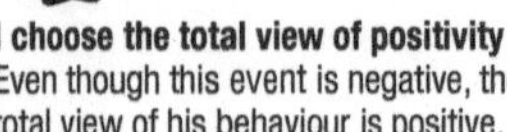

I surrender control
Since I cannot change this situation, I choose to let go of it.

I choose to put this event in perspective This event is not a catastrophe because it is not life threatening. It can be viewed as a trivial life event, a normal life problem that needs to be solved not dramatised.

I choose to view this event as average, falling within the normal range
This event is not exceptional; many people have gone through this.

It's temporary - "this too shall pass"
Life is constantly changing and moving through phases and this situation will also change.

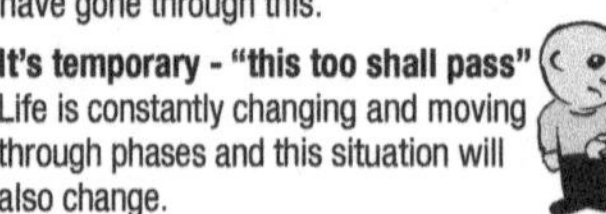

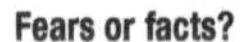

Fears or facts?
Why fear? It may not happen!

I choose to focus on this as a learning experience
Every problem that comes my way is an opportunity for me to learn about my strengths and weaknesses, others and life.

Feel soothing emotions:

I choose to feel warm, loving emotions. I do this by focusing on my heart and letting love, trust forgiveness, compassion, hope or gratitude fill my heart space.

Behave constructively:

I choose to work in part acts:
I will break the overwhelming job into manageable parts.

Do the difficult:
I will face what I fear and act with self-discipline.

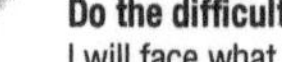

I choose to solutionise:
I will find a solution by taking advice or doing research.

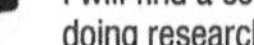

Prioritise myself:
I will keep my life balanced by meeting friends, doing exercise or laughing.

Compartmentalise:
I will not let this event cloud my whole day; I will focus on something else now.

Utilise calming strategies:

When I:
- relax,
- breathe deeply,
- go for a run,
- shower,
- lie down,
- read,
- watch TV,
- climb into a mental helicopter,
- practice mindfulness/meditation,

my mind and body calm down.

Step Four: The Self Motivation Process

Endorse yourself for any growth no matter how small.

In the past I would have...

____

____

But this time I...

____

____

Tick off the traits that you strengthened when you worked down your anxiety:

☐ generosity	☐ peacefulness
☐ kindness	☐ self-discipline
☐ compassion	☐ forgiveness
☐ consideration	☐ courage
☐ helpfulness	☐ responsibility
☐ respectfulness	☐ reliability
☐ honesty	☐ loyalty
☐ fairness	☐ love
☐ patience	☐ humility

Rate your anxiety on a scale of 0 to 100%:

[____]%

O

W

Week 12

Week twelve is the final week. Congratulate yourself on coming this far. There are just three tools left for you to learn and apply. They are all excellent tools and coming at the end in no way implies that they are the least important. The three tools are:

1. Learning experience: thinking tool
2. Build your character: behavioural tool
3. Slowing down: calming tool

Learning experience: thinking tool

When you feel defeated, you will feel anxious. It seems like another person, or an event, has had the upper hand. However, if you felt victorious, then you would be calm and confident. This tool will enable you to see every situation as one where you can be victorious. How? By believing that you have gained from the experience no matter how difficult, complicated or negative that it seemed.

> You are stuck in traffic. You start to panic about getting to your meeting on time. You feel powerless. As long as you feel the traffic is a negative event in your life, you will feel disempowered and frustrated. However, the minute that you believe that you gain from being stuck in traffic, you will feel empowered and less stressed.

You could say to yourself:

- "Now is a perfect time to practise meditation as I will not have time later."
- "I am always rushing around. This is teaching me to learn to slow down and to plan better so that I am not so frantic. Next time I will give myself more travel time."
- "While I am here, I will check my emails. What difference does it make if I do it now or later in the office. In fact, doing it now is advantageous because I get them out of the way."

> Your ageing mother keeps asking you for help. You are not enjoying her dependence on you and feel worried about what the future holds.

As long as you feel that your mother, or your life, is beating you down, you will feel stressed. The minute your perception changes and you view this period in your life as an opportunity for growth, you will feel energised and optimistic. For instance, you could perceive this time as your time to give back to your mother for all she has done for you over the years. Or you could intuit that you have tended to be quite selfish in the past and now you can develop selflessness and kindness.

Every single situation in life is an opportunity to learn something new. Sometimes it is a practical lesson like planning your travel time better. But often, the lesson pertains to personal growth. In fact, in some really difficult situations where external change is impossible, internal growth is the only place progress is possible.

When you utilise this tool in this way, it helps you to live a value-based life. Life is not only about external achievement. It can also be about striving to be a better person even in a challenging situation. Like Covey (17), I believe that there are universally good values which every human being intuitively knows. These values assist you to develop a fine character and to behave in the world in an ethical, responsible manner. This is discussed further in "**build your character**" on page 344.

EXERCISE 41

What do you think can be gained from being stuck in traffic?
    a) business arena: <u>I will learn to pace myself better and leave more than enough time in future.</u>
    a) personal arena: <u>I will practice the tool surrender control and strengthen patience.</u>

What do you think can be gained from the following:

1. Having to wait in a long queue:
    a) business arena ______________________
    b) personal arena ______________________

2. Not getting a promotion:
    a) business arena ______________________
    b) personal arena ______________________

3. Losing a bargain:
    a) business arena ______________________
    b) personal arena ______________________

4. Having your authority overridden:
    a) business arena ______________________
    b) personal arena ______________________

5. Being moved to a different department:
   a) business arena ....
   b) personal arena ....

6. Having a neighbour scream at you:
   a) business arena ....
   b) personal arena ....

7. Running out of petrol on the way to an appointment:
   a) business arena ....
   b) personal arena ....

8. Overpaying for an article:
   a) business arena ....
   b) personal arena ....

Build your character: behavioural tool

Character is an old fashioned word. Today we are impressed by money and status. A person can be a scoundrel but if he drives a fancy car we are impressed. Or a person can be famous as a rock star and idolised, but no accounting is made of his drug taking, womanising or irresponsible behaviour.

Character is the foundation of healthy living. When you live according to eternal and universal values, you can feel good about yourself no matter how much money or status you have. These values help lower anxiety about not being good enough in society.

Good character also lowers stress by removing choices. When every option is available there can be confusion, but when your character informs your choice, it becomes easier. Let's say you are offered a bribe. First you may agonise about whether you should accept it or not. Then, if you do accept the bribe, it can lead to fear that you will be found out. However, when you live by ethical values, and respect good character, you will immediately choose to be honest. Your choice was simple and ensured that you did not get stressed.

Values include:

- generosity
- diligence
- kindness
- gratitude
- compassion
- humility
- consideration
- orderliness
- helpfulness
- perseverance
- respectfulness
- growth
- honesty
- respect for self
- fairness
- respect for others
- patience
- positivity
- peacefulness
- flexibility
- self-discipline
- resourcefulness
- forgiveness
- decisiveness
- courage
- loyalty
- responsibility
- love
- reliability
- humility

By now you will have noticed that by practising the four-step process, and ticking off the traits that you strengthened when you worked down your anxiety, the more you have internalised these values. Living according to universally good values, centres you. It enables you to have meaningful goals, and increases happiness. It also helps to reduce anxiety, because you now have a focus and direction. Moreover, values assist you to have self-leadership and be pro-active, rather than reactive, to events and the behaviour of others.

Slowing down: calming tool

Simply slowing down in your day, and becoming more aware of what is happening around you, is a form of mindfulness.

Do you know the expression: "Stop and smell the roses?" Well that is exactly what slowing down is. The next time you have a break, instead of checking your emails, spend ten minutes looking around you and appreciating what surrounds you. Consider taking a walk around your neighbourhood at half speed. Take this opportunity to look around and notice as many details as possible. Take note especially of any detail you may have missed previously when you walked at a faster pace.

EXERCISE 42

Think about times in your day where you could slow down.

Write them down.

From today make a conscious effort to slow down where possible.

DAILY MONITORING DIARY WEEK ENDING ....

Day	M	T	W	T	F	S	S
Overall Anxiety Rating for the day (0-10)							
1. EXERCISE							
How long?							
Anxiety level before (0-10)							
Anxiety level after (0-10)							
2. BREATHING							
How long?							
Anxiety level before (0-10)							
Anxiety level after (0-10)							
3. RELAXATION							
How long?							
Anxiety level before (0-10)							
Anxiety level after (0-10)							
4. PERVASIVE PESSIMISTIC THINKING							
How often this type of thought occurred							
Belief in thoughts before challenging (0-10)							
Belief in thoughts after challenging (0-10)							

Day	M	T	W	T	F	S	S
5. CATASTROPHIC THINKING							
How often this type of thought occurred							
Belief in thoughts before challenging (0-10)							
Belief in thoughts after challenging (0-10)							
6. PERMANENT PESSIMISTIC THINKING							
How often this type of thought occurred							
Belief in thoughts before challenging (0-10)							
Belief in thoughts after challenging (0-10)							
7. MINDFULNESS (FORMAL, GROUNDING, INFORMAL MINDFULNESS)							
How long?							
Anxiety level before (0-10)							
Anxiety level after (0-10)							
8. ROMANTIC THINKING							
How often this type of thought occurred							
Belief in thoughts before challenging (0-10)							
Belief in thoughts after challenging (0-10)							

Day	M	T	W	T	F	S	S
9. NEGATIVE JUDGEMENTAL THINKING							
How often this type of thought occurred							
Belief in thoughts before challenging (0-10)							
Belief in thoughts after challenging (0-10)							
10. CAN'T LET GO THINKING							
How often this type of thought occurred							
Belief in thoughts before challenging (0-10)							
Belief in thoughts after challenging (0-10)							
11. MEDITATION							
How long?							
Anxiety level before (0-10)							
Anxiety level after (0-10)							
12. EXCEPTIONAL THINKING							
How often this type of thought occurred							
Belief in thoughts before challenging (0-10)							
Belief in thoughts after challenging (0-10)							

Date: ___________

Anxiety Management Worksheet

The purpose of this worksheet is to help you to see every stressful event as an opportunity for
1. greater understanding of yourself, your anxiety and the people around you, and
2. practicing tools to manage your anxiety.

Step One: An Event

Briefly describe an event when you became anxious. Give such details as time, place and people involved, and end with "That's when I began to work myself up..."

____

____

____

______________________________________ Rate your anxiety on a scale of 0 to 100%: [   ] %

E

Step Two: The Working-Up Process

Learn about your working up process by identifying your thoughts, feelings, behaviours and bodily reactions during the event.
Tick the ones that most resonate with you.

Undermining Beliefs

B

I fear that I have lost...

- [ ] approval
- [ ] control
- [ ] co-operation
- [ ] face
- [ ] respect
- [ ] success
- [ ] trust
- [ ] validation
- [ ] love

This event proves that I am...

- [ ] stupid
- [ ] abnormal
- [ ] incompetent
- [ ] lazy
- [ ] irresponsible
- [ ] a total failure
- [ ] undisciplined
- [ ] untogether
- [ ] useless

I worry that I will suffer...

- [ ] mental collapse
- [ ] illness
- [ ] financial hardship

What I want is...

- [ ] total control
- [ ] respect
- [ ] success
- [ ] perfection
- [ ] comfort
- [ ] fairness
- [ ] tranquility
- [ ] all the answers
- [ ] for life to go smoothly
- [ ] to be all things to all people

Self-destructive Behaviour

Active
- [ ] get violent
- [ ] swear
- [ ] slam doors
- [ ] run away
- [ ] overeat
- [ ] harm myself
- [ ] criticise

Passive
- [ ] take it too seriously
- [ ] give up
- [ ] wallow in self pity
- [ ] sulk
- [ ] space out
- [ ] procrastinate
- [ ] give in
- [ ] be controlled

Intense Feelings

Angry feelings
- [ ] hateful
- [ ] aggravated
- [ ] annoyed
- [ ] hostile
- [ ] outraged
- [ ] punitive
- [ ] resentful
- [ ] vengeful

Fearful feelings
- [ ] helpless
- [ ] hopeless
- [ ] disappointed
- [ ] sad
- [ ] attacked
- [ ] worn out
- [ ] rejected
- [ ] jealous
- [ ] afraid
- [ ] exploited
- [ ] lonely
- [ ] abandoned
- [ ] guilty
- [ ] insulted
- [ ] confused
- [ ] disillusioned
- [ ] misunderstood
- [ ] trapped

Bodily Reactions (limbic system)

I am uncomfortable because I am experiencing...

- [ ] tremors
- [ ] nausea
- [ ] sweaty palms
- [ ] stomach-ache
- [ ] pounding heart
- [ ] general tension
- [ ] fatigue
- [ ] imagination on fire
- [ ] headache
- [ ] dry mouth
- [ ] jaw clenching
- [ ] shortness of breath

Continued over

B   **F**   **L**

Step Three: The Working-Down Process

Begin with, "Suddenly I realised that I was anxious and that I had choices..." This is the step of self-leadership and trust in one's ability to handle the situation.

Choose helpful thoughts:

I choose to depersonalise
There is no intention to hurt me. He is doing the best he can with the tools he has at the moment.

I choose realism over romanticism
Life presents many obstacles. I lower or raise standards as needed.

There is no right or wrong
Unless it is a moral issue, I will see it simply as a difference of opinion and/or taste.

I choose the total view of positivity
Even though this event is negative, the total view of his behaviour is positive.

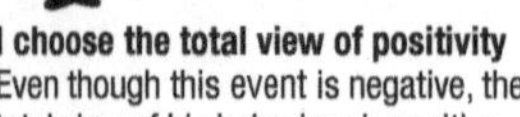

I surrender control
Since I cannot change this situation, I choose to let go of it.

I choose to put this event in perspective This event is not a catastrophe because it is not life threatening. It can be viewed as a trivial life event, a normal life problem that needs to be solved not dramatised.

I choose to view this event as average, falling within the normal range
This event is not exceptional; many people have gone through this.

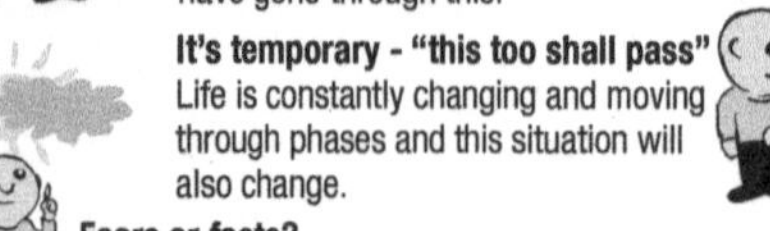

It's temporary - "this too shall pass"
Life is constantly changing and moving through phases and this situation will also change.

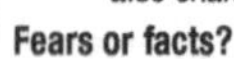

Fears or facts?
Why fear? It may not happen!

I choose to focus on this as a learning experience
Every problem that comes my way is an opportunity for me to learn about my strengths and weaknesses, others and life.

Feel soothing emotions:

I choose to feel warm, loving emotions. I do this by focusing on my heart and letting love, trust forgiveness, compassion, hope or gratitude fill my heart space.

Behave constructively:

I choose to work in part acts:
I will break the overwhelming job into manageable parts.

Do the difficult:
I will face what I fear and act with self-discipline.

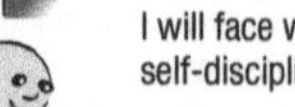

I choose to solutionise:
I will find a solution by taking advice or doing research.

Prioritise myself:
I will keep my life balanced by meeting friends, doing exercise or laughing.

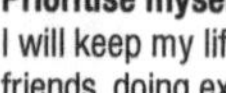

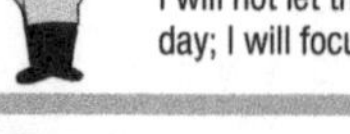

Compartmentalise:
I will not let this event cloud my whole day; I will focus on something else now.

Utilise calming strategies:

When I:
- relax,
- breathe deeply,
- go for a run,
- shower,
- lie down,
- read,
- watch TV,
- climb into a mental helicopter,
- practice mindfulness/meditation,

my mind and body calm down.

Step Four: The Self Motivation Process

Endorse yourself for any growth no matter how small.

In the past I would have...

____

____

But this time I...

____

____

Tick off the traits that you strengthened when you worked down your anxiety:

☐ generosity	☐ peacefulness	
☐ kindness	☐ self-discipline	
☐ compassion	☐ forgiveness	
☐ consideration	☐ courage	
☐ helpfulness	☐ responsibility	
☐ respectfulness	☐ reliability	
☐ honesty	☐ loyalty	
☐ fairness	☐ love	
☐ patience	☐ humility	

Rate your anxiety on a scale of 0 to 100%:

⬇

______ %

O

W

Date: ___________

Anxiety Management Worksheet

The purpose of this worksheet is to help you to see every stressful event as an opportunity for
1. greater understanding of yourself, your anxiety and the people around you, and
2. practicing tools to manage your anxiety.

Step One: An Event

Briefly describe an event when you became anxious. Give such details as time, place and people involved, and end with "That's when I began to work myself up..."

____

____

____

____   Rate your anxiety on a scale of 0 to 100%: [   ] %

E

Step Two: The Working-Up Process

Learn about your working up process by identifying your thoughts, feelings, behaviours and bodily reactions during the event.
Tick the ones that most resonate with you.

Undermining Beliefs

B

I fear that I have lost...
- ☐ approval
- ☐ control
- ☐ co-operation
- ☐ face
- ☐ respect
- ☐ success
- ☐ trust
- ☐ validation
- ☐ love

This event proves that I am...
- ☐ stupid
- ☐ abnormal
- ☐ incompetent
- ☐ lazy
- ☐ irresponsible
- ☐ a total failure
- ☐ undisciplined
- ☐ untogether
- ☐ useless

I worry that I will suffer...
- ☐ mental collapse
- ☐ illness
- ☐ financial hardship

What I want is...
- ☐ total control
- ☐ respect
- ☐ success
- ☐ perfection
- ☐ comfort
- ☐ fairness
- ☐ tranquility
- ☐ all the answers
- ☐ for life to go smoothly
- ☐ to be all things to all people

Self-destructive Behaviour

Active
- ☐ get violent
- ☐ swear
- ☐ slam doors
- ☐ run away
- ☐ overeat
- ☐ harm myself
- ☐ criticise

Passive
- ☐ take it too seriously
- ☐ give up
- ☐ wallow in self pity
- ☐ sulk
- ☐ space out
- ☐ procrastinate
- ☐ give in
- ☐ be controlled

B

Intense Feelings

Angry feelings
- ☐ hateful
- ☐ aggravated
- ☐ annoyed
- ☐ hostile
- ☐ outraged
- ☐ punitive
- ☐ resentful
- ☐ vengeful

Fearful feelings
- ☐ helpless
- ☐ hopeless
- ☐ disappointed
- ☐ sad

- ☐ attacked
- ☐ worn out
- ☐ rejected
- ☐ jealous
- ☐ afraid
- ☐ exploited
- ☐ lonely
- ☐ abandoned
- ☐ guilty
- ☐ insulted
- ☐ confused
- ☐ disillusioned
- ☐ misunderstood
- ☐ trapped

F

Bodily Reactions (limbic system)

I am uncomfortable because I am experiencing...
- ☐ tremors
- ☐ nausea
- ☐ sweaty palms
- ☐ stomach-ache
- ☐ pounding heart
- ☐ general tension
- ☐ fatigue
- ☐ imagination on fire
- ☐ headache
- ☐ dry mouth
- ☐ jaw clenching
- ☐ shortness of breath

Continued over

L

Step Three: The Working-Down Process

Begin with, "Suddenly I realised that I was anxious and that I had choices..." This is the step of self-leadership and trust in one's ability to handle the situation.

Choose helpful thoughts:

I choose to depersonalise
There is no intention to hurt me. He is doing the best he can with the tools he has at the moment.

I choose realism over romanticism
Life presents many obstacles. I lower or raise standards as needed.

There is no right or wrong
Unless it is a moral issue, I will see it simply as a difference of opinion and/or taste.

I choose the total view of positivity
Even though this event is negative, the total view of his behaviour is positive.

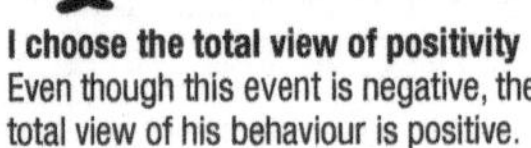

I surrender control
Since I cannot change this situation, I choose to let go of it.

I choose to put this event in perspective This event is not a catastrophe because it is not life threatening. It can be viewed as a trivial life event, a normal life problem that needs to be solved not dramatised.

I choose to view this event as average, falling within the normal range
This event is not exceptional; many people have gone through this.

It's temporary - "this too shall pass"
Life is constantly changing and moving through phases and this situation will also change.

Fears or facts?
Why fear? It may not happen!

I choose to focus on this as a learning experience
Every problem that comes my way is an opportunity for me to learn about my strengths and weaknesses, others and life.

Feel soothing emotions:

I choose to feel warm, loving emotions. I do this by focusing on my heart and letting love, trust forgiveness, compassion, hope or gratitude fill my heart space.

Behave constructively:

I choose to work in part acts:
I will break the overwhelming job into manageable parts.

Do the difficult:
I will face what I fear and act with self-discipline.

I choose to solutionise:
I will find a solution by taking advice or doing research.

Prioritise myself:
I will keep my life balanced by meeting friends, doing exercise or laughing.

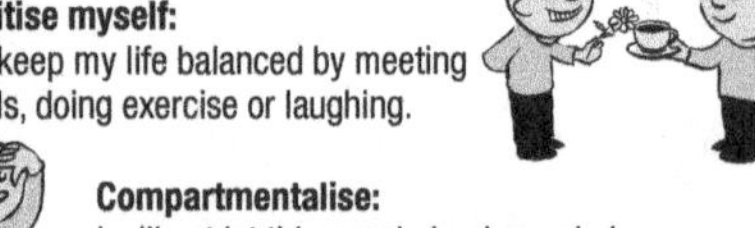

Compartmentalise:
I will not let this event cloud my whole day; I will focus on something else now.

Utilise calming strategies:

When I:
- relax,
- breathe deeply,
- go for a run,
- shower,
- lie down,
- read,
- watch TV,
- climb into a mental helicopter,
- practice mindfulness/meditation,

my mind and body calm down.

Step Four: The Self Motivation Process

Endorse yourself for any growth no matter how small.

In the past I would have...

____

____

But this time I...

____

____

Tick off the traits that you strengthened when you worked down your anxiety:

- ☐ generosity
- ☐ kindness
- ☐ compassion
- ☐ consideration
- ☐ helpfulness
- ☐ respectfulness
- ☐ honesty
- ☐ fairness
- ☐ patience
- ☐ peacefulness
- ☐ self-discipline
- ☐ forgiveness
- ☐ courage
- ☐ responsibility
- ☐ reliability
- ☐ loyalty
- ☐ love
- ☐ humility

Rate your anxiety on a scale of 0 to 100%:

______ %

o   w

Date: ___________

Anxiety Management Worksheet

The purpose of this worksheet is to help you to see every stressful event as an opportunity for
1. greater understanding of yourself, your anxiety and the people around you, and
2. practicing tools to manage your anxiety.

Step One: An Event

Briefly describe an event when you became anxious. Give such details as time, place and people involved, and end with "That's when I began to work myself up…"

____

____

____

____ Rate your anxiety on a scale of 0 to 100%: [ ] %

E

Step Two: The Working-Up Process

Learn about your working up process by identifying your thoughts, feelings, behaviours and bodily reactions during the event. Tick the ones that most resonate with you.

Undermining Beliefs

I fear that I have lost…
- ☐ approval
- ☐ control
- ☐ co-operation
- ☐ face
- ☐ respect
- ☐ success
- ☐ trust
- ☐ validation
- ☐ love

This event proves that I am…
- ☐ stupid
- ☐ abnormal
- ☐ incompetent
- ☐ lazy
- ☐ irresponsible
- ☐ a total failure
- ☐ undisciplined
- ☐ untogether
- ☐ useless

B

I worry that I will suffer…
- ☐ mental collapse
- ☐ illness
- ☐ financial hardship

What I want is…
- ☐ total control
- ☐ respect
- ☐ success
- ☐ perfection
- ☐ comfort
- ☐ fairness
- ☐ tranquility
- ☐ all the answers
- ☐ for life to go smoothly
- ☐ to be all things to all people

Self-destructive Behaviour

Active
- ☐ get violent
- ☐ swear
- ☐ slam doors
- ☐ run away
- ☐ overeat
- ☐ harm myself
- ☐ criticise

Passive
- ☐ take it too seriously
- ☐ give up
- ☐ wallow in self pity
- ☐ sulk
- ☐ space out
- ☐ procrastinate
- ☐ give in
- ☐ be controlled

Intense Feelings

Angry feelings
- ☐ hateful
- ☐ aggravated
- ☐ annoyed
- ☐ hostile
- ☐ outraged
- ☐ punitive
- ☐ resentful
- ☐ vengeful

Fearful feelings
- ☐ helpless
- ☐ hopeless
- ☐ disappointed
- ☐ sad
- ☐ attacked
- ☐ worn out
- ☐ rejected
- ☐ jealous
- ☐ afraid
- ☐ exploited
- ☐ lonely
- ☐ abandoned
- ☐ guilty
- ☐ insulted
- ☐ confused
- ☐ disillusioned
- ☐ misunderstood
- ☐ trapped

Bodily Reactions (limbic system)

I am uncomfortable because I am experiencing…
- ☐ tremors
- ☐ nausea
- ☐ sweaty palms
- ☐ stomach-ache
- ☐ pounding heart
- ☐ general tension
- ☐ fatigue
- ☐ imagination on fire
- ☐ headache
- ☐ dry mouth
- ☐ jaw clenching
- ☐ shortness of breath

B   **F**   **L**

Step Three: The Working-Down Process

Begin with, "Suddenly I realised that I was anxious and that I had choices..." This is the step of self-leadership and trust in one's ability to handle the situation.

Choose helpful thoughts:

I choose to depersonalise
There is no intention to hurt me. He is doing the best he can with the tools he has at the moment.

I choose realism over romanticism
Life presents many obstacles. I lower or raise standards as needed.

There is no right or wrong
Unless it is a moral issue, I will see it simply as a difference of opinion and/or taste.

I choose the total view of positivity
Even though this event is negative, the total view of his behaviour is positive.

I surrender control
Since I cannot change this situation, I choose to let go of it.

I choose to put this event in perspective This event is not a catastrophe because it is not life threatening. It can be viewed as a trivial life event, a normal life problem that needs to be solved not dramatised.

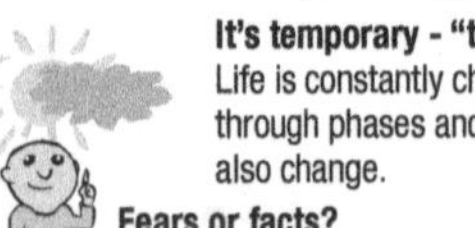

I choose to view this event as average, falling within the normal range
This event is not exceptional; many people have gone through this.

It's temporary - "this too shall pass"
Life is constantly changing and moving through phases and this situation will also change.

Fears or facts?
Why fear? It may not happen!

I choose to focus on this as a learning experience
Every problem that comes my way is an opportunity for me to learn about my strengths and weaknesses, others and life.

Feel soothing emotions:

I choose to feel warm, loving emotions. I do this by focusing on my heart and letting love, trust forgiveness, compassion, hope or gratitude fill my heart space.

Behave constructively:

I choose to work in part acts:
I will break the overwhelming job into manageable parts.

Do the difficult:
I will face what I fear and act with self-discipline.

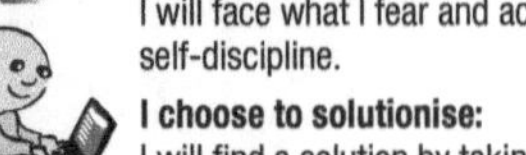

I choose to solutionise:
I will find a solution by taking advice or doing research.

Prioritise myself:
I will keep my life balanced by meeting friends, doing exercise or laughing.

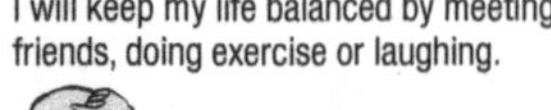

Compartmentalise:
I will not let this event cloud my whole day; I will focus on something else now.

Utilise calming strategies:

When I:
- relax,
- breathe deeply,
- go for a run,
- shower,
- lie down,
- read,
- watch TV,
- climb into a mental helicopter,
- practice mindfulness/meditation,

my mind and body calm down.

Step Four: The Self Motivation Process

Endorse yourself for any growth no matter how small.

In the past I would have...

____

____

But this time I...

____

____

Tick off the traits that you strengthened when you worked down your anxiety:

☐ generosity	☐ peacefulness
☐ kindness	☐ self-discipline
☐ compassion	☐ forgiveness
☐ consideration	☐ courage
☐ helpfulness	☐ responsibility
☐ respectfulness	☐ reliability
☐ honesty	☐ loyalty
☐ fairness	☐ love
☐ patience	☐ humility

Rate your anxiety on a scale of 0 to 100%:

[____] %

O

W

Date: _______________

Anxiety Management Worksheet

The purpose of this worksheet is to help you to see every stressful event as an opportunity for
1. greater understanding of yourself, your anxiety and the people around you, and
2. practicing tools to manage your anxiety.

Step One: An Event

Briefly describe an event when you became anxious. Give such details as time, place and people involved, and end with "That's when I began to work myself up..."

E

____

____

____

_________________________________ Rate your anxiety on a scale of 0 to 100%: [   ] %

Step Two: The Working-Up Process

Learn about your working up process by identifying your thoughts, feelings, behaviours and bodily reactions during the event.
Tick the ones that most resonate with you.

Undermining Beliefs

B

I fear that I have lost...
- ☐ approval
- ☐ success
- ☐ control
- ☐ trust
- ☐ co-operation
- ☐ validation
- ☐ face
- ☐ love
- ☐ respect

This event proves that I am...
- ☐ stupid
- ☐ a total failure
- ☐ abnormal
- ☐ undisciplined
- ☐ incompetent
- ☐ untogether
- ☐ lazy
- ☐ useless
- ☐ irresponsible

I worry that I will suffer...
- ☐ mental collapse
- ☐ illness
- ☐ financial hardship

What I want is...
- ☐ total control
- ☐ tranquility
- ☐ respect
- ☐ all the answers
- ☐ success
- ☐ for life to go smoothly
- ☐ perfection
- ☐ comfort
- ☐ to be all things to all people
- ☐ fairness

Self-destructive Behaviour

Active
- ☐ get violent
- ☐ swear
- ☐ slam doors
- ☐ run away
- ☐ overeat
- ☐ harm myself
- ☐ criticise

Passive
- ☐ take it too seriously
- ☐ give up
- ☐ wallow in self pity
- ☐ sulk
- ☐ space out
- ☐ procrastinate
- ☐ give in
- ☐ be controlled

Intense Feelings

Angry feelings
- ☐ hateful
- ☐ attacked
- ☐ aggravated
- ☐ worn out
- ☐ annoyed
- ☐ rejected
- ☐ hostile
- ☐ jealous
- ☐ outraged
- ☐ afraid
- ☐ punitive
- ☐ exploited
- ☐ resentful
- ☐ lonely
- ☐ vengeful
- ☐ abandoned
- ☐ guilty

Fearful feelings
- ☐ insulted
- ☐ helpless
- ☐ confused
- ☐ hopeless
- ☐ disillusioned
- ☐ disappointed
- ☐ misunderstood
- ☐ sad
- ☐ trapped

Bodily Reactions (limbic system)

I am uncomfortable because I am experiencing...
- ☐ tremors
- ☐ nausea
- ☐ sweaty palms
- ☐ stomach-ache
- ☐ pounding heart
- ☐ general tension
- ☐ fatigue
- ☐ imagination on fire
- ☐ headache
- ☐ dry mouth
- ☐ jaw clenching
- ☐ shortness of breath

Continued over

B   **F**   **L**

Step Three: The Working-Down Process

Begin with, "Suddenly I realised that I was anxious and that I had choices..." This is the step of self-leadership and trust in one's ability to handle the situation.

Choose helpful thoughts:

I choose to depersonalise
There is no intention to hurt me. He is doing the best he can with the tools he has at the moment.

I choose realism over romanticism
Life presents many obstacles. I lower or raise standards as needed.

There is no right or wrong
Unless it is a moral issue, I will see it simply as a difference of opinion and/or taste.

I choose the total view of positivity
Even though this event is negative, the total view of his behaviour is positive.

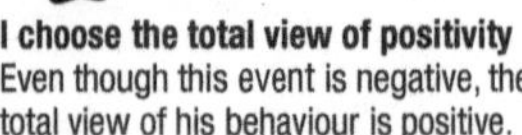

I surrender control
Since I cannot change this situation, I choose to let go of it.

I choose to put this event in perspective This event is not a catastrophe because it is not life threatening. It can be viewed as a trivial life event, a normal life problem that needs to be solved not dramatised.

I choose to view this event as average, falling within the normal range
This event is not exceptional; many people have gone through this.

It's temporary - "this too shall pass"
Life is constantly changing and moving through phases and this situation will also change.

Fears or facts?
Why fear? It may not happen!

I choose to focus on this as a learning experience
Every problem that comes my way is an opportunity for me to learn about my strengths and weaknesses, others and life.

Feel soothing emotions:

I choose to feel warm, loving emotions. I do this by focusing on my heart and letting love, trust forgiveness, compassion, hope or gratitude fill my heart space.

Behave constructively:

I choose to work in part acts:
I will break the overwhelming job into manageable parts.

Do the difficult:
I will face what I fear and act with self-discipline.

I choose to solutionise:
I will find a solution by taking advice or doing research.

Prioritise myself:
I will keep my life balanced by meeting friends, doing exercise or laughing.

Compartmentalise:
I will not let this event cloud my whole day; I will focus on something else now.

Utilise calming strategies:

When I:
- relax,
- breathe deeply,
- go for a run,
- shower,
- lie down,
- read,
- watch TV,
- climb into a mental helicopter,
- practice mindfulness/meditation,
  my mind and body calm down.

Step Four: The Self Motivation Process

Endorse yourself for any growth no matter how small.

In the past I would have...

____

____

But this time I...

____

____

Tick off the traits that you strengthened when you worked down your anxiety:

☐ generosity	☐ peacefulness
☐ kindness	☐ self-discipline
☐ compassion	☐ forgiveness
☐ consideration	☐ courage
☐ helpfulness	☐ responsibility
☐ respectfulness	☐ reliability
☐ honesty	☐ loyalty
☐ fairness	☐ love
☐ patience	☐ humility

Rate your anxiety on a scale of 0 to 100%:

⬇

________ %

O

W

Date: ___________

Anxiety Management Worksheet

The purpose of this worksheet is to help you to see every stressful event as an opportunity for
1. greater understanding of yourself, your anxiety and the people around you, and
2. practicing tools to manage your anxiety.

Step One: An Event

Briefly describe an event when you became anxious. Give such details as time, place and people involved, and end with "That's when I began to work myself up..."

____

____

____

____ Rate your anxiety on a scale of 0 to 100%: [   ] %

E

Step Two: The Working-Up Process

Learn about your working up process by identifying your thoughts, feelings, behaviours and bodily reactions during the event.
Tick the ones that most resonate with you.

B

Undermining Beliefs

I fear that I have lost...
- ☐ approval
- ☐ control
- ☐ co-operation
- ☐ face
- ☐ respect
- ☐ success
- ☐ trust
- ☐ validation
- ☐ love

This event proves that I am...
- ☐ stupid
- ☐ abnormal
- ☐ incompetent
- ☐ lazy
- ☐ irresponsible
- ☐ a total failure
- ☐ undisciplined
- ☐ untogether
- ☐ useless

I worry that I will suffer...
- ☐ mental collapse
- ☐ illness
- ☐ financial hardship

What I want is...
- ☐ total control
- ☐ respect
- ☐ success
- ☐ perfection
- ☐ comfort
- ☐ fairness
- ☐ tranquility
- ☐ all the answers
- ☐ for life to go smoothly
- ☐ to be all things to all people

Self-destructive Behaviour

Active
- ☐ get violent
- ☐ swear
- ☐ slam doors
- ☐ run away
- ☐ overeat
- ☐ harm myself
- ☐ criticise

Passive
- ☐ take it too seriously
- ☐ give up
- ☐ wallow in self pity
- ☐ sulk
- ☐ space out
- ☐ procrastinate
- ☐ give in
- ☐ be controlled

Intense Feelings

Angry feelings
- ☐ hateful
- ☐ aggravated
- ☐ annoyed
- ☐ hostile
- ☐ outraged
- ☐ punitive
- ☐ resentful
- ☐ vengeful

Fearful feelings
- ☐ helpless
- ☐ hopeless
- ☐ disappointed
- ☐ sad
- ☐ attacked
- ☐ worn out
- ☐ rejected
- ☐ jealous
- ☐ afraid
- ☐ exploited
- ☐ lonely
- ☐ abandoned
- ☐ guilty
- ☐ insulted
- ☐ confused
- ☐ disillusioned
- ☐ misunderstood
- ☐ trapped

Bodily Reactions (limbic system)

I am uncomfortable because I am experiencing...
- ☐ tremors
- ☐ nausea
- ☐ sweaty palms
- ☐ stomach-ache
- ☐ pounding heart
- ☐ general tension
- ☐ fatigue
- ☐ imagination on fire
- ☐ headache
- ☐ dry mouth
- ☐ jaw clenching
- ☐ shortness of breath

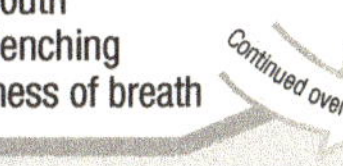

B   **F**   **L**

Step Three: The Working-Down Process

Begin with, "Suddenly I realised that I was anxious and that I had choices..." This is the step of self-leadership and trust in one's ability to handle the situation.

Choose helpful thoughts:

I choose to depersonalise
There is no intention to hurt me. He is doing the best he can with the tools he has at the moment.

I choose realism over romanticism
Life presents many obstacles. I lower or raise standards as needed.

There is no right or wrong
Unless it is a moral issue, I will see it simply as a difference of opinion and/or taste.

I choose the total view of positivity
Even though this event is negative, the total view of his behaviour is positive.

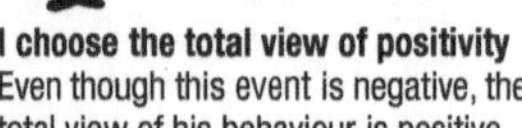

I surrender control
Since I cannot change this situation, I choose to let go of it.

I choose to put this event in perspective This event is not a catastrophe because it is not life threatening. It can be viewed as a trivial life event, a normal life problem that needs to be solved not dramatised.

I choose to view this event as average, falling within the normal range
This event is not exceptional; many people have gone through this.

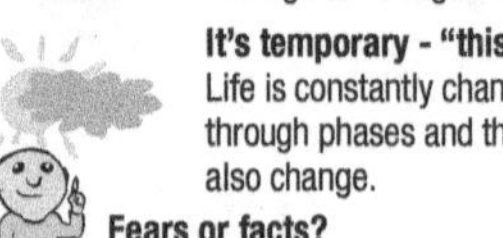

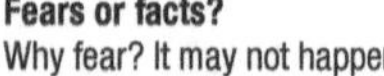

It's temporary - "this too shall pass"
Life is constantly changing and moving through phases and this situation will also change.

Fears or facts?
Why fear? It may not happen!

I choose to focus on this as a learning experience
Every problem that comes my way is an opportunity for me to learn about my strengths and weaknesses, others and life.

Feel soothing emotions:

I choose to feel warm, loving emotions. I do this by focusing on my heart and letting love, trust forgiveness, compassion, hope or gratitude fill my heart space.

Behave constructively:

I choose to work in part acts:
I will break the overwhelming job into manageable parts.

Do the difficult:
I will face what I fear and act with self-discipline.

I choose to solutionise:
I will find a solution by taking advice or doing research.

Prioritise myself:
I will keep my life balanced by meeting friends, doing exercise or laughing.

Compartmentalise:
I will not let this event cloud my whole day; I will focus on something else now.

Utilise calming strategies:

When I:
- relax,
- breathe deeply,
- go for a run,
- shower,
- lie down,
- read,
- watch TV,
- climb into a mental helicopter,
- practice mindfulness/meditation,

my mind and body calm down.

Step Four: The Self Motivation Process

Endorse yourself for any growth no matter how small.

In the past I would have...

____

____

But this time I...

____

____

Tick off the traits that you strengthened when you worked down your anxiety:

- ☐ generosity
- ☐ kindness
- ☐ compassion
- ☐ consideration
- ☐ helpfulness
- ☐ respectfulness
- ☐ honesty
- ☐ fairness
- ☐ patience

- ☐ peacefulness
- ☐ self-discipline
- ☐ forgiveness
- ☐ courage
- ☐ responsibility
- ☐ reliability
- ☐ loyalty
- ☐ love
- ☐ humility

Rate your anxiety on a scale of 0 to 100%:

☐ %

O

W

Date: _______________

Anxiety Management Worksheet

The purpose of this worksheet is to help you to see every stressful event as an opportunity for
1. greater understanding of yourself, your anxiety and the people around you, and
2. practicing tools to manage your anxiety.

Step One: An Event

Briefly describe an event when you became anxious. Give such details as time, place and people involved, and end with "That's when I began to work myself up..."

Rate your anxiety on a scale of 0 to 100%: ______ %

E

Step Two: The Working-Up Process

Learn about your working up process by identifying your thoughts, feelings, behaviours and bodily reactions during the event.

Tick the ones that most resonate with you.

Undermining Beliefs

B

I fear that I have lost...
- ☐ approval
- ☐ control
- ☐ co-operation
- ☐ face
- ☐ respect
- ☐ success
- ☐ trust
- ☐ validation
- ☐ love

This event proves that I am...
- ☐ stupid
- ☐ abnormal
- ☐ incompetent
- ☐ lazy
- ☐ irresponsible
- ☐ a total failure
- ☐ undisciplined
- ☐ untogether
- ☐ useless

I worry that I will suffer...
- ☐ mental collapse
- ☐ illness
- ☐ financial hardship

What I want is...
- ☐ total control
- ☐ respect
- ☐ success
- ☐ perfection
- ☐ comfort
- ☐ fairness
- ☐ tranquility
- ☐ all the answers
- ☐ for life to go smoothly
- ☐ to be all things to all people

Self-destructive Behaviour

Active
- ☐ get violent
- ☐ swear
- ☐ slam doors
- ☐ run away
- ☐ overeat
- ☐ harm myself
- ☐ criticise

Passive
- ☐ take it too seriously
- ☐ give up
- ☐ wallow in self pity
- ☐ sulk
- ☐ space out
- ☐ procrastinate
- ☐ give in
- ☐ be controlled

Intense Feelings

Angry feelings
- ☐ hateful
- ☐ aggravated
- ☐ annoyed
- ☐ hostile
- ☐ outraged
- ☐ punitive
- ☐ resentful
- ☐ vengeful

Fearful feelings
- ☐ helpless
- ☐ hopeless
- ☐ disappointed
- ☐ sad
- ☐ attacked
- ☐ worn out
- ☐ rejected
- ☐ jealous
- ☐ afraid
- ☐ exploited
- ☐ lonely
- ☐ abandoned
- ☐ guilty
- ☐ insulted
- ☐ confused
- ☐ disillusioned
- ☐ misunderstood
- ☐ trapped

Bodily Reactions (limbic system)

I am uncomfortable because I am experiencing...
- ☐ tremors
- ☐ nausea
- ☐ sweaty palms
- ☐ stomach-ache
- ☐ pounding heart
- ☐ general tension
- ☐ fatigue
- ☐ imagination on fire
- ☐ headache
- ☐ dry mouth
- ☐ jaw clenching
- ☐ shortness of breath

Continued over

B   **F**   **L**

Step Three: The Working-Down Process

Begin with, "Suddenly I realised that I was anxious and that I had choices..." This is the step of self-leadership and trust in one's ability to handle the situation.

Choose helpful thoughts:

I choose to depersonalise
There is no intention to hurt me. He is doing the best he can with the tools he has at the moment.

I choose realism over romanticism
Life presents many obstacles. I lower or raise standards as needed.

There is no right or wrong
Unless it is a moral issue, I will see it simply as a difference of opinion and/or taste.

I choose the total view of positivity
Even though this event is negative, the total view of his behaviour is positive.

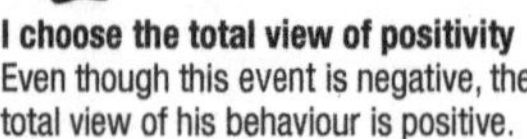

I surrender control
Since I cannot change this situation, I choose to let go of it.

I choose to put this event in perspective
This event is not a catastrophe because it is not life threatening. It can be viewed as a trivial life event, a normal life problem that needs to be solved not dramatised.

I choose to view this event as average, falling within the normal range
This event is not exceptional; many people have gone through this.

It's temporary - "this too shall pass"
Life is constantly changing and moving through phases and this situation will also change.

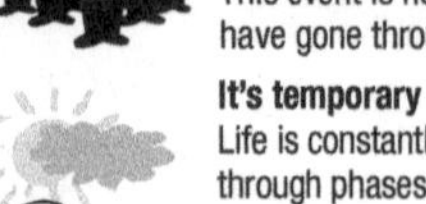

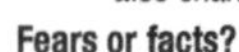

Fears or facts?
Why fear? It may not happen!

I choose to focus on this as a learning experience
Every problem that comes my way is an opportunity for me to learn about my strengths and weaknesses, others and life.

Feel soothing emotions:

I choose to feel warm, loving emotions. I do this by focusing on my heart and letting love, trust forgiveness, compassion, hope or gratitude fill my heart space.

Behave constructively:

I choose to work in part acts:
I will break the overwhelming job into manageable parts.

Do the difficult:
I will face what I fear and act with self-discipline.

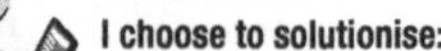

I choose to solutionise:
I will find a solution by taking advice or doing research.

Prioritise myself:
I will keep my life balanced by meeting friends, doing exercise or laughing.

Compartmentalise:
I will not let this event cloud my whole day; I will focus on something else now.

Utilise calming strategies:

When I:
- relax,
- breathe deeply,
- go for a run,
- shower,
- lie down,
- read,
- watch TV,
- climb into a mental helicopter,
- practice mindfulness/meditation,

my mind and body calm down.

Step Four: The Self Motivation Process

Endorse yourself for any growth no matter how small.

In the past I would have...

____

____

But this time I...

____

____

Tick off the traits that you strengthened when you worked down your anxiety:

☐ generosity	☐ peacefulness
☐ kindness	☐ self-discipline
☐ compassion	☐ forgiveness
☐ consideration	☐ courage
☐ helpfulness	☐ responsibility
☐ respectfulness	☐ reliability
☐ honesty	☐ loyalty
☐ fairness	☐ love
☐ patience	☐ humility

Rate your anxiety on a scale of 0 to 100%:

________ %

Date: _____________

Anxiety Management Worksheet

The purpose of this worksheet is to help you to see every stressful event as an opportunity for
1. greater understanding of yourself, your anxiety and the people around you, and
2. practicing tools to manage your anxiety.

Step One: An Event

Briefly describe an event when you became anxious. Give such details as time, place and people involved, and end with "That's when I began to work myself up…"

____

____

____

____ Rate your anxiety on a scale of 0 to 100%: [ ] %

E

Step Two: The Working-Up Process

Learn about your working up process by identifying your thoughts, feelings, behaviours and bodily reactions during the event.
Tick the ones that most resonate with you.

Undermining Beliefs

B

I fear that I have lost...

- ☐ approval
- ☐ control
- ☐ co-operation
- ☐ face
- ☐ respect
- ☐ success
- ☐ trust
- ☐ validation
- ☐ love

This event proves that I am...

- ☐ stupid
- ☐ abnormal
- ☐ incompetent
- ☐ lazy
- ☐ irresponsible
- ☐ a total failure
- ☐ undisciplined
- ☐ untogether
- ☐ useless

I worry that I will suffer...

- ☐ mental collapse
- ☐ illness
- ☐ financial hardship

What I want is...

- ☐ total control
- ☐ respect
- ☐ success
- ☐ perfection
- ☐ comfort
- ☐ fairness
- ☐ tranquility
- ☐ all the answers
- ☐ for life to go smoothly
- ☐ to be all things to all people

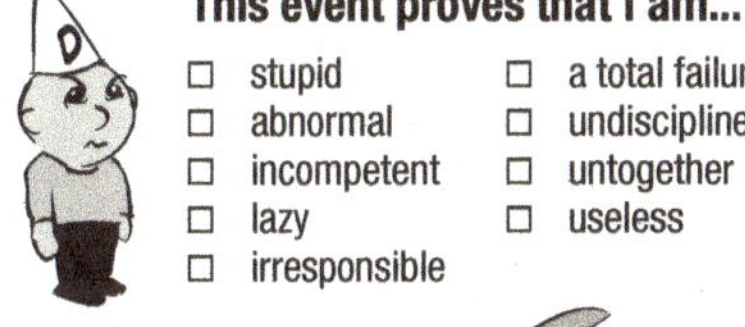

Self-destructive Behaviour

Active

- ☐ get violent
- ☐ swear
- ☐ slam doors
- ☐ run away
- ☐ overeat
- ☐ harm myself
- ☐ criticise

Passive

- ☐ take it too seriously
- ☐ give up
- ☐ wallow in self pity
- ☐ sulk
- ☐ space out
- ☐ procrastinate
- ☐ give in
- ☐ be controlled

Intense Feelings

Angry feelings

- ☐ hateful
- ☐ aggravated
- ☐ annoyed
- ☐ hostile
- ☐ outraged
- ☐ punitive
- ☐ resentful
- ☐ vengeful

Fearful feelings

- ☐ helpless
- ☐ hopeless
- ☐ disappointed
- ☐ sad
- ☐ attacked
- ☐ worn out
- ☐ rejected
- ☐ jealous
- ☐ afraid
- ☐ exploited
- ☐ lonely
- ☐ abandoned
- ☐ guilty
- ☐ insulted
- ☐ confused
- ☐ disillusioned
- ☐ misunderstood
- ☐ trapped

Bodily Reactions (limbic system)

I am uncomfortable because I am experiencing...

- ☐ tremors
- ☐ nausea
- ☐ sweaty palms
- ☐ stomach-ache
- ☐ pounding heart
- ☐ general tension
- ☐ fatigue
- ☐ imagination on fire
- ☐ headache
- ☐ dry mouth
- ☐ jaw clenching
- ☐ shortness of breath

Continued over

B   **F**   **L**

Step Three: The Working-Down Process

Begin with, "Suddenly I realised that I was anxious and that I had choices..." This is the step of self-leadership and trust in one's ability to handle the situation.

Choose helpful thoughts:

I choose to depersonalise
There is no intention to hurt me. He is doing the best he can with the tools he has at the moment.

I choose realism over romanticism
Life presents many obstacles. I lower or raise standards as needed.

There is no right or wrong
Unless it is a moral issue, I will see it simply as a difference of opinion and/or taste.

I choose the total view of positivity
Even though this event is negative, the total view of his behaviour is positive.

I surrender control
Since I cannot change this situation, I choose to let go of it.

I choose to put this event in perspective This event is not a catastrophe because it is not life threatening. It can be viewed as a trivial life event, a normal life problem that needs to be solved not dramatised.

I choose to view this event as average, falling within the normal range
This event is not exceptional; many people have gone through this.

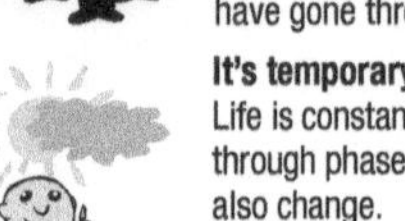

It's temporary - "this too shall pass"
Life is constantly changing and moving through phases and this situation will also change.

Fears or facts?
Why fear? It may not happen!

I choose to focus on this as a learning experience
Every problem that comes my way is an opportunity for me to learn about my strengths and weaknesses, others and life.

Feel soothing emotions:

I choose to feel warm, loving emotions. I do this by focusing on my heart and letting love, trust forgiveness, compassion, hope or gratitude fill my heart space.

Behave constructively:

I choose to work in part acts:
I will break the overwhelming job into manageable parts.

Do the difficult:
I will face what I fear and act with self-discipline.

I choose to solutionise:
I will find a solution by taking advice or doing research.

Prioritise myself:
I will keep my life balanced by meeting friends, doing exercise or laughing.

Compartmentalise:
I will not let this event cloud my whole day; I will focus on something else now.

Utilise calming strategies:

When I:
- relax,
- breathe deeply,
- go for a run,
- shower,
- lie down,
- read,
- watch TV,
- climb into a mental helicopter,
- practice mindfulness/meditation,

my mind and body calm down.

Step Four: The Self Motivation Process

Endorse yourself for any growth no matter how small.

In the past I would have...

____

____

But this time I...

____

____

Tick off the traits that you strengthened when you worked down your anxiety:

☐	generosity	☐	peacefulness
☐	kindness	☐	self-discipline
☐	compassion	☐	forgiveness
☐	consideration	☐	courage
☐	helpfulness	☐	responsibility
☐	respectfulness	☐	reliability
☐	honesty	☐	loyalty
☐	fairness	☐	love
☐	patience	☐	humility

Rate your anxiety on a scale of 0 to 100%:

________ %

O

W

Summing up the 90 days

In what ways do you think you have grown over the past 90 days?

What have you gained from the techniques you've practised?

What skills have you been using the most and finding helpful in reducing anxiety?

What has been difficult for you during this process?

What changes have you noticed within yourself?

What have you learned about yourself?

What are your plans to keep up the practice of relaxation, breathing, mindfulness and meditation?

How do you plan to keep exercising regularly?

What is your long-term plan to ensure that you continue to fill
out anxiety management worksheets?

....

....

....

....

Please feel free to contact me at any time for further help on
+ 61 2 9328 5899.

In order to facilitate your journey to tranquillity, visit my
website **www.anxietysolutionscbt.com** to receive all the latest
information on anxiety and its management, and to access free
resources and giveaways.

References

1. www.bspg.com.au/dam/bsg/product?client=BEYOND-
    BLUE&prodid=BL/0384&type=file. The official statistic for
    anxiety is one in four.

2. Doidge, N. *The brain that changes itself: Stories of personal
    triumph from the frontiers of brain science*, Penguin Group,
    2007

3. Simply Google Wikipedia, *DSM 5*, Anxiety Online or
    Beyond Blue to find credible sites rich in valuable infor-
    mation about anxiety. Some examples include:
    - www.beyondblue.org.au/the-facts/anxiety/
      what-causes-anxiety
    - www.beyondblue.org.au/the-facts/anxiety/
      treatments-for-anxiety
    - www.mindhealthconnect.org.au/anxiety
    - www.psychology.org.au/publications/tip_sheets/
      anxiety/

4. http://gabriellemarieloomis.com/blog/
    3-keys-to-create-positive-lasting-change/

5. www.anxietyonline.org.au/pages/about-us

6. These come from reputable sources and can be down-
    loaded on any smart phone
    - Smiling Mind — Meditation made easy
    - I Can Be Free: Relax, Remove fear & anxiety

- Digipill: Sleep, relaxation and mindfulness
- Mindfulness: The Art of Being
- I Can Be Calm
- The Now: Mindful Living
- End Anxiety: Free Guided meditation and relaxation program
- 7 cups of tea - free anxiety relief, depression help, therapy & counseling

7. Deci, E. L., R. M., "The 'what' and 'why' of goal pursuits: Human needs and the self-determination of behaviour." *Psychological Inquiry*, Volume 11, 227–268, 2000

8. Klosko, J. S. & Sanderson, W. C., *Cognitive-behavioural treatment for depression*, Jason Aronson, Inc., 1999

9. www.beckinstituteblog.org/2012/12/cbt-plus-medication-is-effective-for-treatment-resistant-depression/

10. Rossouw, P., *Focused neuropsychotherapy training manual*, Mediros Clinical Solutions, Mediros Pty Ltd, 2012

11. www.australiangeographic.com.au/topics/science-environment/2014/12/shark-attacks-in-australia-a-timeline/

12. Greenberger, D. & Padesky, C. A. *Mind Over Mood*, Guildford Press, 1995

13. Adahan, M. *EMETT*, Feldman Publishers, 1987

14. Rossouw, P. & Henson, C. *Brainwise leadership*, Learning Quest, 2013

15. Seligman, M. E. P. *Learned optimism*, Random House, 1992

16. Macquarie Dictionary, Revised 3rd Edition, Macquarie University, 2004

17. Covey, S. R. *The seven habits of highly effective people*, Simon & Schuster Ltd., 1993

18. www.blackdoginstitute.org.au

19. Childre, D. & Rozman, D. *Transforming anxiety: The heartmath solution for overcoming fear and worry and creating serenity*, New Harbinger Publications Inc., 2006

20. Cousins, N. *Anatomy of an illness — As perceived by the patient*, W. W. Norton & Company, 1979

21. UCLA laughter clinic: Cousins Centre for Psychoneuroimmunology — www.semel.ucla.edu/cousins

22. Nikolic, N. ACT — http://strategicpsychology.com.au/acceptance-and-commitment-therapy/

23. *Alcoholics Anonymous*, Third Edition, A. A. World Services, Inc., 1976

24. Hernstein, R. J. & Murray, C. *The bell curve: Intelligence and class structure in American life*, Free Press Paperbacks, 1994